SENSORY PROFILE

User's Manual

Winnie Dunn, Ph.D., OTR, FAOTA

THE
PSYCHOLOGICAL
CORPORATION®

A Harcourt Assessment Company

■ Reproducing Pages From This Book

As described below, some of the pages in this book may be reproduced for instructional use (not for resale). To protect your book, make a photocopy of each reproducible page. Then use that copy as a master for photocopying.

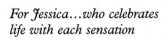

*For Jessica...who celebrates
life with each sensation*

About the Author

Winnie Dunn is professor and chairperson of the Occupational Therapy Department at the University of Kansas Medical Center. She has researched the *Sensory Profile* for 10 years. Dr. Dunn is a Fellow of the American Occupational Therapy Association (AOTA) and a member of the American Occupational Therapy Foundation's Academy of Research. She also has earned the AOTA's Award of Merit and has received AOTA's Service Award several times.

Dr. Dunn has taught at the University of Kansas Medical Center; Rockhurst College; Kent State University; University of Missouri-Kansas City; University of Missouri-Columbia; William Jewell College; and Webster University, Extension Service of St. Louis Program. She formerly was director of Exemplary Services at the University of Missouri; coordinator of Postgraduate Education and Professional Development, specialized consultant for Lighthouse Preschool for Exceptional Children, coordinator of Pediatric Outreach Programs, and occupational therapist for high-risk preschool and school-based therapy at St. Luke's Hospital of Kansas City; and occupational therapist/learning disabilities specialist at Liberty Public School in Liberty, Missouri.

In addition, Dr. Dunn has published extensively, authoring or co-authoring more than 80 journal articles, monographs, books, book chapters, and book reviews. She also has served on the editorial boards for *Physical and Occupational Therapy in Pediatrics, Cognitive Rehabilitation,* and the *Occupational Therapy Journal of Research.* She has presented hundreds of papers and workshops during her career.

Dr. Dunn earned her bachelor of science degree in Occupational Therapy and her master of science degree in Education/Learning Disabilities at the University of Missouri in Columbia, Missouri. She earned her doctorate in Neuroscience-Special Studies at the University of Kansas in Lawrence, Kansas. In addition, she is a Registered Occupational Therapist and holds lifetime teaching certificates in Learning Disabilities K–12 and Early Childhood/Special Education, and as a School Psychological Examiner and Educational Resource Teacher.

■ Contents

■ Chapter 1

■ Chapter 2

■ Chapter 3

■ Chapter 4

■ Chapter 5

■ Chapter 6

■ Chapter 7

■ Chapter 8

■ List of Figures

■ List of Tables

Preface

October 1994 will always be a benchmark date in my history. It was during this month that events and decisions I made transformed my professional path forever. Actually, what happened that month was a sojourn back to thoughts I had nearly 20 years earlier, but in 1994 I finally was able to appreciate what my random thoughts might mean.

In the early part of the month I was conducting a workshop on service provision in the schools. Although most of the participants were enthusiastic about the evolution of school-based practice as an integrated way to provide services, there were a few members who were very unhappy at the prospects that I was laying out before them. These people were more interested in continuing more traditional types of services and found my suggestions difficult to consider.

On my journey home from this workshop, I felt discouraged. I had been writing, studying, and talking about integrated services for more than 15 years, and wondered when this knowledge might be accepted as routine practice rather than as the radical message some still were receiving. Furthermore, I felt that I had conveyed my message in every possible way and couldn't think of any other ways to package it. During that journey home, I decided that I would have to stop writing about service provision and would have to severely limit speaking engagements on the topic because I already had said what I knew to say.

This decision felt heavy; I had the idea that this would come to be known in occupational therapy history as my contribution to the profession. I was very proud of my work on service provision, but could feel myself entering the professional vortex…that place where past contributors are regarded for their historic contributions to the evolution of thought.

Later that same month, after living through two weeks of somberness, the October 1994 *American Journal of Occupational Therapy* (AJOT) contained the first pilot study of the *Sensory Profile*. My life would never be the same. In the first two days, I received five calls from colleagues I had never met who had read this article and wanted to participate in other studies. From then until now, I have had a steady stream of contacts from colleagues in many disciplines asking questions, giving me feedback, sending data, letting me know of their studies, etc. The result of all of this "dancing" is the work before you today.

I now see that I needed to let people digest what I had to say about services in schools and trust that the knowledge would advance because many were attending to it by 1994. I also needed to let go of this work so that I was available for the work that was coming along; I wouldn't have had the energy to do both topics justice.

I also discovered that I have been thinking about the topic of sensory processing in daily life for a very long time. I found handouts I made for a workshop in 1978 in which I was trying to characterize the features of a child's behavior and performance using a sensory processing point of view. The diagram was very complicated and hard to follow, and I remember that my audience was intrigued but baffled by my suggestions that this would be a simplified way to characterize our observations. Amazingly, the work I have done in the last 4 years contains nearly the same concepts as that 1978 handout, but I seem to be able to think and communicate my ideas more clearly now (thank goodness for maturity!).

So this work for me very clearly is a "coming home." During the 20 years from that first attempt, I have engaged in a myriad of professional activities that enabled me to come back to this place with more insights. The work on the *Sensory Profile* reflects all of my central beliefs and capitalizes on the specialized knowledge that I have worked hard to acquire over these two decades. It reflects family-centered care in that the *Sensory Profile* asks care providers to tell us how children behave in daily life and has been shown to be a very discriminating set of data for planning. It reflects my passion for understanding the nervous system and its impact on performance. Finally, the *Sensory Profile* links theoretical knowledge to daily life; I believe that performance in daily life is the only true reflection of all other aspects of function, and I am proud that I have contributed a measure that honors that relationship.

So here we are. I have gathered knowledge, data, colleagues, mentees, and friends and have basted all of it together with my perspective to make this fabulous tool that celebrates the best of me, you, and our wisdom about children's sensory processing and their families' experiences of daily life with them…

"…as Anna says about making a quilt, '…. The right colors will enhance your quilt; the wrong choices will dull their colors—hide their original beauty. There are no rules you can follow; you have to go by instinct and you have to be brave…' "

spoken by Finn: *How to Make an American Quilt*
(Moorhouse, 1995)

Wrap yourselves in the *Sensory Profile* and the "comfort" it gives you in understanding children a little better…and with the insights it brings you, gather new bits of knowledge for our next "quilt."

winnie dunn

Acknowledgments

Many people have added their time and talents to the creation of the *Sensory Profile*. I would like to thank the following people who contributed to the collective research: Carol Berry, Andrea Bilics, Marie Carey, Mary Cater, Stephanie Foster, Kathryn Grace, June Holstrom, Deb Kugel, Susan Lizotte, Jan Marson, Rosane Myers, Tamara Sarracino, Joy Sawh, and Susan Withey.

I also would like to acknowledge the significant contributions to our knowledge and the development of this assessment made by Lucy Jane Miller, Daniel McIntosh, Vivian Shyu, Tana Brown, Mary Pat Gilbert, Christy Hill, and Kathleen Westman.

I would like to thank many individuals at The Psychological Corporation for their behind-the-scenes contributions: Valarie Spiser-Albert, Acquisitions Editor, for her vision and faith in the *Sensory Profile;* Gay Lynn Lamey, Project Director, and Pam Parmer, Supervising Editor, for their support and direction throughout the development phase of the manual and record forms—reviewing, editing, designing, and producing the final product; Dr. Charles "Chuck" Wilkins, Project Director, for his review of the technical chapters and his expertise in psychometrics; Marian Zahora, Designer, for her imagery and contributions to the design of the *Sensory Profile*; Meg Grant, Marketing Strategist, for her thoughtful innovations in marketing; and Jan Laurent, Project Director, for her in-depth review of the manual.

My sincere thanks go to the following graduate students who collected and analyzed *Sensory Profile* data on children with various diagnoses: Donna Bennett, Julie Ermer, and Mary Kientz. Tec Chapman and Robin Wells, I also thank you for your contribution to data collection.

In addition, I would like to acknowledge the following undergraduate students for their help entering and analyzing data: Julie Arndt, Suzanne Churchill, Matt Cohara, Gina Dopson, Amy Green, Tricia Hare, Keziben Ismail, Kim Kelley-Evans, Emily Johnson, Melanie Lynn, Deirdre Newcomer, Traci Ridder, Laura Robertson, Sara Robertson, Kori Turney, Amy Vaughan, and Emily Wurtenberger. Other undergraduate students who entered and analyzed data are: Hilary Brown, Tammy Christiansen, Deb Ephraim, Kristin Helmer, and Amy Yunek.

I also want to thank Helen Courvoisie, Lois Heying, Kristie Middendorf, Jamie Odle, Teresa Pinder, Cay Reilly, Lorene Tierney, and Larissa Witter for their efforts in collecting data, and Stephan Corsale, Mariana D'Amico, Barbara Sides, Melanie Specter, and Renee Watling for their contributions to the database.

Finally, I would like to acknowledge the following people for their work providing data on the normal population and on therapists' placement of *Sensory Profile* items:

Mary Alessio	Catriona Binder-Macleod	Tina Collop
Liz Alia	Patricia Brannon	Linda Coogle Stephens
Delores Arroyo	Rosemary Brophy	Christine Cook
Sun Ann Bainter	Nierenberg	Janice Corson
Mary Elizabeth Baron	Estherbeth Buchbinder	Barbara Cracchiolo
Pamela Bauman	Mary Buck	Anne Cronin
Mary Baumgartner	Ellen Carll-Bennett	Patricia Cunningham
Margaret Behar	Audrey Chaput	Sandra Dallaire
Barbara Berman	Ruth Clatos	Donita Davis
Susan Biagini	Cheryl Colangelo	Catherine DeLeon

Diane Demaio-Feldman
Sharon Dugan
Susan Dykema
Norma Eigles
Kathleen Engebretson
Julie Ermer
Sally Fennema-Jansen
Susan Finn
Ann Fisher-Evangelista
Jennifer Flanagan
Sherley Fosmire
Carole Fournier
Doreen Fraits-Hunt
Suzanne Frank
Emily Frank
Emily Garrett Sager
Kristen Gillogly
    Grayson
Irene Gordon
Susan Guertin
Karen Hardy
Margaret Mary Hare
Roseann Hatchett
Cindy Hatch-Rasmussen
Elizabeth Hebert
Patricia Heckenbach
Julie Herbert
Carol Hesch
Dorothy Hess
Debra Hinkle
    Gauthreaux
Jennifer Hoffman
Margaret Hoffman
Robin Hoffman
Cynthia Horgard
Catherine Hostetler
Darlene Hughes
Susan Ireland Murray
Karen Louise Johnson
Amy Johnson
Debra Kabrich
Joanne Kania
Jerelyn Kidd Bresnan
Virginia Knight
J. Patricia Knutson
Theresa Hollar

Jane Koomar
Colleen Kremer
Mary Louise Kueber
Julie Ann Lake
Maryjo Laughlin
Lana Ledet
Jill Leffler-Lyons
Harriet Levin
Diane Long
Linda Luecke
Lea Manny
Sandra Martin
Elizabeth Maruyama
Margaret McCormack
    Singer
Susan McDuff
Marie McNamera
Connie Jo Meadows
    Blanco
Lisa Anne Meoli
Lucille Messina
Mary Frances Meyer
Kathryn Miesner
Carol Miller
Heather Miller
Maryanne Moisan
Nancy Mooers
Ruth Morales
Ellen Morrow
Debra Myers
Phyllis Nayak
Patricia Neville
Barbara O'Brien
Ann Marie O'Reilly
Connie Ortman
Nancy Ossman
Gretchen Parker
Marcie Passic
Lisa Payne
Teresa Pinder
Mary Pogosky-Grassi
Esther Jean Quinn
Cynthia Radue
Maryann Radowski
Sharon Readinger
Margaret Roggensack

Eileen Rosenbaum
Jean Ann Savina
Virginia Scardina
Marcia Scott
Teresa Shire
Olivia Shugart
Susan Siler
Nora Simmons Dunn
Vera Ann Simpson
Anne Small
Eileen Somers
Margaret Mary Spring
Llaine St Pierre
Gertrude Stark-Goeckel
Carrie Strauch
Susan Swartz
Judy Taft
Carrie Taguma
M. Kim Talmor
Jody Tate
Sarah Thomas
Michelle Tierney
Linda Tirella
Carol Tornello
Janet Tredwell
Lynne Tupper
Mary Ann Turner
Sheryl Vail
Sonya Vanhorn
Phyllis Verhage
Margaret Visentin
Corinne Vivian
Jeanette Voelm
Rebecca Wallace
Elaine Walter
Carolyn Wendt
Mary Lee Wilde
Jennifer Wineberg
Teri Wiss
Cheryl Wojton
Sheila Wolford
Kathryn Wotta
Sharon Wu
Beth Zabel
Kelly Zaros

CHAPTER 1

■ Overview

The *Sensory Profile* provides a standard method for professionals to measure a child's sensory processing abilities and to profile the effect of sensory processing on functional performance in the daily life of a child. The profile is most appropriate for children 5–10 years of age. See Chapter 5 for information on how to use it with 3- and 4-year-olds. The *Sensory Profile* was designed to contribute to a comprehensive assessment of a child's sensory performance when combined with other evaluations, observations, and reports to determine the child's status for diagnostic and intervention planning.

The *Sensory Profile* is a judgment-based caregiver questionnaire. Each item describes children's responses to various sensory experiences. The caregiver who has daily contact with the child completes the questionnaire by reporting the frequency with which these behaviors occur (Always, Frequently, Occasionally, Seldom, or Never). The therapist or other professional then scores the responses on the questionnaire. Certain patterns of performance on the *Sensory Profile* are indicative of difficulties with sensory processing and performance. In these cases, the team serving the child follows up on the relationship between sensory processing and performance difficulties. Occupational therapists have expertise in sensory processing as part of their professional preparation. Other professionals can acquire this expertise through post-professional education.

The *Sensory Profile* consists of 125 items grouped into three main sections: Sensory Processing, Modulation, and Behavioral and Emotional Responses.

The **Sensory Processing** section indicates the child's responses to the basic sensory systems. Sensory processing is further broken down into six sensory processing systems: Auditory, Visual, Vestibular, Touch, Multisensory, and Oral Sensory Processing.

The **Modulation** section reflects the child's regulation of neural messages through facilitation or inhibition of various types of responses. Modulation is broken down into five areas of sensory modulation: Sensory Processing Related to Endurance/Tone, Modulation Related to Body Position and Movement, Modulation of Movement Affecting Activity Level, Modulation of Sensory Input Affecting Emotional Responses, and Modulation of Visual Input Affecting Emotional Responses and Activity Level.

The **Behavioral and Emotional Responses** section reflects the child's behavioral outcomes of sensory processing, which is broken down into Emotional/Social Responses, Behavioral Outcomes of Sensory Processing, and Items Indicating Thresholds for Response.

Items on the *Caregiver Questionnaire* unite to form nine meaningful groups or factors: Sensory Seeking, Emotionally Reactive, Low Endurance/Tone, Oral Sensory Sensitivity, Inattention/Distractibility, Poor Registration, Sensory Sensitivity, Sedentary, and Fine Motor/Perceptual. The factors identify items on the *Caregiver Questionnaire* that characterize children by their responsiveness to sensory input (i.e., overly responsive or underresponsive).

A short form of the *Sensory Profile* was designed specifically to target sensory modulation rather than the more multidimensional aspects of development (see Chapter 7). Researchers selected 38 items from the *Sensory Profile* that were the most discriminatory. Children who exhibit these particular behaviors very likely have sensory processing issues that affect performance and therefore require further assessment. The *Short Sensory Profile* is most appropriate for screening programs and research protocols.

■ Purpose

The *Sensory Profile* is a tool for linking performance strengths and barriers with the child's sensory processing patterns. Its purpose is to evaluate the possible contributions of sensory processing to the child's daily performance patterns and to provide information about both the child's tendencies to respond to stimuli and which sensory systems are likely to be contributing to or creating barriers to functional performance.

■ Rationale

The Education for All Handicapped Children Act (Public Law 94-142), which was amended and expanded in 1990 by the Individuals With Disabilities Education Act (IDEA, Public Law 101-476), mandates that children have the right to a free, appropriate public education provided in the least restrictive environment. When children begin to struggle to be successful in school and in related skill areas, a team of professionals collaborates with families to identify supports and barriers to successful performance. The law indicates that the team must explore the child's needs in a comprehensive way, including finding alternative learning strategies, conducting formal assessments, and completing skilled observations, as well as interviewing and requesting information from parents, teachers, physicians, and other service or care providers.

When a child is referred for an evaluation, the members of the interdisciplinary team bring unique frames of reference to the assessment process, including interpreting the same behavior in several ways. Regardless of the frame of reference a professional uses, each team member has the responsibility to link hypotheses about the child's abilities to the child's performance. Some assessment methods yield good diagnostic information but do not provide clear links to performance; other assessment methods enable professionals to verify performance problems, but provide no mechanism for linking this information to frames of reference for theory-based decision making.

The *Sensory Profile* uses a sensory integrative and neuroscience frame of reference and supports a family-centered care philosophy by involving the caregivers in the data-gathering process. The *Sensory Profile* provides the necessary link between performance in daily life and theory to facilitate theory-based decision making.

■ Benefits

Following are benefits to the caregiver and professional using the *Sensory Profile*.

1. The *Sensory Profile* provides a natural way to include families in the information-gathering process. Caregivers complete the profile, reporting their own experiences with their child. Evaluation tools that solicit the caregivers' expertise support family-centered care models of practice.

2. Caregivers report a therapeutic benefit from completing the *Sensory Profile*. The items are familiar to caregivers living with children who have sensory processing problems. Reading about their children's "idiosyncratic" behaviors during assessment provides validation that there is something real about their family's struggle and suggests that there may be some ways to deal with it.

3. The *Sensory Profile* provides professionals with a way to capture the child's responses during the natural course of daily life, a task difficult or impossible to achieve with formal evaluations in unfamiliar settings. For all professionals, a child's functional performance in daily life must be a central focus. Because there are few evaluation tools that measure performance in daily life, the *Sensory Profile* is a viable solution.

4. The *Sensory Profile* is constructed so that professionals can engage in theory-based decision making during comprehensive assessment and intervention planning. Principles of neuroscience, sensory integration, and occupational performance are embedded in the items and scoring structure. By following the guidelines for use in this manual, professionals can make decisions that are consistent with these theoretical principles.

5. The *Sensory Profile* provides both a measure of current performance and an indication of intervention directions. Test results provide information about the child's level of responsivity to sensory events (e.g., hyperresponsive or hyporesponsive). Because the *Sensory Profile* is organized into sections, test results also suggest which sensory systems might be interfering with the child's performance and which daily life tasks might be more difficult. The information gained from the *Sensory Profile* provides status measurement of current performance levels; the section scores and the factor structure of the *Sensory Profile* provide guideposts for planning interventions with the families and other caregivers.

■ Goals and Features

A primary goal of the *Sensory Profile* research process was to develop an evaluation tool for professionals to gather information about children's sensory processing abilities that support and/or interfere with functional performance. The *Sensory Profile*:

1. captures salient information about a child's sensory processing;

2. clearly links sensory processing with the child's daily life performance;

3. provides information for theory-based decision making;

4. includes caregivers as critical members of the team;

5. is applicable for children with all types of disabilities and severity levels;

6. is easy to administer, score, and interpret; and

7. is quick to administer.

■ Test Components

The *Sensory Profile* consists of a *User's Manual, Caregiver Questionnaire, Summary Score Sheet,* and the *Short Sensory Profile.*

User's Manual

The *User's Manual* contains information about the rationale, theory, and development of the *Sensory Profile* and specific information about the administration, scoring, and interpretation of the scores. The manual also contains a worksheet on items and factors relating to attention deficit/hyperactivity disorder (ADHD), as well as case studies and intervention suggestions.

Caregiver Questionnaire

The *Caregiver Questionnaire* contains 125 items that describe children's responses to daily sensory experiences. Caregivers complete the form by indicating the frequency of the child's responses (Always, Frequently, Occasionally, Seldom, or Never) to various sensory experiences. The For Office Use Only section includes keys for icons, thresholds, and scoring.

Summary Score Sheet

The *Summary Score Sheet* provides a summary of the child's scores. It contains an area to record the child's demographic information, a Factor Grid to help summarize the child's scores into nine factor groupings, a Factor Summary to plot factor raw score totals, and a Section Summary to plot section raw score totals.

Short Sensory Profile

The *Short Sensory Profile* is a 38-item caregiver questionnaire and score sheet designed for use in screening and research protocols.

■ Administration Time

Caregivers report that it takes 30 minutes to complete the full *Caregiver Questionnaire* and 10 minutes to complete the *Short Sensory Profile.* The *Summary Score Sheet* will take the examiner 20–30 minutes to complete.

■ User Qualifications

Individuals from many different professions can administer the *Sensory Profile.* Both service providers and researchers will find the test results useful. Service providers such as occupational therapists, teachers, psychologists, speech-language pathologists, and physicians might use it to gain a picture of a child's performance during daily life, as well as areas of strength and concern that can provide the foundation for intervention planning. Basic science researchers might include the instrument in their protocols as a functional measure of sensory responsivity. Applied science researchers might use it to gather data linking sensory processing to daily life.

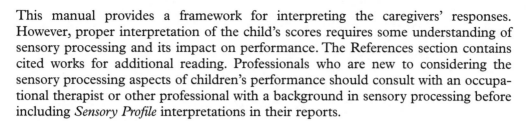

This manual provides a framework for interpreting the caregivers' responses. However, proper interpretation of the child's scores requires some understanding of sensory processing and its impact on performance. The References section contains cited works for additional reading. Professionals who are new to considering the sensory processing aspects of children's performance should consult with an occupational therapist or other professional with a background in sensory processing before including *Sensory Profile* interpretations in their reports.

■ Cut Scores and Classification System

Researchers defined a classification system by determining cut scores for each of the section and factor raw score totals. The classification system describes the child's sensory processing abilities for each section and factor as either:

- Typical Performance
- Probable Difference
- Definite Difference

The classification system helps the professional quickly determine whether a child's performance on any of the section or factor groupings is of concern. Chapter 3 provides an explanation of the derivation of cut scores and the classification system.

CHAPTER 2

■ Theoretical and Conceptual Features

■ Conceptual Model for the *Sensory Profile*

The *Sensory Profile* characterizes children's behaviors and performance in relation to sensory processing. Research findings led to a new conceptual model that hypothesizes that there is an interaction between neurological thresholds and behavioral responses (Dunn, 1997a). This model presents the neurological thresholds and behavioral responses as continua that interact with each other. The interaction of these two continua provides a method for explaining how children process sensory information and provides guidance for intervention planning. Figure 2.1 on page 8 illustrates the conceptual model and its components.

Neurological threshold refers to the amount of stimuli required for a neuron or neuron system to respond. At one end of this continuum, thresholds are very high; this means it would take a *lot* of stimuli to meet the threshold and fire the neurons. At the other end of this continuum, thresholds are very low; this means it takes *very little* stimuli to meet the threshold and fire the neurons.

Behavioral response refers to the way people act in consideration of their thresholds. At one end of this continuum, children respond in accordance with their thresholds. This means they would have a tendency to let the nervous system respond (or not respond), and they would behave consistently with this neural activity. At the other end of the behavioral continuum, children respond to counteract their thresholds. This means they would work against their thresholds as a way to reach homeostasis.

Principles and Features of the Neurological Threshold Continuum

The entire nervous system operates based on excitation and inhibition. Excitation occurs when the neurons are more likely to respond or are activated. Inhibition occurs when the likelihood of responding is decreased or responses are blocked. It is the balance of these operations that determine when responses are generated; some refer to this balance of the neurological continuum as *modulation*. Modulation is the brain's regulation of neural messages by facilitating or inhibiting responses. When modulation is intact, the nervous system responds to some stimuli while ignoring other stimuli, and the child generates an appropriate adaptive response to the situation.

In the neuroscience literature, the extreme ends of the neurological threshold continuum are called *habituation* and *sensitization*. Habituation is a process that represents

Neurological Threshold Continuum	Behavioral Response Continuum	
	Acting in ACCORDANCE With Threshold	Acting to COUNTERACT Threshold
HIGH (habituation)	Poor Registration	Sensation Seeking
LOW (sensitization)	Sensitivity to Stimuli	Sensation Avoiding

Figure 2.1 ■ **Relationships Between Behavioral Responses and Neurological Thresholds***

the nervous system's recognition that something familiar has occurred. At the cellular level, we can say that the neuron has experienced the firing pattern, and after a time, this familiar pattern no longer needs attention. At a system level, children need habituation to cope with the myriad of stimuli available at any moment in their day. Without habituation, children would be distracted continually by each new stimulus, including how their clothing feels, the sounds in the hall, the flowers blowing in the breeze outside the window, the sound and feel of saliva being swallowed, etc. Humans need habituation to focus their attention to tasks at hand. When people have difficulty with habituation, they may appear distractible, agitated, or inattentive. Their nervous systems keep interrupting ongoing performance to notice each new stimulus that comes along.

Sensitization is the nervous system mechanism that enhances potentially important stimuli. Some stimuli require attention right away, although they might be familiar. This is particularly true when the organism anticipates harm or danger associated with the stimulus. Once the nervous system identifies a stimulus as one requiring heightened attention, more neurons can be recruited to make the message more powerful and subsequently generate an immediate and powerful response. For example, although the smell of smoke could be a technically small stimulus in the room after bedtime, this stimulus could trigger sensitization (based on its potential harmfulness),

*Reprinted with permission from Dunn, W., The impact of sensory processing abilities on the daily lives of young children and their families: A conceptual model. *Infants and Young Children, 9*(4), 23–35, copyright © 1997, Aspen Publishers.

so that the person would arouse (even from sleep) and take immediate action to gather more information and/or get out of harm's way. Children develop and use sensitization through life experiences as they grow up so that they can remain attentive to their surroundings while engaged in play and other learning.

As children grow, their nervous systems are evolving and their experiences are shaping the nervous system's evolution. As part of this process, a balance of habituation and sensitization must develop to support adaptive behavior (i.e., appropriate responses to environmental demands). The point along the neurological continuum that is the most likely to generate a response for a particular child is called that child's *threshold* for that stimulus. There is a range of thresholds that support adaptive behavior and thresholds that are outside of acceptable ranges for functional performance. Children whose thresholds are too high tend to be underresponsive (i.e., it takes a lot of stimuli to reach the threshold, as when children don't respond to cues around them). Children whose thresholds are too low tend to be overly responsive (i.e., very little stimuli causes a reaction, as when children are distracted by every stimulus).

Principles and Features of the Behavioral Response Continuum

Children have interests, skills, and preferences about how to spend their time. These choices are not merely a matter of nervous system operations or all children would behave exactly alike. These individual behavioral differences are the subject of the behavioral sciences just as nervous system fluctuations are the subject of the neurosciences.

Goal-directed behavior has many features, including internal and external conditions for acting on a situation and a motivation to act. Children must have experiences that present opportunities for certain behaviors. This is a "necessary-but-not-sufficient" criterion for goal-directed behavior. The child also must have an incentive to act in a certain way. They must see that acting in certain ways will move them toward the goal, and they must have some level of interest in the act of "doing."

Children let us know their behavioral interests and tendencies by their persistence (or lack thereof) at a task. As with the neurological continuum, there is a range of performance in the center that supports adaptive behavior. There are behavioral patterns at the ends of the continuum that are maladaptive and result in unsuccessful performance. At one end of the behavioral continuum, children are so driven to perform certain rituals that these rituals interfere with the routines of daily life. At the other end of the continuum, children are so disengaged from the ongoing circumstances around them that they miss the experience of daily life routines.

The Behavioral Response continuum shown in Figure 2.1 places Acting in Accordance With Threshold at one end of the continuum and Acting to Counteract Threshold at the other end. Acting in accordance with one's threshold means that the child behaves more passively and consistently with neurological thresholds. For example, children with high thresholds who act in accordance with these thresholds appear unaware of their surroundings, so their high thresholds are rarely challenged. Acting to counteract thresholds means that the child behaves more actively to work against thresholds. For example, children with high thresholds who counteract these thresholds continuously generate activity to create more stimuli so that their thresholds can be met more frequently. Chapter 5 provides more detailed examples.

Using this continuum within a sensory processing perspective, you can see that children have preferences for certain sensory stimuli and that sensory input can be supportive or disruptive to different children. For some children, music in the background provides sensory support, increasing the level of arousal so that work can be more productive. For other children, background music creates a distraction, interrupting thinking and performance. Some children like the opportunity to get messy in art class, while others find ways to avoid putting their hands into paint or glue because it feels "yucky." Each of these behaviors provides insight about the children's sensory processing needs and preferences, enabling professionals to use this information to design more effective learning strategies for the children.

Constellations of Performance

The neurological threshold and behavioral response continuums can help you understand children's performance. However, neither continuum provides sufficient information to understand the complexity of children's responses. The proposed model of sensory processing offers a wider set of possible interpretations of children's behavior by enabling you to consider the neurological and behavioral features of performance as they affect each other.

Studies using the *Sensory Profile* support this model of sensory processing (Dunn, 1997a; Ermer & Dunn, 1998; Dunn & Brown, 1997; Kientz & Dunn, 1997) and enable you to consider what the performance constellations would look like at each corner of the model. The corners represent the extreme forms of responsiveness for each combination. For example, the performance constellation of poor registration, according to the conceptual model, represents high neurological thresholds and a tendency to act in accordance with these thresholds. Sensitivity to stimuli represents low neurological thresholds and a tendency to act in accordance with these thresholds. Sensation seeking represents high neurological thresholds with a tendency to act to counteract these thresholds, and sensation avoiding represents low neurological thresholds with a tendency to act to counteract these thresholds. See Chapter 5 for details about how to use this model to interpret *Sensory Profile* data.

■ Rationale for Evaluating Sensory Responsiveness in Daily Life

The literature on neuroscience and sensory integrative theory provides a rich source of information as you assess, plan, and provide intervention for people with special needs (Ayres, 1975, 1980; Fisher, Murray, & Bundy, 1994). Recent neuroscience literature emphasizes modulation of input as a critical function of the central nervous system (CNS) (Kandel, Schwartz, & Jessell, 1993). The sensory integrative theory's primary postulate is that learning occurs when a person has the ability to receive accurate sensory information, process it, and use it to organize behaviors (Fisher & Murray, 1991). The literature on sensory integration places a strong emphasis on processing sensory information as a key factor in the ability to exhibit adaptive responses (Ayres, 1980; Fisher, Murray, & Bundy, 1994). The actual process of integrating sensory information is a construct discussed in both the neuroscience and sensory integration literature. However, caregivers and professionals are concerned with the child's ability to manage daily life. Information that only enables the team to develop hypotheses about theoretical constructs without linking those ideas to the routines of daily life has little utility in serving the child and family. Professionals must have an understanding of the principles of neuroscience and sensory integration, and the corresponding use of that knowledge in natural contexts such as home and school.

Neuroscience

From a neuroscience perspective, modulation of input is critical to the function of the CNS. Modulation is the ability of the CNS to monitor and regulate information for the generation of appropriate responses (Dunn, 1997b). Modulation occurs by regulating habituation and sensitization responses. Habituation occurs when the CNS recognizes stimuli; in this case, the CNS decreases transmission among the cells. Sensitization occurs when the CNS perceives sensations as unfamiliar or potentially harmful and generates a heightened response. Both of these actions are considered part of learning in the CNS.

Another aspect of modulation is the development of thresholds for responding (Dunn, 1997b). CNS thresholds are established by genetic endowment and personal life experiences (Clarke & Clarke, 1976; Kandel, 1993). Children with poor sensory processing seem to display exceedingly high thresholds (i.e., habituation, hyposensitivity) or exceedingly low thresholds (i.e., sensitization, hypersensitivity). When thresholds are too high, children react less readily to stimuli, take a longer time to respond, and appear lethargic (Dunn, 1997a). When thresholds are too low, children react too quickly and frequently to stimuli, and appear to be overly excitable or hyperactive (Dunn, 1997a).

Sensory Integration

From a sensory integrative perspective, learning occurs when a person receives accurate sensory information, processes it, and uses it to organize behaviors. When children receive inaccurate or unreliable sensory input, then their ability to process the information and create responses is disrupted (Dunn, 1991). Poor sensory processing can take many forms (Ayres, 1980) and must be inferred from observations of children's behavior and performance. Poor sensory processing can take the form of overresponsivity (e.g., becoming agitated when someone brushes against you [tactile defensiveness]) or lack of responsivity (e.g., must be tapped on the shoulder several times to gain attention). Families and service providers have hypothesized that poor sensory responsivity can affect performance (e.g., Ayres & Mailloux, 1981; Magrun, McCue, Ottenbacher, & Keefe, 1981; Ottenbacher, Scoggins, & Wayland, 1981).

Performance in Daily Life

Professionals working in early intervention and public school programs have come to realize that it is both possible and useful to apply neuroscience and sensory integrative principles to children's natural life settings. In a pilot study investigating the application of sensory integrative principles in classrooms, Kemmis and Dunn (1996) found that the knowledge from this frame of reference could be successfully applied within classroom routines as part of collaborative consultation. The therapist-teacher dyads selected functional tasks with which the students were struggling in their classroom routines. They then designed interventions, based on knowledge about the students' sensory processing difficulties, that would improve the functional performance of those classroom tasks. The students in the study met about 70% of their Individual Educational Plan (IEP) goals after a year of classroom-based intervention planning.

In another study conducted in public schools, Cox (1996) found that occupational therapists identified relationships among the functional tasks of eating lunch at school and sensory processing. Therapists observed videotapes of students with sensory processing difficulties (the therapists were blind to the students' problem areas) while the students ate lunch with their peers. The therapists recorded observations about the task of eating lunch and identified the sensorimotor, cognitive, and psychosocial skills they observed. Sensory processing skills were a prominent part of their observations, along with observations of task performance. For example, therapists wrote about a child's ability to notice (or not notice) food on the face (i.e., the touch sensation of the food on the skin) in addition to recording how the child used utensils and put food into his or her mouth.

These findings provide initial evidence that there is a link between sensory processing and functional performance at school. Further work is needed to create a more direct link between functional performance and sensory processing abilities. To accomplish this goal, it is critical to have a framework for applying this theoretical knowledge in natural contexts.

The Ecology of Human Performance (EHP) framework provides this theoretical link. The EHP framework emphasizes a person's contexts as a critical variable in his or her ability to perform functional tasks in his or her life (Dunn, Brown, & McGuigan, 1994). This framework suggests that professionals must broaden the focus of data gathering to include not only information about the person's skills, but also to identify clearly what the person wants or needs to do (i.e., functional performance needs) and where the person needs to perform the task (i.e., the context). For example, washing one's face and hands before a meal presents one set of performance challenges when the person does this at home in the bathroom sink and another when he or she does it at the sink in the back of a classroom where many other students are gathering.

Three types of data need to be gathered to expand our knowledge of the application of neuroscience and sensory integration within natural contexts. First, we need data that informs us about the frame of reference being applied (i.e., sensory integration). Second, we need data about the child's functional performance. Third, we need systematic data about the context of performance so that its impact on the child's performance can be evaluated. The *Sensory Profile* directly addresses the first two of these data-gathering needs and incorporates the third by providing information from caregivers about their children's responses to sensory events in daily life.

CHAPTER 3

Research and Development of the Instrument

Brief History of the Development of the *Sensory Profile*

The *Sensory Profile* originally was compiled as part of research to test the application of sensory integration theory within consultative services in classrooms (Dunn, 1994; Kemmis & Dunn, 1996). In these studies, researchers used the instrument to determine which sensory processing difficulties the children seemed to be having so that consultative intervention could address the children's sensory processing needs within the classroom. These studies indicated that one could address sensory processing in the context of the daily routines and expectations of the classroom, and achieve successful outcomes. Although these findings were interesting and informative for practice, therapists expressed strong interest in discovering more about the *Sensory Profile* as a measure for such purposes as contributing to comprehensive assessment or designing effective interventions.

The American Occupational Therapy Foundation, the University of Kansas School of Allied Health, the Kansas Occupational Therapy Association, and the Federal Maternal and Child Health Bureau supported graduate students who worked on various aspects of the *Sensory Profile* development from 1993 to 1999.

Item Development

Researchers completed a literature review of sensory histories to develop items that characterize unusual responses to various sensory experiences in children's daily lives. Each item was written as a behavioral statement (e.g., "Prefers to be in the dark"). The original *Caregiver Questionnaire* contained 99 items (Dunn, 1994). Following pilot testing, 26 items were added to improve the clarity and range of the behavioral descriptions for caregivers, for a total of 125 items (Dunn & Westman, 1997).

The items initially were grouped by categories traditionally used in the literature and in sensory histories:

Six sensory systems

1. touch (24 items)
2. movement (22 items)
3. body position (11 items)
4. visual (18 items)
5. auditory (10 items)
6. taste/smell (10 items)

Two behavior categories

   7. activity level (6 items)

   8. social/emotional (24 items)

In 1997, to refine the item groupings, 155 therapists from the Sensory Integration Special Interest Section of the American Occupational Therapy Association (AOTA) participated in a study. The therapists reported the sensory or behavioral category they believed each item on the *Caregiver Questionnaire* represented. They received a randomized list of the questionnaire's items with the eight category choices: touch, movement, body position, visual, auditory, taste/smell, activity level, and social/emotional. Therapists also could indicate secondary categories for each item.

Description of Item Categories

The results of this study indicated that it was useful to group the items differently to derive the most meaning from the data collected on a child. The *Sensory Profile* now reflects that grouping:

- Sensory Processing contains six item categories that reflect particular types of sensory processing as part of daily life.

- Modulation contains five item categories that reflect various combinations of modulation of input for use in daily life.

- Behavioral and Emotional Responses contains three item categories that reflect emotional and behavioral responses that might be indicative of a child's sensory processing abilities.

Sensory Processing

Auditory Processing. The items included in the Auditory section measure the child's responses to things heard (e.g., "Is distracted or has trouble functioning if there is a lot of noise around").

Visual Processing. The Visual section includes items that measure the child's responses to things seen (e.g., "Is bothered by bright lights after others have adapted to the light").

Vestibular Processing. This section measures the child's responses to movement (e.g., "Becomes anxious or distressed when feet leave the ground").

Touch Processing. The Touch section measures the child's responses to stimuli that touch the skin (e.g., "Becomes irritated by shoes or socks").

Multisensory Processing. Items in this section measure the child's responses to activities that contain a combined sensory experience (e.g., "Seems oblivious within an active environment").

Oral Sensory Processing. The Oral Sensory section measures the child's responses to touch and taste stimuli to the mouth (e.g., "Limits self to particular food textures/temperatures").

Modulation

Sensory Processing Related to Endurance/Tone. This section measures the child's ability to sustain performance (e.g., "Poor endurance/tires easily").

Modulation Related to Body Position and Movement. Items in this section measure the child's ability to move effectively (e.g., "Takes movement or climbing risks during play that compromise personal safety").

Modulation of Movement Affecting Activity Level. This section measures the child's demonstration of activeness (e.g., "Spends most of the day in sedentary play").

Modulation of Sensory Input Affecting Emotional Responses. These items measure the child's ability to use body senses to generate emotional responses (e.g., Rigid rituals in personal hygiene").

Modulation of Visual Input Affecting Emotional Responses and Activity Level. Items in this section measure the child's ability to use visual cues to establish contact with others (e.g., "Stares intensively at objects or people").

Behavioral and Emotional Responses

Emotional/Social Responses. Items in this section indicate the child's psychosocial coping strategies (e.g., "Has fears that interfere with daily routine").

Behavioral Outcomes of Sensory Processing. Items in this section indicate the child's ability to meet performance demands (e.g., "Has difficulty tolerating changes in plans and expectations").

Items Indicating Thresholds for Response. This section includes items that indicate the child's level of modulation (e.g., "Jumps from one activity to another so that it interferes with play").

■ Research

The research on the *Sensory Profile* took place from 1993 to 1999, and included more than 1,200 children with and without disabilities between the ages of 3 and 14.

Examiner Selection

One hundred sixty-six occupational therapists participated as examiners in the research. Researchers randomly selected examiners from the roster of the Sensory Integration Special Interest Section of the AOTA.

Description of the Sample of Children Without Disabilities

Examiners provided a sample of 1,037 children without disabilities between the ages of 3 and 10 years. Examiners tested 524 girls and 510 boys (gender was not reported on three children). Children were excluded from the sample if caregivers reported that the children were receiving special education services and were on regular prescription medication (78 children were excluded from an original sample of 1,115 children, for this reason). Table 3.1 (see page 16) reports the number of children in the sample by age in one-year intervals.

Table 3.1		
Sample by Age		
Age (in years and months)	***n***	**% of Sample**
3.0–3.11	139	13.4
4.0–4.11	138	13.3
5.0–5.11	140	13.5
6.0–6.11	124	12.0
7.0–7.11	139	13.4
8.0–8.11	127	12.2
9.0–9.11	110	10.6
10.0–10.11	120	11.6
Total	1,037	100

Table 3.2 reports the distribution of the sample by gender.

Table 3.2		
Sample by Gender		
Gender	***n***	**% of Sample**
Female	524	50.5
Male	510	49.2
Did not report	3	.3
Total	1,037	100

Table 3.3 reports the distribution of the sample by the geographic regions of the United States. Figure 3.1 shows the breakdown of the states by region: Northeast, North Central, South, and West.

Table 3.3		
Sample by Region		
Region	***n***	**% of Sample**
Northeast	303	29.2
North Central	308	29.7
South	262	25.3
West	152	14.7
Did not report	12	1.1
Total	1,037	100

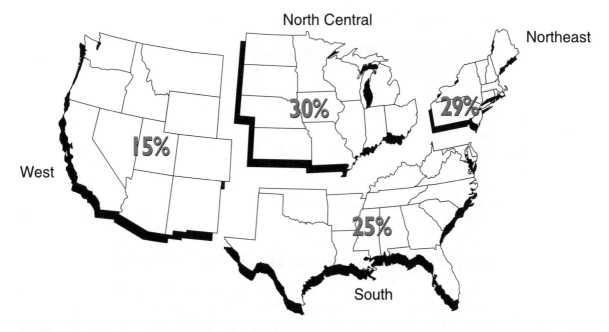

North Central

Northeast

West

South

Figure 3.1 ■ **Geographic Regions of the United States for the Sample**

Note: 1% did not report region

Table 3.4 reports the distribution of the sample by race/ethnicity.

Table 3.4		
Sample by Race/Ethnicity		
Race	**n**	**% of Sample**
Native American	9	.9
Asian	12	1.2
African American	16	1.5
Hispanic	15	1.4
White	948	91.4
Other	25	2.4
Did not report	12	1.2
Total	1,037	100

Table 3.5 reports the distribution of the sample by income.

Table 3.5		
Sample by Income		
Income	**n**	**% of Sample**
$10,000 or less	94	9.1
$11,000–30,000	467	45.0
$31,000–50,000	259	25.0
$51,000–70,000	92	8.9
Did not report	125	12.0
Total	1,037	100

Table 3.6 reports the distribution of the sample by community locations.

Table 3.6		
Sample by Community		
Community	**n**	**% of Sample**
Rural	196	18.9
Suburban	631	60.9
Urban	161	15.5
Did not report	49	4.7
Total	1,037	100

Description of the Sample of Children With Disabilities

Researchers conducted studies with smaller samples of children with various disabilities to establish validity. Children in the studies had been identified previously as having attention deficit/hyperactivity disorder (ADHD) ($n = 61$, ages 3–15), autism/pervasive developmental disorder (PDD) ($n = 32$, ages 3–13), Fragile X disorder ($n = 24$, ages 3–17), or a sensory modulation disorder ($n = 21$, ages 4–9). The studies also included a small group of children with other disabilities (e.g., behavior or learning disabilities other than those listed).

■ Development of Scores

Researchers scored and analyzed all *Caregiver Questionnaires* from the research sample (i.e., descriptive statistics, multivariate analysis of variance, principal component factor analysis) to formulate a scoring structure and provide validity evidence.

Factor Analysis

Researchers conducted a principal-components factor analysis on the sample of children without disabilities ($n = 1,037$) to determine whether items clustered meaningfully into independent groupings (Dunn & Brown, 1997). The initial factor analysis yielded 17 factors that accounted for 59.6% of the variance (i.e., nearly 60% of the variation among the scores of the children could be accounted for by these factors). Upon examination of the initial factors, a nine-factor solution was determined to be the most interpretable. These nine factors accounted for 47.8% of the variance. Researchers eliminated from the analysis any items that had weaker relationships within the factor structure (i.e., with commonalties of <.40) (Gorsuch, 1983). Forty-four items were eliminated from the final factor groupings.

Development of the Classification System and Cut Scores

A classification system was derived by establishing cut scores for each section and factor raw score totals. The classification system (Typical Performance, Probable Difference, and Definite Difference) provides an estimate of the child's likely performance in that section or factor. Researchers derived the cut scores from the research sample of children without disabilities between the ages of 3 and 10 years.

■ Types of Scores and Classification System

Section and Factor Raw Scores

Table 3.7 (see page 20) reports the mean raw scores and standard deviations by section, and Table 3.8 (see page 21) reports the mean raw scores and standard deviations by factor for each one-year age group from the *Sensory Profile* research sample of children without disabilities.

There was very little difference in the mean raw scores across the age groups. These scores indicate that children's sensory processing abilities do not change developmentally after the age of 5. Chapter 5 contains information on interpreting scores for children ages 3–4, and Appendix A provides appropriate cut scores for these children.

Although the mean raw scores and standard deviation *(SD)* for each section did not increase developmentally after age 5, three items that form Factor 9 (Fine Motor/ Perceptual) and two other factors did reflect the developmental skill levels of 3- and 4-year-olds. Therefore, you must consider these differences when interpreting the cut scores on the *Summary Score Sheet* for younger children. See Chapter 5 for interpretation information on children ages 3–4 years.

Cut scores for the classification system were established as follows:
- Typical Performance corresponds to scores at or above the point 1 *SD* below the mean for children without disabilities,
- Probable Difference corresponds to scores at or above the point 2 *SD* below the mean, but lower than 1 *SD* below the mean, for children without disabilities, and
- Definite Difference corresponds to scores below the point 2 *SD* below the mean for children without disabilities.

This method for determining cut scores was selected for several reasons. First, these decisions are based on the data collected from a large sample of children and therefore represent actual trends in children's performance in the population sampled. Second, you can use the *Sensory Profile* to determine whether sensory processing difficulties are interfering with a particular child's performance. By using the scores from the children without disabilities (who scored higher and more homogeneously than disability groups in all categories), your ability to identify children who may need further attention is maximized. In many cases, the −1 *SD* score for the children without disabilities falls toward the +1 *SD* level for disability groups (see Appendix C for a graphic comparison of mean and standard deviation patterns across groups), suggesting that using these standard deviation cut scores enables you to identify children who are in at-risk categories. Finally, the *Sensory Profile* only provides one source of information; by identifying a Probable Difference group, you can study all the assessment data, considering sensory processing correlates, and take a smaller chance of overlooking this aspect of a child's difficulty.

Low and High Threshold Items

Although scores were not developed to determine a child's differential responses to low or high threshold items, the *Caregiver Questionnaire* is designed so that you can determine how scores cluster (low, high, neither low nor high threshold) within the sections. Chapter 5 contains information on the interpretation of low and high threshold items.

Table 3.7

Mean Raw Scores and Standard Deviations for the Sensory Profile Sections

Age	n	Auditory Processing		Visual Processing		Vestibular Processing		Touch Processing		Multisensory Processing		Oral Sensory Processing		Sensory Processing Related to Endurance/Tone	
		Mean	SD	Mean	SD	Mean	SD	Mean	SD	Mean	SD	Mean	SD	Mean	SD
3.0	139	33.4	2.98	34.6	4.7	49.6	3.7	78.2	7.9	28.9	3.0	51.2	6.0	42.98	2.69
4.0	138	33.4	3.35	36.16	3.9	50.5	3.57	79.65	6.47	29.6	2.8	51.4	6.96	42.41	3.63
5.0	140	33.47	4.04	36.1	4.45	51.14	3.59	81.27	6.56	29.98	2.86	52.58	6.47	42.8	2.85
6.0	124	33.19	4.01	36.67	4.43	51.01	3.6	79.35	7.13	30.13	2.95	52.52	6.36	42.92	3.1
7.0	139	34.02	5.22	37.52	4.88	51.69	3.46	80.62	7.92	30.45	2.92	52.49	6.93	42.86	3.31
8.0	127	33.13	3.84	37.36	4.16	51.7	3.11	81.61	7.17	30.43	2.68	53.04	6.39	42.52	3.52
9.0	110	34.14	3.72	37.43	3.93	51.5	3.15	81.62	7.28	30.93	2.43	53.12	6.17	42.46	3.79
10.0	120	34	4.1	37.49	4.74	52.07	3.05	82.25	8.11	31.05	2.85	53.57	5.8	42.2	3.64

Age	n	Modulation Related to Body Position and Movement		Modulation of Movement Affecting Activity Level		Modulation of Sensory Input Affecting Emotional Responses		Modulation of Visual Input Affecting Emotional Responses and Activity Level		Emotional/Social Responses		Behavioral Outcomes of Sensory Processing		Items Indicating Thresholds for Response	
		Mean	SD	Mean	SD	Mean	SD	Mean	SD	Mean	SD	Mean	SD	Mean	SD
3.0	139	42.83	4.01	25.94	3.5	17.98	1.81	15.69	2.41	70.68	6.29	22.36	2.81	12.4	1.66
4.0	138	43.61	4.14	25.93	3.08	17.96	1.78	16.5	1.98	70.87	6.87	24.11	2.74	12.8	1.59
5.0	140	44.8	3.93	26.27	3.54	18.24	1.85	16.63	2.09	71.29	7.99	24.9	2.98	13.15	1.44
6.0	124	44.83	3.76	26.45	3.67	18.03	1.86	16.99	2.06	70.22	8.22	24.93	2.63	13.03	1.54
7.0	139	45.61	3.97	27.47	3.13	18.15	1.83	17.18	2.16	71.41	8.37	25.46	2.83	13.52	1.41
8.0	127	45.69	3.47	27	3.49	18.12	1.85	16.76	2.1	70.59	8.97	25.21	2.86	13.4	1.45
9.0	110	45.89	3.56	26.24	3.16	18.23	1.79	17.05	2.12	70.87	8.63	25.7	2.8	13.36	1.53
10.0	120	46.12	3.81	26.8	3.23	18.06	2.27	17.18	2.1	70.88	9.22	25.66	2.95	13.31	1.61

Table 3.8

Mean Raw Scores and Standard Deviations for the Sensory Profile Factors

Age	n	Sensory Seeking		Emotionally Reactive		Low Endurance/Tone		Oral Sensory Sensitivity		Inattention/Distractibility		Poor Registration		Sensory Sensitivity		Sedentary		Fine Motor/Perceptual	
		Mean	SD	Mean	SD	Mean	SD	Mean	SD	Mean	SD	Mean	SD	Mean	SD	Mean	SD	Mean	SD
3.0	139	67.8	9.12	65	6.65	42.98	2.69	37.79	5.4	29.03	2.83	36.05	3.54	17.87	2.33	14.87	2.49	8.24	2.88
4.0	138	69.7	8.2	65.26	7.27	42.41	3.63	37.77	5.98	29.25	2.85	36.68	3.1	17.95	2.45	14.48	2.53	11.36	2.61
5.0	140	71.67	9.2	65.99	8.37	42.8	2.85	38.97	5.8	28.98	3.34	36.9	2.77	18.36	2.12	14.59	2.84	12.2	2.1
6.0	124	71.25	8.66	64.75	8.45	42.92	3.1	38.79	5.81	28.63	3.7	36.53	3.16	18.56	1.94	14.79	2.63	12.84	1.78
7.0	139	73.3	8.91	66.24	8.93	42.86	3.31	38.74	6.05	28.68	3.51	36.8	3.14	18.58	1.89	15.47	2.37	13.2	1.7
8.0	127	74.1	7.33	65.22	9.13	42.52	3.52	39.23	5.43	27.89	3.7	36.66	3.35	18.37	2.09	14.95	2.64	13.42	1.8
9.0	110	73.75	7.9	65.7	9	42.46	3.79	39.1	5.43	28.6	3.6	36.73	3.38	18.76	1.58	14.43	2.84	13.49	1.65
10.0	120	75.39	8.14	65.43	9.85	42.2	3.64	39.68	5.14	28.54	4.06	36.6	3.18	18.47	2	14.78	2.7	13.68	1.54

CHAPTER 4

▇ Administration Instructions and Scoring

▇ General Testing Considerations

Before using the *Sensory Profile*, familiarize yourself with the *User's Manual* and *Caregiver Questionnaire*. Orient yourself to the instrument's purpose as well as to the items and rating scale on the *Caregiver Questionnaire* in case the caregiver has any questions. Follow all administration and scoring procedures to maintain test reliability and to ensure that interpretations of results are based on the standard procedures used to develop this instrument.

Caregiver Questionnaire *Layout*

The *Caregiver Questionnaire* was designed to be user-friendly for caregivers as well as informative to professionals. It contains instructions and a response key for caregivers, and item-specific information such as icons and item thresholds for you. The three columns under the Item heading have the following purposes (see Figure 4.1 on page 24).

The first column under the Item heading indicates the category from which the item originated. The key shown on page 24 (Figure 4.2) indicates the category the icon represents. The second column under the heading indicates the threshold of the item. A blank space indicates that the item is neither a low nor a high threshold item. L indicates low threshold, and H represents high threshold. The third column under the heading indicates the actual item number.

You may use these three columns to further refine your interpretations of a child's sensory processing abilities by looking at the scores in relation to item category or item threshold level. Chapter 5 contains additional information about how to use these columns in the interpretation process.

Administering the Sensory Profile

There are three general ways in which you can administer the *Sensory Profile*.

1. Send the *Caregiver Questionnaire* to the caregiver with a cover letter explaining the purpose of the instrument. Be sure to include your phone number in case the caregiver has questions about the form.

Sensory Processing

	Item		A. Auditory Processing	ALWAYS	FREQUENTLY	OCCASIONALLY	SELDOM	NEVER
𝓸	L	1	Responds negatively to unexpected or loud noises (for example, cries or hides at noise from vacuum cleaner, dog barking, hair dryer)					
𝓸	L	2	Holds hands over ears to protect ears from sound					
𝓸	L	3	Has trouble completing tasks when the radio is on					
𝓸	L	4	Is distracted or has trouble functioning if there is a lot of noise around					
𝓸	L	5	Can't work with background noise (for example, fan, refrigerator)					
𝓸	H	6	Appears to not hear what you say (for example, does not "tune-in" to what you say, appears to ignore you)					
𝓸	H	7	Doesn't respond when name is called but you know the child's hearing is OK					
𝓸	H	8	Enjoys strange noises/seeks to make noise for noise's sake					
			Section Raw Score Total					

Comments

Figure 4.1 ■ Item Layout

ICON KEY	
𝓸	Auditory
👁	Visual
🏃	Activity Level
👄	Taste/Smell
🧍	Body Position
→	Movement
✸	Touch
♡	Emotional/Social

Figure 4.2 ■ Icon Key

2. Have the caregiver complete the form in your office or clinic while you are evaluating the child.

3. Help the caregiver fill out the *Caregiver Questionnaire*. Use this procedure if the caregiver has difficulty reading because of language differences or reading disabilities.

If the caregiver asks questions, provide clarification without indicating a correct response. Encourage the caregiver to consider how frequently the child engages in the behaviors of interest. It may be helpful to have the caregiver use the item in a sentence with the child's name (e.g., Johnny *frequently* "walks on toes."). This will help the caregiver identify and link the child's behaviors to the statements presented on the form.

Establishing a Rapport

It is important that caregivers believe that the information you are requesting is critical to your work and that the time they take to complete the materials is invaluable to the process of planning for the child. If you send materials home to the caregiver, include a letter with a brief explanation of the instrument and why the information is important to the assessment process. Explain the caregiver's central role in providing a picture of the child's performance and the caregiver's concerns about daily life.

■ Specific Administration Procedures

Before giving the *Caregiver Questionnaire* to the caregiver, fill in the child's name and birth date on top of the first page as well as your name (Service Provider's Name) and discipline. Explain the purpose of the *Sensory Profile* to the caregiver (or provide that information in a cover letter). Have the caregiver write his or her name, relationship to the child, and the date on the first page of the form. Ask the caregiver to read the items and check the box that best describes the frequency with which he or she sees the following behaviors in the child. Instruct the caregiver to use the following key to mark responses.

Always: When presented with the opportunity, your child **always** responds in this manner, 100% of the time.

Frequently: When presented with the opportunity, your child **frequently** responds in this manner, about 75% of the time.

Occasionally: When presented with the opportunity, your child **occasionally** responds in this manner, about 50% of the time.

Seldom: When presented with the opportunity, your child **seldom** responds in this manner, about 25% of the time.

Never: When presented with the opportunity, your child **never** responds in this manner, 0% of the time.

Emphasize the importance of completing all the items. Encourage the caregiver to provide additional comments about the child's behaviors in the Comments sections. Section F (Oral Sensory Processing) also contains space for caregivers to record comments specific to each item (e.g., the caregiver may list foods the child craves). Explain to the caregiver that he or she need only provide information about the child's behaviors and that you will fill in the section raw score totals.

Once the caregiver has completed the form, make sure all items have been answered. If the caregiver has left any item blank, ask him or her to complete the item. You may need to clarify the item for the caregiver.

Note: If any item is left blank, you cannot compute a raw score total for that section or for any factor that contains that item. If the caregiver marks an X next to the item number because he or she has determined that a particular item is not applicable due to age or the child has not had the opportunity to experience the behavior, you cannot compute a raw score total for that section or for any factor that contains that item.

■ Scoring the *Caregiver Questionnaire*

After you have made sure each item has a response, score each response according to the following:

Always = 1 point

Frequently = 2 points

Occasionally = 3 points

Seldom = 4 points

Never = 5 points

If the caregiver places a mark between two categories, record the more frequent score:

Between Never and Seldom, record Seldom (4 points)

Between Seldom and Occasionally, record Occasionally (3 points)

Between Occasionally and Frequently, record Frequently (2 points)

Between Frequently and Always, record Always (1 point)

Note: Frequent behaviors receive lower scores; therefore, children get lower scores for undesirable performance and higher scores for desirable performance. Also, remember that the items are written so that more frequent behavior is undesirable.

To determine the section raw score total, add the item scores for each section. Write that score in the box labeled Section Raw Score Total following each section (see Figure 4.3).

Sensory Processing

	Item		A. Auditory Processing	ALWAYS	FREQUENTLY	OCCASIONALLY	SELDOM	NEVER
?	L	1	Responds negatively to unexpected or loud noises (for example, cries or hides at noise from vacuum cleaner, dog barking, hair dryer)	X_1				
?	L	2	Holds hands over ears to protect ears from sound		X_2			
?	L	3	Has trouble completing tasks when the radio is on			X_3		
?	L	4	Is distracted or has trouble functioning if there is a lot of noise around		X_2			
?	L	5	Can't work with background noise (for example, fan, refrigerator)	X_1				
?	H	6	Appears to not hear what you say (for example, does not "tune-in" to what you say, appears to ignore you)					X_5
?	H	7	Doesn't respond when name is called but you know the child's hearing is OK					X_5
?	H	8	Enjoys strange noises/seeks to make noise for noise's sake				X_4	
			Section Raw Score Total			23		

Comments

Figure 4.3 ■ Scoring the *Caregiver Questionnaire*

Threshold Information From the Caregiver Questionnaire

Although you do not compute a score for threshold behaviors, the *Caregiver Questionnaire* was designed to make it easy for you to consider the child's responses in relation to thresholds. In each section, the items have been divided to enable you to scan the form for low and high threshold items. To determine whether a specific item is a low threshold, a high threshold, or neither a low nor high threshold item, look at the second column. L stands for low threshold, H represents high threshold, and a blank box indicates that the item is neither a low nor a high threshold item. In Figure 4.4, Items 47 and 48 are neither high nor low threshold items; Item 49 is a low threshold item; and Items 50–53 are high threshold items. See Chapter 5 for information on the relevance and interpretations of low scores on high or low threshold items.

Item			E. Multisensory Processing	ALWAYS	FREQUENTLY	OCCASIONALLY	SELDOM	NEVER
👁		47	Gets lost easily (even in familiar places)					
🏃		48	Has difficulty paying attention					
👁	L	49	Looks away from tasks to notice all actions in the room					
👂	H	50	Seems oblivious within an active environment (for example, unaware of activity)					
🧍	H	51	Hangs on people, furniture, or objects even in familiar situations					
🧍	H	52	Walks on toes					
✋	H	53	Leaves clothing twisted on body					
			Section Raw Score Total					

Comments

Figure 4.4 ■ Item Threshold Information

■ Using the *Summary Score Sheet*

The *Summary Score Sheet* includes space to record demographic information about the child, the Factor Grid, the Factor Summary, and the Section Summary. Fill in the demographic information on the first page of the *Summary Score Sheet*, including the child's name, gender, the date, information on who completed the *Caregiver Questionnaire* and his or her relationship to the child, the service provider's name, a checklist for services the child receives, a checklist for the child's conditions, and space to record additional comments.

Transfer any pertinent caregiver comments from the Comments sections to the bottom of the front page of the *Summary Score Sheet*.

Computing Chronological Age

Calculate the child's chronological age by subtracting the child's birth date from the date the *Caregiver Questionnaire* was completed. In doing so, remember:

1. When borrowing days from months, always borrow 30 days regardless of the month.

2. When borrowing months from years, always borrow 12 months.

For example, the chronological age of a child whose caregiver filled out the questionnaire on June 18, 1999, and whose birth date is June 20, 1991 is 7 years 11 months and 28 days (see Figure 4.5).

	YEAR	MONTH	DAY
Date Tested	99 98	6 17	18 48
Date of Birth	91	6	20
Chronological Age	7	11	28

Figure 4.5 ■ Computing Chronological Age

27

Completing the Factor Grid

The Factor Grid is located on pages 2 and 3 of the *Summary Score Sheet*. Each factor is divided into three columns (see Figure 4.6). The first column contains an icon to indicate the category from which the item originated. The second column indicates the item number that corresponds to the item number on the *Caregiver Questionnaire*. The third column is where you write the item raw scores.

To calculate the child's factor raw score totals, transfer item raw scores from the *Caregiver Questionnaire* to the corresponding item number on the Factor Grid. Add the Raw Score column for each factor and record the totals in the box labeled Factor Raw Score Total.

Factor Grid

Instructions: Transfer from the *Caregiver Questionnaire* the item raw score that corresponds with each item listed. Add the Raw Score column to get the Factor Raw Score Total for each factor.

FACTOR 1 Sensory Seeking — Item	Raw Score		FACTOR 2 Emotionally Reactive — Item	Raw Score		FACTOR 3 Low Endurance/Tone — Item	Raw Score		FACTOR 4 Oral Sensory Sensitivity — Item	Raw Score		FACTOR 5 Inattention/Distractibility — Item	Raw Score
8	2		92	5		66	4		55	3		3	3
24	3		100	4		67	3		56	4		4	4
25	1		101	3		68	4		57	4		5	5
26	2		102	5		69	2		58	5		6	4
44	4		103	3		70	5		59	3		7	5
45	5		104	4		71	4		60	4		48	3
46	1		105	4		72	4		61	5		49	4
51	2		106	3		73	4		62	5		Factor Raw Score Total	28
80	3		107	3		74	3		63	4			
81	1		108	4		Factor Raw Score Total	33		Factor Raw Score Total	37			
82	1		109	5									
83	2		110	5									
84	1		111	3									
89	2		112	4									
90	3		121	3									
94	1		122	4									
123	2		Factor Raw Score Total	62									
Factor Raw Score Total	36												

Figure 4.6 ■ Scoring the Factor Grid

Completing the Factor Summary

The Factor Summary, located on page 3 of the *Summary Score Sheet,* provides an additional way to consider the child's scores. The factors reveal patterns related to the child's responsivity to stimuli in the environments. Transfer the child's score for each factor to the corresponding Factor Raw Score Total column of the Factor Summary. Plot the child's factor raw score total by marking an X in the appropriate classification column, (i.e., Typical Performance, Probable Difference, Definite Difference) that corresponds to the raw score total for each factor (see Figure 4.7).

Factor Summary

Instructions: Transfer the child's score for each factor to the column labeled Factor Raw Score Total. Then plot these totals by marking an X in the appropriate classification column (Typical Performance, Probable Difference, Definite Difference).*

Factor	Factor Raw Score Total	Typical Performance	Probable Difference	Definite Difference
1. Sensory Seeking	36 /85	85 ---------- 63	62 ---------- 55	54 --X----- 17
2. Emotionally Reactive	62 /80	80 ------X-- 57	56 ---------- 48	47 ---------- 16
3. Low Endurance/Tone	33 /45	45 ---------- 39	38 ---------- 36	35 --X----- 9
4. Oral Sensory Sensitivity	37 /45	45 --X----- 33	32 ---------- 27	26 ---------- 9
5. Inattention/Distractibility	28 /35	35 ------X- 25	24 ---------- 22	21 ---------- 7
6. Poor Registration	30 /40	40 ---------- 33	32 ---------- 30	29 ---------- 8
7. Sensory Sensitivity	15 /20	20 ---------- 16	15 ---------- 14	13 ---------- 4
8. Sedentary	17 /20	20 --X----- 12	11 ---------- 10	9 ---------- 4
9. Fine Motor/Perceptual	6 /15	15 ---------- 10	9 --------- 8	7 --X----- 3

*Classifications are based on the performance of children without disabilities (*n* = 1,037).

Figure 4.7 ■ Scoring the Factor Summary

Completing the Section Summary

The Section Summary is located on page 4 of the *Summary Score Sheet.* It provides a visual summary of the child's sensory processing, modulation, and behavior/emotional response abilities. Transfer the child's score for each section from the *Caregiver Questionnaire* to the corresponding column labeled Section Raw Score Total. Plot the child's section raw score totals by marking an X in the classification column that corresponds to the raw score total for each section (see Figure 4.8 on page 30).

Section Summary

Instructions: Transfer the child's score for each section to the Section Raw Score Total column.
Then plot these totals by marking an X in the appropriate classification column
(Typical Performance, Probable Difference, Definite Difference).*

Sensory Processing	Section Raw Score Total		Typical Performance	Probable Difference	Definite Difference
A. Auditory Processing	23	/40	40 ---------- 30	29 ---------- 26	25 ---X----- 8
B. Visual Processing	33	/45	45 ------X- 32	31 ---------- 27	26 ---------- 9
C. Vestibular Processing	45	/55	55 ---------- 48	47---------- 4X	44 ---------- 11
D. Touch Processing	73	/90	90 ---------- 7X	72---------- 65	64 ---------- 18
E. Multisensory Processing	25	/35	35 ---------- 27	26 ---X---- 24	23 ---------- 7
F. Oral Sensory Processing	50	/60	60 ---X--- 46	45 ---------- 40	39 ---------- 12
Modulation					
G. Sensory Processing Related to Endurance/Tone	35	/45	45 ---------- 39	38 ---------- 36	X6 ---------- 9
H. Modulation Related to Body Position and Movement	40	/50	50 ---------- 41	X0 ---------- 36	35 ---------- 10
I. Modulation of Movement Affecting Activity Level	17	/35	35 ---------- 23	22 ---------- 19	18 -X----- 7
J. Modulation of Sensory Input Affecting Emotional Responses	17	/20	20 --------X16	15 ---------- 14	13 ---------- 4
K. Modulation of Visual Input Affecting Emotional Responses and Activity Level	15	/20	20 ---------- X6	14 ---------- 12	11 ---------- 4
Behavior and Emotional Responses					
L. Emotional/Social Responses	60	/85	85 ---------- 63	62 -X----- 55	54 ---------- 17
M. Behavioral Outcomes of Sensory Processing	25	/30	30 ----X--- 22	21 ---------- 19	18 ---------- 6
N. Items Indicating Thresholds for Response	13	/15	15 -------X 12	11 ---------- 10	9 ---------- 3

*Classifications are based on the performance of children without disabilities (*n* = 1,037).

Figure 4.8 ■ **Scoring the Section Summary**

CHAPTER 5

Interpretation

This chapter provides insights about how to interpret a child's performance on the *Sensory Profile* so that you can design more effective intervention strategies. The *Summary Score Sheet* was designed to simplify the scoring process, to facilitate comparisons of a child's performance to a sample of children without disabilities ($n = 1,037$), and to enable you to consider the performance differences across disability groups to make further interpretations. When combined with other data (i.e., other formal tests, observations, reports, referral concerns), you will be able to make decisions about the meaning of the child's *Sensory Profile* scores in relation to performance in daily life.

Using the Classification System for Interpretation

The *Sensory Profile* enables you to communicate a child's sensory processing abilities to parents and teachers as a profile of scores. It uses a classification system to organize the possible scores into three groups based on the performance of the sample of children without disabilities ($n = 1,037$). The classification system's cut scores are provided on the *Summary Score Sheet* to aid in your interpretation process.

Classification System

Cut scores were determined for each section and factor in the following manner:

Typical Performance is scores at or above the point 1 *SD* below the mean. Section and factor raw score totals that fall within this range indicate typical sensory processing abilities. This range indicates that the child performed like a child in the top 84% of the research sample of children ($n =1,037$). See Figure 5.1 on page 32 for a graphic representation of the classification system.

Probable Difference is scores at or above the point 2 *SD* below the mean, but lower than 1 *SD* below the mean. Section and factor raw score totals that fall within this range indicate questionable areas of sensory processing abilities. This range indicates that the child's performance was between the 2nd and 16th percentile, representing 14% of the population sample.

Definite Difference is scores below the point 2 *SD* below the mean. Section and factor raw score totals that fall within this range indicate sensory processing problems. This range indicates that the child is performing like a child in the lowest 2% of the research sample.

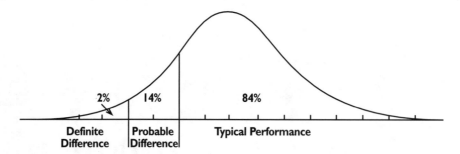

■ Using the Theoretical Model of Sensory Processing for Interpretation

Dunn (1997a) proposed a theoretical model for sensory processing based on the child's neurological thresholds and behavioral response patterns, as discussed in Chapter 2. In this model, the neurological threshold continuum is illustrated on the vertical axis, and the behavioral response continuum is illustrated on the horizontal axis (see Figure 5.2).

Low thresholds (bottom) and high thresholds (top) anchor the neurological threshold continuum. With a low threshold, the nervous system responds frequently to stimuli because it does not take very much input to reach the threshold and activate the system. With high thresholds, the nervous system does not respond to stimuli because it takes a lot of input to reach the threshold; therefore the system is dormant much of the time. Functional performance relies on a balance of activation so that the child can be alert to selected stimuli while screening out other stimuli.

The behavioral response continuum is anchored by acting in accordance (left) and acting to counteract (right) one's thresholds (see Figure 5.2). When children act in accordance with thresholds, they tend to respond in a more passive way to whatever comes along. When children act to counteract their thresholds, they tend to actively work to oppose their thresholds. These tendencies to respond are based on genetics, experience, and task demands.

These continuua interact with each other to create four basic quadrants of responsivity. It is important to keep in mind that:

1. If a child has behaviors consistent with one of these quadrants, that by itself does not constitute a reason for concluding that the child is dysfunctional. When a child has performance difficulties in daily life, behaviors consistent with these quadrants can shed light on possible reasons for the child's difficulty and ways to address the performance problem.

2. Children can exhibit any combination of these patterns of behaviors, and the patterns can coexist because they represent various forms of modulation.

Figure 5.3 on page 34 contains a summary of interpretation considerations related to this theoretical model of sensory processing. Each quadrant is discussed to help you organize your thinking.

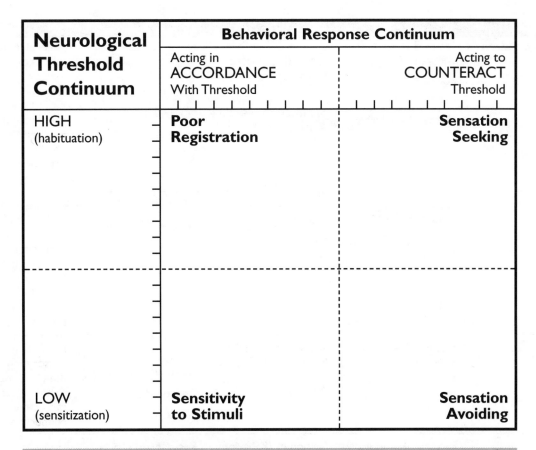

Neurological Threshold Continuum	Behavioral Response Continuum	
	Acting in ACCORDANCE With Threshold	Acting to COUNTERACT Threshold
HIGH (habituation)	Poor Registration	Sensation Seeking
LOW (sensitization)	Sensitivity to Stimuli	Sensation Avoiding

Figure 5.2 ■ **Relationships Between Behavioral Responses and Neurological Thresholds***

Poor Registration

General Features

Behavior consistent with poor registration represents high neurological thresholds and a tendency to act in accordance with those thresholds. Children who have poor registration tend to appear uninterested and can have a flat or dull affect. Children with poor registration have low energy levels and act as if they are overly tired all the time. The rationale for this, using the sensory processing model, is that the brain is not getting what it needs to generate responses, and the child's tendency to respond in accordance with high thresholds leads to an apathetic, self-absorbed appearance. It is hypothesized that children with poor registration have inadequate neural activation to support sustained performance and therefore may miss salient cues in the context to support ongoing responsivity.

Sections and Factors to Consider

Low scores on Factor 3 (Low Endurance/Tone) and Factor 6 (Poor Registration) are indicants of this category of responsivity, as is Section G (Sensory Processing Related to Endurance/Tone).

Note: It is possible that Factor 8 (Sedentary) and Section I (Modulation of Movement Affecting Activity Level) also could be related to poor registration; however,

Model Category	Associated Factors	Related Section Headings	Behavior Indicators	Intervention Approach
Poor Registration	Factor 3 (Low Endurance/Tone) Factor 6 (Poor Registration) *Factor 8 (Sedentary)	Section G (Sensory Processing Related to Endurance/ Tone) *Section I (Modulation of Movement Affecting Activity Level)	Uninterested Dull affect Withdrawn "Overly tired" Apathetic Self-absorbed	Make all experiences more concentrated with sensory information so that there is more likelihood that the thresholds will be met and the child will be able to notice and respond to cues in the environment.
Sensitivity to Stimuli	Factor 4 (Oral Sensory Sensitivity) Factor 5 (Inattention/ Distractibility) Factor 7 (Sensory Sensitivity)	Section A (Auditory Processing) Section F (Oral Sensory Processing)	Distractible Hyperactive	Provide the child with sensory experiences as part of ongoing performance that supports him or her to continue the task, and minimize the chances for thresholds to be fired repeatedly.
Sensation Seeking	Factor 1 (Sensory Seeking)	Section H (Modulation Related to Body Position and Movement)	Active Continuously engaging Fidgety Excitable	Incorporate additional sensory input into the child's routines so that thresholds can be met while conducting daily life.
Sensation Avoiding	Factor 2 (Emotionally Reactive) *Factor 8 (Sedentary)	Section M (Behavioral Outcomes of Sensory Processing)	Resistant to change Reliant on rigid rituals	Honor the child's need to limit unfamiliar input and broaden the sensory processing range within acceptable rituals.

Indicates section and factors that need further interpretations to determine to which model category they contribute.

Figure 5.3 ■ Summary of Interpretation Using the Theoretical Model of Sensory Processing

these groupings of behaviors also might be indicators of sensation avoiding if the child has been successful at creating a context that keeps him or her away from unwanted stimuli. To make this discrimination, you must consider the child's history. Children who are sensation avoiders will have indications of noticing and rejecting stimuli in their histories, while those who are poor registerers will have a history of dullness and being withdrawn.

Intervention Planning

If a child is identified as having poor registration, direct intervention planning toward enhancing task features and contextual cues. This increases the chance that the child's thresholds will be met and neural responses generated. You can do this by increasing the contrast of stimuli (e.g., placing a contrasting color on the child's desk surface to make the paper more noticeable) or by decreasing the predictability of routines (e.g., changing the route to the cafeteria, requiring the child to get up to hand in each row of seatwork rather than waiting for the whole page to be completed).

The overall goal is to make all experiences more concentrated with sensory information so there is more likelihood that the thresholds will be met and the child will be able to notice and respond to cues in the environment.

Sensitivity to Stimuli

General Features

Behavior consistent with sensitivity to stimuli represents low neurological thresholds and a tendency to act in accordance with those thresholds. Children who have sensitivity to stimuli tend to be distractible and may display hyperactivity. They have a pattern of directing their attention to the latest stimulus that presents itself, which draws them away from whatever they are trying to accomplish. They might be cautious about proceeding in some situations because they missed something (while being distracted), or might become upset either by their own difficulties with tracking tasks or with others who are interrupting them. It can be hypothesized that children who have sensitivity to stimuli have overreactive neural systems that make them aware of every stimulus that becomes available, and these children do not have the commensurate ability to habituate to these stimuli.

Sections and Factors to Consider

Low scores on Factor 4 (Oral Sensory Sensitivity), Factor 5 (Inattention/Distractibility), Factor 7 (Sensory Sensitivity), Section A (Auditory Processing), and Section F (Oral Sensory Processing) are indicators of this sensory-processing category. Each of these factors and sections contain behaviors that describe ways children are distracted from ongoing performance.

Intervention Planning

It is important to understand the meaning of these distractible behaviors when planning interventions. Be careful about withholding stimuli from these children; they still need input to operate, but cannot tolerate the influx of random input because their mechanisms of habituation are underdeveloped. For this child, you must understand how the nervous system, particularly the sensory systems, operates to establish the balance of power. Each sensory system has a component that enables arousal and alerting, and another component that supports discriminatory skills and mapping of self and environment. Children with sensory sensitivity do not need any more arousal and alerting; this mechanism is already informing them of new stimuli too often. Therefore, discriminatory input that supports organized patterns of information to the brain without generating additional arousal must be provided. Discriminatory input includes firm touch-pressure on the surface of the skin (as opposed to light touch), linear patterns of movement (as opposed to angular movement such as spinning or bending over) and predictable patterns of visual and auditory cues (as opposed to unexpected stimuli). For example, finding a waist-high bookshelf for the child's supplies and books instead of having his or her items in the compartment under his seat would reduce the angular movement input of bending down to get things out of the desk during class (Dunn, 1997b).

The overall goal is to provide the child with sensory experiences as part of ongoing performance that support the child to continue a task and to minimize the chances for the thresholds to be fired repeatedly.

Sensation Seeking

General Features

Behavior consistent with sensation seeking represents high neurological thresholds with a tendency to act to counteract these thresholds. Children who are sensation seekers are active and continuously engaged in their environments. These children add sensory input to every experience in daily life. They make noises while working, fidget, rub or explore objects with their skin, chew on things, and wrap body parts around furniture or people as ways to increase input during tasks. They may appear excitable or seem to lack consideration for safety while playing. One might hypothesize that children who are sensation seekers have inadequate neural activation (as do those with poor registration), but they are driven to meet their thresholds and so create opportunities to increase input to meet their high thresholds.

Sections and Factors to Consider

Low scores on Factor 1 (Sensory Seeking) and Section H (Modulation Related to Body Position and Movement) are the indicators of sensation seeking.

Intervention Planning

Begin intervention planning for these children with skilled observation. Because these children create sensation for themselves, their behavior tells us what sensory input they need. Their performance problems are related to the interference of their seeking behaviors to ongoing performance, so the most effective strategy is to incorporate needed sensory input into daily routines. When caregivers can include the sensory input the children need while they are conducting their lives (e.g., during eating, personal hygiene, dressing, seatwork), the children don't have to stop what they are doing to load up on sensory input to stay alert.

Be careful not to make the mistake of observing what the child *likes* related to sensory input and then using that as a reinforcer. For example, do not tell the child that when he or she accomplishes some learning task, he or she can do whatever he or she craves. This theoretical model of sensory processing suggests that the child is demonstrating what he or she *needs* and you must provide it *first* to enable performance, rather than make it contingent on performance.

Children who rock and fidget in their chairs need vestibular input; don't make them be still to complete seatwork and earn recess. They *need* to move about as a part of being ready and available for learning. One way to provide vestibular input is to send these children on errands throughout the day. Although this might be seen as a behavioral intervention, it is also a sensory one when you consider the body movement input available when moving about the school. You also could use a rocking or swivel chair, a T-stool, or a very malleable cushion to provide ongoing movement input while completing seatwork. The selection depends on the classroom setting, the teacher's needs, and the child's preferences.

The overall goal is to incorporate additional sensory input into the child's routines so that thresholds can be met while conducting daily life.

Sensation Avoiding

General Features

Behavior consistent with sensation avoiding represents low neurological thresholds with a tendency to act to counteract these thresholds. Children who are sensation avoiders engage in very disruptive behaviors. It is hypothesized that meeting thresholds occurs too often, and this event is uncomfortable or frightening to the child. In this case, the coping strategy is to keep these events at bay. Children do this by either withdrawing or engaging in an emotional outburst that enables them to get out of the threatening situation. Children who are sensation avoiders also might create rituals for their daily lives, and by their behavior, entice others to support these rituals. For example, the child might have a good morning getting ready for school if his or her parent awakens the child a certain way, serves a certain breakfast food, and allows the child to wear certain clothing items. That same child might have a bad day if the ritual is altered. The parent learns what constitutes a good day and attempts to recreate it each day to facilitate getting the child ready for school. From a behavioral perspective, this child might be stubborn or controlling. However, from a sensory processing perspective, the child is creating a situation to limit sensory input to those events that are familiar and therefore easy for the nervous system to interpret. Children who avoid sensation are resistant to changes because change represents an opportunity to be bombarded with unfamiliar (and potentially harmful) stimuli.

Sections and Factors to Consider

Low scores on Factor 2 (Emotionally Reactive) and Section M (Behavioral Outcomes of Sensory Processing) inform us about sensation avoiding. The behaviors represented in these groups of items indicate difficulty with unfamiliar or unexpected stimuli, which then generates negative emotional responses. Factor 8 (Sedentary) also can be indicative of sensation avoiding if the child has developed such clear routines that sensory thresholds are never challenged. When exploring the child's history, there will be behaviors that are more defiant if the child is a sensation avoider.

Intervention Planning

The most important thing to remember when planning interventions for children who avoid sensation is to honor their need to reduce sensory input. There is something about unfamiliar input that generates sensitization, which interferes with ongoing performance. Forcing the child "to get used to it" and to confront intense sensory input without systematic planning generates more defiant and withdrawing behaviors, making him or her even more unavailable for learning. These defiant behaviors must be understood as indications of the difficulty the child is having habituating, and a power struggle over this primal response to protect oneself must be avoided. This does not mean that you leave the child with the narrow range of acceptable input. Rather, you must carefully construct events to introduce a wider range of sensory experiences so the child can develop habituation for them. An easy way to do this is to take one of the child's imbedded rituals and expand it in one sensory way at a time. For example with the getting ready for school ritual, the parent might mix two cereals together (with texture differences) and leave everything else the same. Then when the child has processed that as part of the ritual, the parent can change something else.

The overall goal is to honor the child's need to limit unfamiliar sensory input and gradually broaden the sensory processing experiences within child's accepted rituals.

Using Threshold Patterns for Interpretation

The *Caregiver Questionnaire* was organized to provide you with an additional method for considering the child's pattern of performance. In addition to scoring the sections and the factors (which are summarized on the *Summary Score Sheet*), you can examine the caregiver responses to see if there are explicit patterns of performance that indicate high or low thresholds. Please note that there are no specific scores related to item threshold patterns; items were coded to give you another way to consider the meaning of the child's performance in the interpretation process.

Consider item threshold patterns only if the child has scores that are of concern on the Section or the Factor Score Summaries. Children without sensory processing issues also will have some variability in response. Therefore, as with any of the scores, it is only necessary to consider the meaning of these scores when the child is having problems with performance in daily life.

In the second column within the item heading on the *Caregiver Questionnaire*, you will see a code (L or H) indicating the threshold level characterized by that item (see Figure 5.4).

- Blank indicates that this item does not contribute to threshold information.
- L indicates that this item contributes to low threshold information (i.e., either indicates sensory sensitivity or sensory avoiding patterns of performance).
- H indicates that this item contributes to high threshold information (i.e., either indicates poor registration or sensory seeking patterns of performance).

Item			H. Modulation Related to Body Position and Movement	ALWAYS	FREQUENTLY	OCCASIONALLY	SELDOM	NEVER
♡		75	Seems accident-prone					
👁		76	Hesitates going up or down curbs or steps (for example, is cautious, stops before moving)					
→	L	77	Fears falling or heights					
→	L	78	Avoids climbing/jumping or avoids bumpy/uneven ground					
→	L	79	Holds onto walls or banisters (for example, clings)					
→	H	80	Takes excessive risks during play (for example, climbs high into a tree, jumps off tall furniture)					
→	H	81	Takes movement or climbing risks during play that compromise personal safety					
→	H	82	Turns whole body to look at you					
🜨	H	83	Seeks opportunities to fall without regard to personal safety					
🜨	H	84	Appears to enjoy falling					
			Section Raw Score Total					

Comments

Figure 5.4 ■ **Threshold Level**

Some children will have a scattering of scores across items within a section, while other children will have a more distinct pattern in which they have higher scores (i.e., no trouble with this type of processing because 5 = Never) for one threshold group and lower scores (i.e., difficulty with this type of processing because 1= Always) for the other threshold group.

Pattern 1: Contrast Between High and Low Threshold Items in a Section

For example, in Section A (Auditory Processing) there are five items that indicate low thresholds and three items that indicate high thresholds (see Figure 5.5). The first pattern you can observe is that the low threshold item scores cluster together and the high threshold item scores cluster together, but the two groups are separated from each other. Figure 5.5 shows that the child's pattern indicates a tendency for low threshold responses to auditory events in daily life. You then would recommend managing the environmental noise for this child so he or she can function without having sounds interfere throughout the day. For example, the teacher might provide earphones during seatwork or allow this child to go to the library to study in a carrel. The family might turn the television off during mealtime so that the child can partic-ipate more actively in the family interactions without becoming irritable.

Sensory Processing

Item			A. Auditory Processing	ALWAYS	FREQUENTLY	OCCASIONALLY	SELDOM	NEVER
👂	L	1	Responds negatively to unexpected or loud noises (for example, cries or hides at noise from vacuum cleaner, dog barking, hair dryer)	X				
👂	L	2	Holds hands over ears to protect ears from sound		X			
👂	L	3	Has trouble completing tasks when the radio is on		X			
👂	L	4	Is distracted or has trouble functioning if there is a lot of noise around		X			
👂	L	5	Can't work with background noise (for example, fan, refrigerator)		X			
👂	H	6	Appears to not hear what you say (for example, does not "tune-in" to what you say, appears to ignore you)				X	
👂	H	7	Doesn't respond when name is called but you know the child's hearing is OK			X		
👂	H	8	Enjoys strange noises/seeks to make noise for noise's sake					X
			Section Raw Score Total			*21*		

Comments

Figure 5.5 ■ Pattern 1

Pattern 2: Item Scores in a Section Are Variable Among High and Low Threshold Items

The second pattern you can observe is that the child's item scores are scattered without a particular pattern among the high and low threshold items. If the child's scores are primarily high or in the Typical Performance range, then there is not a problem with this section. When the scores are primarily low or in the Definite Difference range, then this section may indicate poor modulation. In Figure 5.6, the child's pattern indicates average to poor responsivity across all eight items in the Auditory Processing section. This pattern suggests that this child has poor modulation of auditory input, which may be interfering with daily life. You should investigate behaviors that indicate the child's high or low responsivity during the day and make recommendations about managing daily routines based on these observations. In this situation, the teacher and parents will have to recognize behaviors that indicate overresponsiveness or lack of responsiveness and act accordingly. For example, the child might seem agitated when exiting the bus on some days, suggesting overresponsiveness to the sounds on the bus. On these days, the teacher might find a quiet activity for the beginning of the day to mediate that experience. On other days, the child might seem oblivious to friends' invitations to play on the playground. The teacher might provide additional cues for the child on these days to prevent social isolation because of poor auditory responsiveness.

Sensory Processing

Item			A. Auditory Processing	ALWAYS	FREQUENTLY	OCCASIONALLY	SELDOM	NEVER
🦻	L	1	Responds negatively to unexpected or loud noises (for example, cries or hides at noise from vacuum cleaner, dog barking, hair dryer)	X				
🦻	L	2	Holds hands over ears to protect ears from sound				X	
🦻	L	3	Has trouble completing tasks when the radio is on			X		
🦻	L	4	Is distracted or has trouble functioning if there is a lot of noise around		X			
🦻	L	5	Can't work with background noise (for example, fan, refrigerator)			X		
🦻	H	6	Appears to not hear what you say (for example, does not "tune-in" to what you say, appears to ignore you)	X				
🦻	H	7	Doesn't respond when name is called but you know the child's hearing is OK		X			
🦻	H	8	Enjoys strange noises/seeks to make noise for noise's sake		X			
			Section Raw Score Total			*18*		

Comments

Figure 5.6 ■ **Pattern 2**

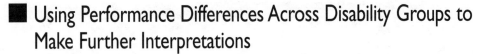

Using Performance Differences Across Disability Groups to Make Further Interpretations

If a child scores within the Typical Performance range for children without disabilities on all sections and factors, there is no need for further interpretations of section or factor scores. However, if the child scores below the Typical Performance range for children without disabilities on at least one section or factor, you may find if useful to consider how children with various disabilities performed on that section or factor.

A range of scores from –1 *SD* to +1 *SD* from the mean was plotted for four groups of children: children without disabilities, children with ADHD, children with autism/PDD, and children with other disabilities. For a description of the four groups refer to Chapter 3. Appendix C displays these relationships for all sections and factors. The X represents the mean for the groups, while the brackets represent –1 *SD* and +1 *SD* for each group. (Keep in mind that the data on the groups of children who have ADHD, autism, or other disabilities do not directly match in age, gender, or any other stratification variables the sample of children without disabilities.)

Performance Differences Between Disability Groups and Children Without Disabilities

Factor 1

For Factor 1 (Sensory Seeking), 81.1% of the children without disabilities scored 65 points or higher (out of 85 possible points), while 81.7% of the children with ADHD and 77.8% of children with autism scored below 65 points. As you can see in Figure 5.7 on page 42, all the disability groups performed poorer overall on Factor 1 than the children without disabilities.

Factor 2

This pattern also exists in Factor 2 (Emotionally Reactive), on which 77.1% of the children without disabilities scored 60 points or higher (out of 80 possible points), while 87.3% of the children with ADHD and 100% of the children with autism scored below 60 points. This suggests that children respond differently to emotionally reactive items on the *Sensory Profile* depending on whether or not they have one of these disabilities.

Factor 5

The same pattern of separation between the children with and without disabilities occurs for Factor 5 (Inattention/Distractibility); 88.8% of children without disabilities obtained a score 25 points or higher (out of 35 possible points), while 94.4% of children with ADHD and 79.2% of children with autism scored lower than 25 points.

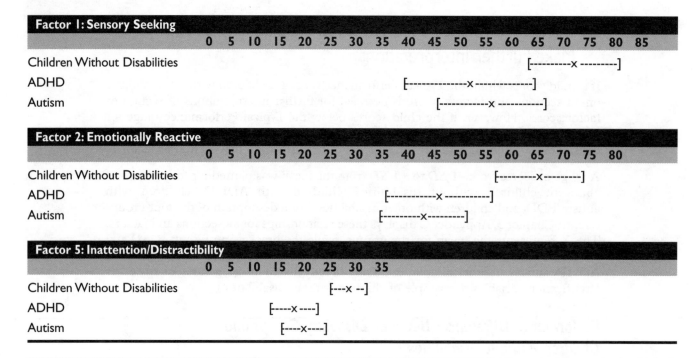

Factor 1: Sensory Seeking

	0	5	10	15	20	25	30	35	40	45	50	55	60	65	70	75	80	85

Children Without Disabilities   [---------x---------]

ADHD   [-------------x-------------]

Autism   [-----------x-----------]

Factor 2: Emotionally Reactive

	0	5	10	15	20	25	30	35	40	45	50	55	60	65	70	75	80

Children Without Disabilities   [---------x---------]

ADHD   [-----------x-----------]

Autism   [---------x---------]

Factor 5: Inattention/Distractibility

	0	5	10	15	20	25	30	35

Children Without Disabilities   [---x --]

ADHD   [----x----]

Autism   [----x----]

Figure 5.7 ■ **Performance Differences Between Groups**

Performance Differences for Particular Disability Groups

Factor 4

In Factor 4 (Oral Sensory Sensitivity), children without disabilities performed higher on average than children with ADHD, who performed higher than children with autism (see Figure 5.8).

Factor 9

The same results occur in Factor 9 (Fine Motor/Perceptual); children who have autism had more difficulties with these behaviors (see Figure 5.8).

Example 1

Let's consider the meaning of these data for your decision-making process and for program planning. As shown in Figure 5.9, a child obtained a score of 55 points out of a possible 85 on Factor 1 (Sensory Seeking). This score is below the Typical Performance range for children without disabilities and within 1 *SD* of the mean for children with autism and those with ADHD. This does not mean that this child has autism or ADHD. However, it is likely that this child is engaging in sensory-seeking behaviors more than children without disabilities.

Note: Remember that frequent behaviors receive lower scores; therefore, children get lower scores for undesirable performance and higher scores for desirable performance.

In Example 1, you would consider the referral concerns and performance problems to see whether sensory-seeking behaviors are interfering with this child's success at home or at school. For example, if the teacher reported that this child was not getting seat-

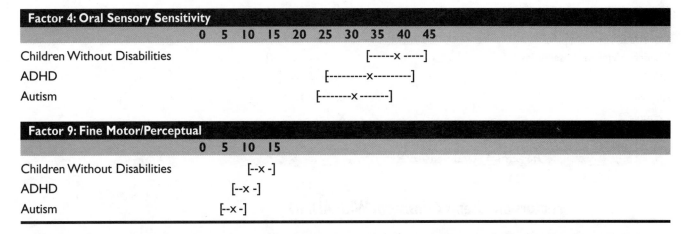

Figure 5.8 ■ **Factor 4 and Factor 9 Comparisons of Children Without Disabilities and Children With ADHD or Autism**

work completed in a timely manner, you might hypothesize that he or she is engaging in sensory-seeking behaviors that interfere with seatwork. Perhaps this child is getting up from his or her desk frequently, rocks, moves or fiddles at the desk, makes noises with objects on the desk, or spends a lot of time visually searching the environment. Although some children can do some of these behaviors and still complete their work, these activities may be interfering with this child's performance at school.

Example 2

This child scored 30 out of a possible 45 points for Factor 4 (Oral Sensory Sensitivity). According to the classification system, this child's score is in the Probable Difference range and within 1 *SD* of the mean for children with autism and those with ADHD (see Figure 5.10 on page 44). This score would suggest a need to explore the child's performance related to the oral structure. Follow-up would include observations, interviews, and other investigations about this child's eating, drinking, talking, socializing, and other activities that require oral motor control. You would want to know whether this child selects oral activity throughout the day (e.g., making noises, touching the face and mouth frequently, chewing on objects), because oral activity can provide added arousal to support performance.

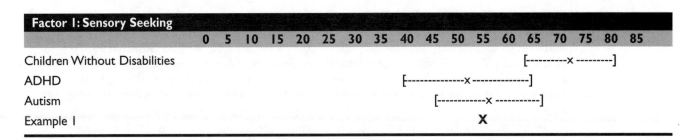

Figure 5.9 ■ **Example 1: Factor 1 (Sensory Seeking)**

Factor 4: Oral Sensory Sensitivity										
	0	5	10	15	20	25	30	35	40	45

Children Without Disabilities   [------x -----]

ADHD   [---------x---------]

Autism   [-------x -------]

Example 2   **X**

Figure 5.10 ■ **Example 2: Factor 4 (Oral Sensory Sensitivity)**

Factors and Items Consistent With ADHD

Bennett and Dunn's (in press) analyses of children without disabilities and children with ADHD identified 43 items from the *Caregiver Questionnaire* representing behaviors that were more common for children with ADHD.

Thirty-one items fell into the following factors:

- Factor 1 (Sensory Seeking)
- Factor 2 (Emotionally Reactive)
- Factor 5 (Inattention/Distractibility)

Factors 1, 2, and 5 contain items that are consistent with the patterns of behavior that are observed in children who have ADHD. If a child's scores on these factors indicate low performance (i.e., Probable Difference or Definite Difference), you might want to look for behaviors such as distractibility, poor frustration tolerance, lack of ability to profit from mistakes, and impulsivity during daily life. The child also might have difficulty with learning new tasks, following directions (including direct, single orders), and completing work, and may have inconsistent work product.

The remaining 12 items that Bennett and Dunn found to be more common for ADHD primarily involve behaviors of visual and tactile processing. These items only cluster for children with ADHD. This grouping represents the Visual/Tactile Processing Cluster on the ADHD worksheet in Appendix B. This finding is consistent with the results of Schaughency (1986), who reported that children who have ADHD have a characteristic pattern of visual and tactile perceptual difficulties.

When referral concerns lead the team to consider features of attentional deficits, consider scoring these 12 items as a cluster (Visual/Tactile Processing Cluster) in addition to completing the *Summary Score Sheet's* Factor and Section Summaries. To calculate the Visual/Tactile Cluster Raw Score Total, transfer the item scores from the *Caregiver Questionnaire* onto a photocopy of the Appendix B worksheet, then add the item scores. Transfer the Cluster Raw Score Total to the summary section of the worksheet as well as the total raw scores for Factors 1, 2, and 5. Then plot the raw score totals by marking Xs in the appropriate classification column (Typical Performance, Probable Difference, Definite Difference) (see Figure 5.11).

This ADHD worksheet can be used as part of comprehensive assessment data for diagnosing ADHD, and can be used to validate parents and teachers' referral concerns. Therapists can include this worksheet with other diagnostic information in the child's record. Even if a child does not meet criteria for the ADHD diagnosis, Probable Difference or Definite Difference scores on this worksheet indicate a need for the team to construct intervention plans related to the child's difficulty with organizing sensory input to design and carry out appropriate responses at home and school.

SUMMARY

Instructions: Transfer the child's score for the cluster and factors to the Raw Score Total column. Then plot these totals by marking an X in the appropriate classification column (Typical Performance, Probable Difference, Definite Difference).

	Raw Score Total	Typical Performance	Probable Difference	Definite Difference
Visual/Tactile Processing Cluster (see above)	*26* /60	60 ---------- 46	45 ---------- 41	40 ----X---- 12
Factor 1 Sensory Seeking	*53* /85	85 ---------- 63	62 ---------- 55	54 X--------- 17
Factor 2 Emotionally Reactive	*49* /80	80 ---------- 57	56 --------X48	47 ---------- 16
Factor 5 Inattention/Distractibility	*21* /35	35 ---------- 25	24 ---------- 22	X1 ---------- 7

Figure 5.11 ■ **Summary of Scores Relevant to Children With ADHD**

■ Making Interpretations for 3- and 4-Year-Old Children

Because children ages 3 and 4 years perform differently in some ways than older children, you should be cautious when interpreting a 3- or 4-year-old child's responses and conduct further assessment whenever his or her scores fall into the Definite Difference range. It is advisable to use the cut scores in Appendix A for 3- and 4-year-olds when plotting the child's performance on the *Summary Score Sheet*. In particular, 3- and 4-year-olds performed differently on the following sections and factors:

- On Factor 1 (Sensory Seeking), 3- and 4-year-olds without disabilities had slightly lower scores than older children, suggesting that they engaged in these behaviors more often than older children. Therefore 3- and 4-year-olds are sensation seeking more often than older children.

- On Factor 2 (Emotional Reactivity), Factor 5 (Inattention/Distractibility), and Section L (Emotional/Social Responses), 3- and 4-year-olds also had slightly higher scores, suggesting that young children were slightly less reactive and distractible. None of these outcomes are surprising. Young children generally are very intent on exploring their environments, which can affect their ability to respond to environmental stimuli.

- Factor 9 (i.e., items 13, 118, and 119) reflects a developmental skill (fine motor) that 3- and 4-year-olds typically have not yet attained:

  Item 13: has difficulty putting puzzles together (as compared to same age children)

  Item 118: writing is illegible

  Item 119: has trouble staying between the lines when coloring or writing

  Generally it is inappropriate to score Factor 9 for 3- and 4-year-olds.

You must engage in a clinical reasoning process linking the summary of the data with the performance issues raised in the referral to understand the relationships among *Sensory Profile* findings and child's needs/performance to make an effective interpretation.

CHAPTER 6

■ Technical Characteristics

■ Reliability

Test reliability is an indication of the degree to which a test provides a precise and stable score. The reliability of the *Sensory Profile* was estimated using internal consistency. The more reliable a test is, the smaller the standard error of measurement *(SEM)* and the smaller the confidence intervals around a test score.

Internal Consistency

Cronbach's Alpha was calculated to examine the internal consistency for each section of the *Sensory Profile*. Internal consistency indicates the extent to which the items in each section measure a single construct. The values of alpha for the various sections ranged from .47 to .91 as shown in Table 6.1 on page 48.

Standard Error of Measurement

As with all measurement instruments, the scores obtained from the *Sensory Profile* provide only an estimate of the child's true score. Measurement error can occur for a variety of reasons (e.g., caregivers guessing or recording responses incorrectly, examiners giving misinformation, miscalculation of scores, unclear directions or items).

The standard error of measurement is an index of the degree to which obtained scores differ from true scores. The *Sensory Profile* provides a standard error of measurement value for each possible section and factor raw score total (see Table 6.2 on page 49). These values can be used to construct a confidence interval around each section and factor raw score total.

Table 6.1	
Coefficient Alpha	
Sensory Processing	**Coefficient Alpha**
Section A: Auditory Processing	.6585
Section B: Visual Processing	.7480
Section C: Vestibular Processing	.6959
Section D: Touch Processing	.8568
Section E: Multisensory Processing	.6389
Section F: Oral Sensory Processing	.8450
Modulation	
Section G: Sensory Processing Related to Endurance/Tone	.8378
Section H: Modulation Related to Body Position and Movement	.7434
Section I: Modulation of Movement Affecting Activity Level	.6621
Section J: Modulation of Sensory Input Affecting Emotional Responses	.5817
Section K: Modulation of Visual Input Affecting Emotional Responses and Activity Level	.6177
Behavioral and Emotional Responses	
Section L: Emotional/Social Responses	.8986
Section M: Behavioral Outcomes of Sensory Processing	.6386
Section N: Items Indicating Thresholds for Response	.4717
Factors	**Coefficient Alpha**
1. Sensory Seeking	.8906
2. Emotionally Reactive	.9151
3. Low Endurance/Tone	.8378
4. Oral Sensory Sensitivity	.8521
5. Inattention/Distractibility	.7732
6. Poor Registration	.7670
7. Sensory Sensitivity	.8095
8. Sedentary	.8331
9. Fine Motor/Perceptual	.7245

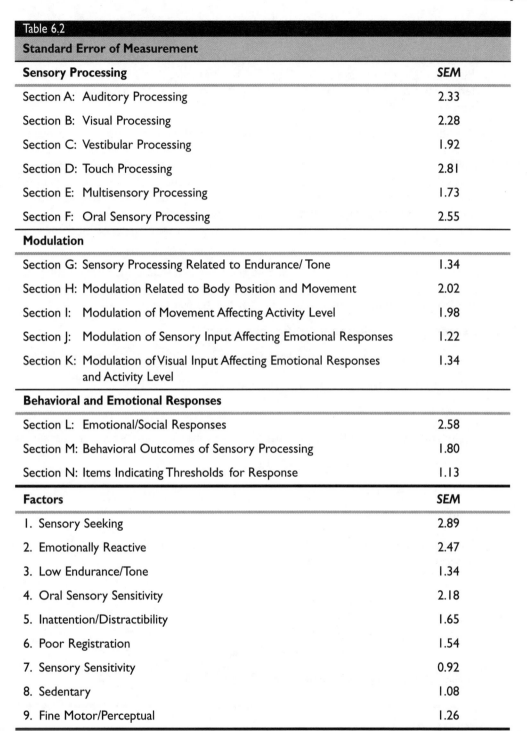

Table 6.2	
Standard Error of Measurement	
Sensory Processing	**SEM**
Section A: Auditory Processing	2.33
Section B: Visual Processing	2.28
Section C: Vestibular Processing	1.92
Section D: Touch Processing	2.81
Section E: Multisensory Processing	1.73
Section F: Oral Sensory Processing	2.55
Modulation	
Section G: Sensory Processing Related to Endurance/ Tone	1.34
Section H: Modulation Related to Body Position and Movement	2.02
Section I: Modulation of Movement Affecting Activity Level	1.98
Section J: Modulation of Sensory Input Affecting Emotional Responses	1.22
Section K: Modulation of Visual Input Affecting Emotional Responses and Activity Level	1.34
Behavioral and Emotional Responses	
Section L: Emotional/Social Responses	2.58
Section M: Behavioral Outcomes of Sensory Processing	1.80
Section N: Items Indicating Thresholds for Response	1.13
Factors	**SEM**
1. Sensory Seeking	2.89
2. Emotionally Reactive	2.47
3. Low Endurance/Tone	1.34
4. Oral Sensory Sensitivity	2.18
5. Inattention/Distractibility	1.65
6. Poor Registration	1.54
7. Sensory Sensitivity	0.92
8. Sedentary	1.08
9. Fine Motor/Perceptual	1.26

Confidence Intervals

A confidence interval is a range of scores within which you can be highly confident that the child's true score actually lies. For example, if you calculate the 95% confidence interval, you can be 95% confident that the child's true score is within this interval.

Confidence intervals are developed assuming the data follows a normal curve. Because 95% of scores under a normal curve are within 1.96 standard deviations *(SD)* of the mean, a 95% confidence interval is found by adding and subtracting 1.96 times the number of standard deviations from the score. To develop a 95% confidence interval for a particular score, the standard deviation of the sample distribution is the standard error of measurement; therefore, the appropriate standard deviation is the standard error of measurement. Therefore, the confidence interval becomes the score +/- 1.96 x *SEM*.

Note that for very high or very low raw scores it is possible that the confidence interval will fall outside the range of possible obtained scores. However, this is not a problem because the confidence interval is for the true score.

Example of calculating a confidence interval

Justin's section raw score total for Section A (Auditory Processing) = 20

SEM for this score = 2.33 (see Table 6.2)

1.96 x 2.33 = 4.57

Subtract 4.57 and add 4.57 to Justin's raw score to get the 95% confidence interval.

For Justin, these numbers would be:

20 – 4.57 = 15.43

20 + 4.57 = 24.57

This calculation gives you 95% confidence that Justin's true score lies somewhere between 15.43 and 24.57 (see Figure 6.1).

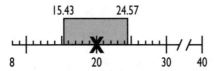

Figure 6.1 ■ **Justin's Confidence Interval for Section A**

Retesting

Although most of the *Sensory Profile* research indicates that sensory processing is a measure of status, there may be times when scores would be expected to change over time (e.g., because of the effect of physiological treatment regimes). When it is appropriate to retest a child, it is important to determine whether a change in a child's score is due to measurement error or an actual change in the child's performance. To do this, take the two test scores and calculate a confidence interval around each score. If these intervals overlap, there is a good chance that the change in the score does not represent true functional progress, but rather may be due to measurement error.

The following example illustrates how to use confidence intervals to examine change in a child's score over time (see Figure 6.2).

Example: Tamara (first test session)

Section raw score total for Section D (Touch Processing) = 65

SEM for this score = 2.81 (see Table 6.2)

1.96 x 2.81 = 5.51

Now subtract and add 5.51 to Tamara's section raw score total for a 95% confidence interval of 59.49 to 70.51. This calculation gives you 95% confidence that Tamara's first test's true score lies somewhere between 59.49 to 70.51.

Tamara (second test session)

Section raw score total for Section D (Touch Processing) = 71

SEM for this score = 2.81 (see Table 6.2)

1.96 x 2.81 = 5.51

Now subtract and add 5.51 to Tamara's section raw score total.

For Tamara, these scores would be:

71 − 5.51 = 65.49

71 + 5.51 = 76.51

So, you can have 95% confidence that Tamara's second score is between 65.49 and 76.51. Now you should plot these two confidence intervals to see whether they are distinct from each other. As Figure 6.2 illustrates, the confidence intervals of Tamara's score from Test 1 and Test 2 overlap. This indicates that the change her score could be due to measurement error rather than real functional progress. Therefore, Tamara has not necessarily made significant improvements and further intervention or assessment may be warranted.

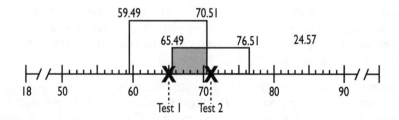

Figure 6.2 ■ **Tamara's Confidence Intervals**

■ Validity

Validity refers to evidence that establishes the extent to which a test measures what it was designed to measure. There are many different types of studies that provide evidence that an instrument is valid. Typical types of validity evidence include content validity and construct validity.

Content Validity

Content validity was established during the development of the *Sensory Profile* by determining that the test sampled the full range of children's sensory processing behaviors and that the items were placed appropriately within sections.

Literature Review. The items for the *Sensory Profile* were compiled from the sensory histories of children and from literature on sensory processing (e.g., Ayres, 1980; Larson, 1982; Royeen & Fortune, 1990). Items were selected as potential test items on the basis of how well they identified sensory-processing difficulties, discriminated among children with and without difficulties, or reported changes in behaviors with intervention.

Expert Review. Eight therapists who were experienced in applying sensory integration theory to practice reviewed the possible list of items and made recommendations about the best wording of similar items, placement of items into the sections, and structure of the evaluation. These therapists also conducted the first pilot study of the *Sensory Profile* (Dunn, 1994) to determine whether children without disabilities displayed these behaviors.

Category Analysis. A national study was conducted to determine the way that experienced therapists would categorize the items if they had no cues (i.e., section headings) about where the items would be placed. Participants included 155 occupational therapists who were members of the Sensory Integration Special Interest Section of the AOTA. They received a randomized list of the items and were asked to select a primary (and secondary, if necessary) category for each item. They used a list of the eight categories from the research edition of the *Sensory Profile*. Results indicated that 80% of therapists agreed on the category placement on 63% of the items (78 out of 125 items). For the remaining items, new categories (other than the initial eight) were developed into which these items meaningfully fell.

Construct Validity

A test has construct validity if it actually measures the underlying construct that it purports to measure. One way to demonstrate construct validity is to show that a test has convergent and discriminant validity. Convergent validity is established when a test correlates highly with other measures of the same construct or other variables that it theoretically would be expected to correlate highly. Discriminant validity is demonstrated when a test has low to moderate correlations with variables that measure different but related constructs.

To examine the convergent and discriminant validity of the *Sensory Profile,* various scores obtained on the *Sensory Profile* were compared with different functional tasks as measured by the *School Function Assessment* (Coster, Deeney, Haltiwanger, & Haley, 1998). Researchers hypothesized a pattern of correlations that would be predicted from theory. The data supported the hypothesized correlations, demonstrating both convergent and discriminant validity.

■ Sensory Profile and School Function Assessment

Scores obtained on the *Sensory Profile* were compared with scores obtained on the *School Function Assessment* (SFA) in order to examine the convergent and discriminant validity of the *Sensory Profile*. It was hypothesized that some school functions would be related to aspects of sensory processing while others would be independent of sensory processing.

Researchers selected the SFA for the initial validity study because professionals and caregivers are interested in children's performance at school. Learning is a complex process requiring many sensorimotor, cognitive, and psychosocial skills. When children have difficulties with learning, you should consider some or all of these factors to determine whether they support or create barriers to performance. The *Sensory Profile* could be a useful measure to sort out strengths and barriers to performance.

Although sensory processing and modulation are core features of the overall information processing systems, not all performance problems are related to poor sensory processing and modulation. To be the most effective in defining the problem and constructing interventions, you must have measures available that can validly identify which performance problems are likely to be related to sensory processing and/or modulation and which are not.

Researchers expected to see the following relationships, which would establish convergent validity.

- High correlations between the SFA performance items and the items in Factor 9 (Fine Motor/Perceptual) on the *Sensory Profile* because both measures evaluate product behaviors such as hand use.
- High correlations between the SFA socialization and behavior interaction sections and the modulation sections and factors on the *Sensory Profile* because children who have difficulty regulating sensory input have difficulty constructing appropriate responses.

Researchers expected to see the following relationships to establish discriminant validity.

- Low correlations between the SFA sections that capture daily routines and the sensory sections of the *Sensory Profile* because children can learn these routines as patterns of performance that do not require planning each time.

Researchers identified children in special education programs, and team members sent the *Sensory Profile* to caregivers. Researchers then selected a random sample of these children ($n = 16$) and asked their teachers to complete the SFA. Researchers calculated correlations between the sections of the SFA (i.e., 21 adaptations items, 21 assistance items, and 21 performance groupings) and the 14 sections and 9 factor scores of the *Sensory Profile*. The correlations are listed in Table 6.3 (see page 54); significant correlations are in bold print.

When interpreting the correlations between the *Sensory Profile* and SFA it is important to understand the scoring for the two measures. On the SFA, lower scores are desirable and indicate less need for supports. On the *Sensory Profile*, the lower scores are undesirable, indicating the child exhibits the behaviors more often. Therefore the expected correlations between the *Sensory Profile* and the SFA are *negative*.

Convergent Validity

As expected, there were large and meaningful correlations between the *Sensory Profile*'s Factor 9 (Fine Motor/Perceptual) and the three sections of the SFA (18 assistance items, 12 adaptation items, 5 performance groupings). Factor 9 contains items that describe product-oriented behaviors (e.g., writing is illegible, has trouble staying between the lines when writing, has difficulty putting puzzles together). See Table 6.3 for the correlations regarding assistance in adaptation items.

Table 6.3

Correlations Between the *Sensory Profile* and the *School Function Assessment*

Sensory Profile			*School Function Assessment*	
	Behavior Regulation		**Positive Interaction**	
Sensory Processing	Adaptations	Assistance	Adaptations	Assistance
Section A: Auditory Processing	-.493	**-.582***	-.379	-.385
Section B: Visual Processing	**-.589***	**-.674***	-.382	-.478
Section C: Vestibular Processing	**-.583***	-.557	-.563	-.493
Section D: Touch Processing	-.348	-.101	.136	-.194
Section E: Multisensory Processing	-.551	**-.670***	-.448	-.502
Section F: Oral Sensory Processing	-.254	-.343	-.035	-.279
Modulation				
Section G: Sensory Processing Related to Endurance/Tone	**-.584***	**-.721****	**-.584***	**-.716****
Section H: Modulation Related to Body Position and Movement	**-.508***	**-.528***	-.330	-.448
Section I: Modulation of Movement Affecting Activity Level	**-.574***	**-.598***	-.489	-.405
Section J: Modulation of Sensory Input Affecting Emotional Responses	**-.529***	**-.517***	-.334	**-.539***
Section K: Modulation of Visual Input Affecting Emotional Responses and Activity Level	-.216	-.320	-.033	-.260
Behavioral and Emotional Responses				
Section L: Emotional/Social Responses	-.346	-.285	-.241	-.175
Section M: Behavioral Outcomes of Sensory Processing	**-.673****	**-.633****	**-.539***	**-.633****
Section N: Items Indicating Thresholds for Responses	**-.796****	**-.650****	**-.538***	**-.694****

	Behavior Regulation		**Positive Interaction**	
Factor	Adaptations	Assistance	Adaptations	Assistance
1. Sensory Seeking	-.434	-.436	-.095	-.328
2. Emotionally Reactive	-.372	-.360	-.245	-.282
3. Low Endurance/Tone	**-.584***	**-.721****	**-.584***	**-.716****
4. Oral Sensory Sensitivity	-.199	-.320	.007	-.300
5. Inattention/Distractibility	**-.582***	**-.584***	-.495	-.373
6. Poor Registration	**-.615***	-.340	-.348	-.388
7. Sensory Sensitivity	-.452	-.478	**-.546***	-.388
8. Sedentary	**-.551***	**-.554***	**-.545***	-.368
9. Fine Motor/Perceptual	-.502	**-.720****	**-.703****	**-.681****

* = correlation is significant at the 0.05 level (2-tailed).

** = correlation is significant at the 0.01 level (2-tailed).

n = 16

The moderate correlations between the Behavioral Regulation and Positive Interaction sections of the SFA and the modulation sections from the *Sensory Profile* also suggest convergent validity. The data provide additional confirmation to the long-recognized relationship among sensory processing, modulation, and children's behavioral and social repertoires.

In addition, there were moderate correlations between the SFA Behavior Regulation and Positive Interaction sections and the *Sensory Profile* Factors 3, 6, and 8 (Low Endurance/Tone, Poor Registration, and Sedentary, respectively) and Factor 5 (Inattention/Distractibility). These factor groupings contain items that indicate low responsiveness (Factors 3, 6, and 8) or overresponsiveness (Factor 5).

Discriminant Validity

The study findings also provide evidence of discriminant validity. Researchers found low correlations between the more detailed performance items on the SFA and the items on the *Sensory Profile* (see Table 6.3). Although all performance requires sensory input and sensory awareness, the sensory processing features of the *Sensory Profile* items seem to be more globally related to overall performance. Therefore, although a specific performance (e.g., manipulating small objects in art class) may have sensory features, specific sensory inputs are not directly related to the more global way children must construct appropriate responses based on their "sense" of the task demands. This would suggest that the *Sensory Profile* is tapping more global sensory processing and therefore is not related to the specific tasks such as those included on the SFA.

Clinical Group Studies

The performance of a number of clinical groups with disabilities was compared to the research sample of children without disabilities to determine whether the *Sensory Profile* could delineate among the groups based on the children's responses to sensory events in daily life. The clinical groups included children with autism and those with ADHD. It should be noted that the two clinical groups did not match the demographic variables (e.g., age, gender, region) of the research sample to which they were compared. See Chapter 3 for a description of the samples of children with and without disabilities.

Children With Autism

Thirty-two children ages 3–13 years who had autism were evaluated. Table 6.4 (see page 56) shows their mean and standard deviations on the sections and factors. On nearly 90% of the items, children with autism performed meaningfully different from children without disabilities, engaging in the behaviors on the *Sensory Profile* more frequently than children without disabilities. Upon further analysis, it was found that the items that were most different scattered across all factors on the *Sensory Profile*, lending evidence to the pervasive nature of this disorder.

Children With ADHD

Sixty-one children ages 3–15 years who had ADHD were evaluated. Table 6.5 shows their mean and standard deviations on the sections and factors. Children with ADHD exhibited 113 of the 125 behaviors (i.e., items) more frequently than children without disabilities. After examining the items further, 43 of the 113 items had raw score

Table 6.4		
Means and Standard Deviations for Children With Autism		
Sensory Processing	**Mean**	**SD**
Section A: Auditory Processing	25.0	5.1
Section B: Visual Processing	30.6	6.7
Section C: Vestibular Processing	42.8	4.7
Section D: Touch Processing	60.1	10.6
Section E: Multisensory Processing	20.7	4.3
Section F: Oral Sensory Processing	38.2	10.0
Modulation		
Section G: Sensory Processing Related to Endurance/Tone	34.4	8.7
Section H: Modulation Related to Body Position and Movement	35.9	5.5
Section I: Modulation of Movement Affecting Activity Level	21.4	3.2
Section J: Modulation of Sensory Input Affecting Emotional Responses	11.7	2.9
Section K: Modulation of Visual Input Affecting Emotional Responses and Activity Level	12.6	2.4
Behavioral and Emotional Responses		
Section L: Emotional/Social Responses	50.9	8.4
Section M: Behavioral Outcomes of Sensory Processing	16.9	3.1
Section N: Items Indicating Thresholds for Response	10.1	2.8
Factors	**Mean**	**SD**
1. Sensory Seeking	56.1	10.4
2. Emotionally Reactive	43.0	8.3
3. Low Endurance/Tone	34.4	8.7
4. Oral Sensory Sensitivity	30.5	7.0
5. Inattention/Distractibility	19.9	4.3
6. Poor Registration	27.5	5.2
7. Sensory Sensitivity	15.0	4.5
8. Sedentary	12.9	3.4
9. Fine Motor/Perceptual	7.1	2.3

differences of more than 1 point on the Likert scale. These 43 items clustered into three factors (Dunn & Brown, 1997) and one additional grouping: Factor 1 (Sensory Seeking), Factor 2 (Emotional Reactivity), Factor 5 (Inattention/ Distractibility), and a grouping of items that tap tactile and visual perception (see Chapter 5 for interpretation of the 43 items).

Table 6.5
Means and Standard Deviations for Children With ADHD

Sensory Processing	Mean	SD
Section A: Auditory Processing	23.8	5.4
Section B: Visual Processing	30.5	5.7
Section C: Vestibular Processing	42.7	7.2
Section D: Touch Processing	65.4	10.1
Section E: Multisensory Processing	22.3	3.8
Section F: Oral Sensory Processing	44.5	9.8
Modulation		
Section G: Sensory Processing Related to Endurance/Tone	36.9	8.0
Section H: Modulation Related to Body Position and Movement	36.6	6.7
Section I: Modulation of Movement Affecting Activity Level	21.8	4.0
Section J: Modulation of Sensory Input Affecting Emotional Responses	14.3	2.7
Section K: Modulation of Visual Input Affecting Emotional Responses and Activity Level	12.6	2.7
Behavioral and Emotional Responses		
Section L: Emotional/Social Responses	53.0	9.6
Section M: Behavioral Outcomes of Sensory Processing	19.3	3.9
Section N: Items Indicating Thresholds for Response	10.0	2.3
Factors	**Mean**	**SD**
1. Sensory Seeking	51.9	12.5
2. Emotionally Reactive	46.0	10.2
3. Low Endurance/Tone	36.9	8.0
4. Oral Sensory Sensitivity	33.5	8.3
5. Inattention/Distractibility	18.0	4.6
6. Poor Registration	30.9	4.5
7. Sensory Sensitivity	16.6	3.2
8. Sedentary	13.7	3.5
9. Fine Motor/Perceptual	9.6	2.5

CHAPTER 7

Daniel N. McIntosh, Ph.D.; Lucy Jane Miller, Ph.D., OTR; Vivian Shyu, M.A.; and Winnie Dunn, Ph.D., OTR, FAOTA.

Overview of the *Short Sensory Profile (SSP)*

In the process of investigating the properties of the *Sensory Profile*, researchers worked to construct a shorter version of the instrument. Helping develop the *Short Sensory Profile* were researchers in Colorado—Daniel N. McIntosh, Ph.D.; Lucy Jane Miller, Ph.D., OTR; and Vivian Shyu, M.A. The team developed the SSP to help service providers in screening settings quickly identify children with sensory processing difficulties so that these children could be referred for comprehensive assessment and effective intervention planning. The SSP also can be used to help researchers easily incorporate a sensory processing measure into their research protocols.

Development of the SSP

There were three phases in the development of the SSP:

- **Phase 1**–Identifying a smaller set of items that met specific psychometric and construct criteria (i.e., were more discriminating for children with and without disabilities) from the full *Sensory Profile*.
- **Phase 2**–Refining the item pool by evaluating the structure of the scale across samples.
- **Phase 3**–Cross-validating the revised structure to select the final set of items for the SSP.

Phase 1: Item Reduction

The goal during Phase 1 was to develop a short caregiver questionnaire that measures sensory modulation during daily life. Therefore, the researchers removed items from the 125-item *Sensory Profile* that did not fit the theoretical construct of sensory modulation. All items that measured social/emotional abilities and fine motor development were excluded because although these behaviors are related to sensory processing, they are products of the sensory modulation process rather than direct sensory events. This left 98 of the original 125 items for consideration.

Data was collected for 117 children between the ages of 3 and 17 years (see Table 7.1 for demographic information about the sample). The children were from four groups:

- Children with disruptions in sensory modulation (n = 21) (see Fisher & Murray, 1991, and Parham & Mailloux, 1996, for a definition of sensory modulation disorder [SMD])
- Children with Fragile X syndrome (n = 24)
- Children with other developmental disabilities (n = 35)
- Children who were developing typically (n = 37)

Table 7.1
Demographic Characteristics

Group	n	Age Mean (SD) Range	Gender Male/Female
Children With Disruption in Sensory Modulation (SMD)	21	6.0 (1.4) 4–9	15/6
Children With Fragile X Syndrome	24	9.3 (3.7) 3–17	16/8
Children With Other Developmental Disorders	35	9.1 (3.0) 4–16	25/10
Children Developing Typically	37	9.0 (3.6) 3–17	26/11
Total Sample	117	8.5 (3.3) 3–17	82/35 (70%/30%)

Master's level occupational therapists identified the children with SMD (excluding children with developmental disorders) based on behaviors during their occupational therapy assessment and a parent interview (McIntosh, Miller, Shyu, & Hagerman, 1998). Researchers identified children with Fragile X syndrome through genetic studies. Children in the developmental disabilities group included those with autism, Tourette's syndrome, and Down syndrome. They were identified based on medical and psychological services diagnoses. Finally, children in the typically developing group showed no evidence of any learning or neuropsychological disorder and did not have a history of prenatal difficulties or medical or educational problems.

The first procedure during Phase 1 was to examine the remaining 98 items to determine which items to retain (those with highest discrimination ability). Researchers selected the group of children with SMD (n =21) and the group of children who were typically developing (n = 37) for this comparison. The first criterion for retaining items was to keep those that achieved at least marginal significance (p < .05) in an item-by-group analysis of variance (ANOVA).

The second criterion for retention of an item was that each item had to have a certain quantitative relationship to other items in the section or factor with which it was grouped. The entire sample (n = 117) and the sample of children with SMD (n = 21) were used for this analysis. The team examined the relationship of each item, for each sample, to both the items in the same sections and the factors from the full version of the *Sensory Profile*. In order to be retained, items had to show either item-to-total correlations greater than .40 with their section or factor score, or a decrease in Cronbach's coefficient alpha of more than .05 on the respective sections or factors if the item was removed. In other words, if an item did not meet either the correlation or alpha standard in either the total (i.e., all 117 children) or SMD sample ($n = 21$), it was deleted.

After these analyses, 51 of the 98 items remained for consideration. They represented seven of the eight original sections and seven of the nine original factors.

Table 7.2 displays item-to-total correlations for the section or factor grouping with which the item correlated most highly. The groupings for the *Short Sensory Profile* were renamed: Tactile Defensiveness, Visual Sensitivity, Taste and Smell Sensitivity, Auditory Filtering, Low and Slow Levels of Processing Stimuli, Seeking Sensation, and Sensory Sensitivity and Low Regulation (McIntosh et al., 1998). Internal reliability (Cronbach's alpha) for this organizational structure was greater than or equal to .80 for both the full sample ($n = 117$) and for the SMD group ($n = 21$).

Table 7.2				
Summary of Item-to-Total Correlations for Preliminary SSP Item Groupings				
Preliminary Groupings	**Groupings From Sensory Profile Sections**	**Groupings From Factor Structure**	**Number of Items**	**Range of Item-to-Total Correlations for These Item Groupings**
Tactile Defensiveness	Touch Processing		7	.43–.71
Visual Sensitivity	Visual Processing		5	.55–.70
Taste and Smell Sensitivity		Factor 4	6	.43–.73
Auditory Filtering		Factor 5	6	.55–.74
Low and Slow Levels of Processing Stimuli		Factor 3	7	.49–.72
Seeking Sensation		Factor 1	7	.58–.78
Sensory Sensitivity			6	.45–.59
Low Regulation			7	items added to represent poor regulation function

Phase 2: Refinement of Items

For Phase 2, a further study was conducted to determine whether the new organization of the *Short Sensory Profile* sections would emerge in an independent sample. This strategy is important to ensure that the structure of the SSP would reflect an organizational structure that would be useful across many groups of children, not just the initial study group (i.e., that it would have generalizability). Therefore, a principal components factor analysis was conducted (Dunn & Brown, 1997) using the data from the *Sensory Profile* research sample of children without disabilities ($n = 1,037$, see Chapter 3 for a description of the sample). Of the 51 items from Phase 1, 46 items were retained. The names of the factors were adjusted to become the sections of the SSP based on some of the changes in item distribution among the factors. The following is a list of the sections on the SSP:

Tactile Sensitivity. The child's response to touch experiences in daily life.

Taste/Smell Sensitivity. The child's response to taste and smell experiences in daily life.

Movement Sensitivity. The child's response to movement experiences in daily life.

Underresponsive/Seeks Sensation. The child's level of noticing sensory events in daily life.

Auditory Filtering. The child's ability to use and screen out sounds in daily life.

Low Energy/Weak. The child's ability to use muscles to move in daily life.

Visual/Auditory Sensitivity. The child's response to sounds and sights in daily life.

Phase 3: Finalization

For Phase 3, researchers calculated the item-to-total correlations and coefficient alpha for each section using the remaining 46 items. Correlations were calculated for the full sample ($n = 117$), the typically developing children ($n = 37$) and for the children with SMD ($n = 21$).

The team then examined the strength of each item's contribution to its section and removed eight items to improve the correlations within sections. The resulting version of the *Short Sensory Profile* contains 38 items.

Researchers also conducted another principal components factor analysis using the *Sensory Profile* national research sample of children ($n = 1,037$) on this final set of 38 items. Table 7.3 shows the loading of each item within its section. The resultant factor structure lends itself to easily interpreted sections.

■ Administration Instructions and Scoring

■ General Testing Considerations

Before using the SSP, review all administration, scoring, and interpretation information included in this chapter. Although the SSP was designed to be self-explanatory for caregivers, it is important that you become familiar with all of the items on the SSP in case the caregiver has questions.

The SSP should take the caregiver about 10 minutes to complete. There are three general ways in which you can administer the SSP:

1. Send the short form to the caregiver with a cover letter explaining the purpose of the instrument. Be sure to include your phone number in case the caregiver has questions about the form.

2. Have the caregiver complete the questionnaire in your office or clinic while you are evaluating the child.

3. Help the caregiver fill out the SSP. Use this procedure if the caregiver has difficulty reading because of language differences or reading disabilities.

Table 7.3

Factor Loadings of Items in the SSP

SSP Item No.	Tactile Sensitivity	Taste/Smell Sensitivity	Movement Sensitivity	Underresponsive/ Seeks Sensation	Auditory Filtering	Low Energy/Weak	Visual/Auditory Sensitivity
1	.360			.356			
2	.283			.401			
3	.415						
4	.608						
5	.445						
6	.580						
7	.506						
8		.659					
9		.688					
10		.670					
11		.863					
12			.777				
13			.744				
14			.742				
15				.568			
16				.571			
17				.521			
18				.686			
19				.585			
20				.509			
21				.520			
22					.529		
23					.687		
24					.526		
25					.592		
26					.653		
27					.581		
28						.777	
29						.705	
30						.658	
31						.608	
32						.539	
33						.655	
34							.562
35			.300				.274
36				.482			.597
37							.417
38							.571

If the caregiver asks questions, provide clarification without indicating a "correct" response. Encourage the caregiver to consider how frequently the child engages in the behaviors of interest. It may be helpful to have the caregiver use the item in a sentence with the child's name (e.g., Johnny *frequently* "has difficulty paying attention"). This will help the caregiver identify and link the child's behaviors to the statements presented on the form.

Establishing a Rapport

It is important that caregivers believe that the information you are requesting is critical to your work and that the time they take to complete the materials is valuable to the process of planning for the child. If you send materials home to the caregiver, include a letter with a brief explanation of the instrument and why the information is important to the assessment process. Explain the caregiver's central role in providing a picture of the child's performance and the caregiver's concerns about daily life.

■ Specific Administration Procedures

Before giving the SSP to the caregiver, fill in the child's name and date of birth on top, as well as your name (Service Provider's Name) and discipline. Explain the purpose of the SSP to the caregiver (or provide that information in a cover letter). Have the caregiver fill in his or her name, relationship to the child, and the date on the top of the form. Ask the caregiver to read each item and check the box that best describes the frequency with which he or she sees the behavior in the child. Instruct the caregiver to use the following key to mark responses.

> **Always:** When presented with the opportunity, your child **always** responds in this manner, 100% of the time.
>
> **Frequently:** When presented with the opportunity, your child **frequently** responds in this manner, about 75% of the time.
>
> **Occasionally:** When presented with the opportunity, your child **occasionally** responds in this manner, about 50% of the time.
>
> **Seldom:** When presented with the opportunity, your child **seldom** responds in this manner, about 25% of the time.
>
> **Never:** When presented with the opportunity, your child **never** responds in this manner, 0% of the time.

Emphasize the importance of completing all the items. Explain to the caregiver you will fill in the section raw score totals.

Once the caregiver has completed the form, make sure that all items have been answered. If the caregiver has left any item blank, ask him or her to complete the item. You may need to clarify the item for the caregiver.

Note: If any item is left blank, you cannot compute a raw score total for that section. If the caregiver marks an X next to an item number because he or she has determined that a particular item is not applicable due to age or the child has not had the opportunity to experience the behavior, you cannot compute a raw score total for that section.

■ Scoring the SSP

After you have made sure each item has a response, score each response according to the following chart:

Always = 1 point

Frequently = 2 points

Occasionally = 3 points

Seldom = 4 points

Never = 5 points

If the caregiver places a mark between two categories, record the more frequent score:

Between Never and Seldom, record Seldom (4 points)

Between Seldom and Occasionally, record Occasionally (3 points)

Between Occasionally and Frequently, record Frequently (2 points)

Between Frequently and Always, record Always (1 point)

Note: Frequent behaviors receive lower scores; therefore, children get lower scores for undesirable performance and higher scores for desirable performance. Also, remember that the items on the *Short Sensory Profile* are written so that more frequent behavior is undesirable.

To determine the section raw score total, add the item scores for each section. Write this score in the box labeled Section Raw Score Total following each section (see Figure 7.1).

Using the Summary Section of the SSP

The Summary Section for the SSP is located on the back of the form at the bottom of the page. Transfer the child's score for each section to the column labeled Section Raw Score Total. Calculate the SSP raw score total by adding all the section totals. Write the SSP raw score total in the box labeled Total (see Figure 7.2 on page 66).

Item	Tactile Sensitivity	ALWAYS	FREQUENTLY	OCCASIONALLY	SELDOM	NEVER
1	Expresses distress during grooming (for example, fights or cries during haircutting, face washing, fingernail cutting)		X₂			
2	Prefers long-sleeved clothing when it is warm or short sleeves when it is cold			X₃		
3	Avoids going barefoot, especially in sand or grass			X₃		
4	Reacts emotionally or aggressively to touch		X₂			
5	Withdraws from splashing water			X₃		
6	Has difficulty standing in line or close to other people		X₂			
7	Rubs or scratches out a spot that has been touched				X₄	
	Section Raw Score Total			*19*		

Figure 7.1 ■ **Scoring the *Short Sensory Profile***

Plot the section raw score totals and the SSP raw score total by marking an X in the appropriate classification column: Typical Performance, Probable Difference, and Definite Difference (see Figure 7.2).

Classification System

Cut scores were determined by preparing a cumulative frequency distribution with the national research sample of children without disabilities ($n = 1,037$) (Dunn & Westman, 1997) and computing the raw score cut scores for $-1\ SD$ and $-2\ SD$. This was done for the SSP total score and for each section. Refer to the Summary section for representation of the raw scores for $1\ SD$ and $2\ SD$ below the mean.

Typical Performance is scores at or above the point 1 *SD* below the mean. Section raw score totals that fall within this range indicate typical sensory processing abilities. This range indicates that the child performed better than the lowest 16% of the research sample of children ($n = 1,037$). See Figure 5.1 for a graphic representation of the classification system.

Probable Difference is scores at or above the point 2 *SD* below the mean, but lower than 1 *SD* below the mean. Section raw score totals that fall within this range indicate questionable areas of sensory processing abilities. This range indicates that the child's performance was between the 2nd and 16th percentile, representing 14% of the population sample.

Definite Difference is scores below the point 2 *SD* below the mean. Section raw score totals that fall within this range indicate sensory processing problems. This range indicates that the child is performing like a child in the lowest 2% of the research sample when compared to the research sample of children without disabilities.

FOR OFFICE USE ONLY

Summary

Instructions: Transfer the score for each section to the Section Raw Score Total column. Plot these totals by marking an X in the appropriate classification column (Typical Performance, Probable Difference, Definite Difference).*

SCORE KEY

1 = Always	4 = Seldom
2 = Frequently	5 = Never
3 = Occasionally	

Section	Section Raw Score Total	Typical Performance	Probable Difference	Definite Difference
Tactile Sensitivity	19 /35	35 -------- 30	29 -------- 27	26 --X---- 7
Taste/Smell Sensitivity	13 /20	20 -------- 15	14 -----X 12	11 --------- 4
Movement Sensitivity	13 /15	15 -------- X̶13̶	12 -------- 11	10 --------- 3
Underresponsive/Seeks Sensation	29 /35	35 ---X-- 27	26 -------- 24	23 --------- 7
Auditory Filtering	24 /30	30 ----X 23	22 -------- 20	19 --------- 6
Low Energy/Weak	26 /30	30 -------- X̶26̶	25 -------- 24	23 --------- 6
Visual/Auditory Sensitivity	17 /25	25 -------- 19	18 -----X 16	15 --------- 5
Total	141 /190	190 ------- 155	154 ------- 142	1X1 --------- 38

*Classifications are based on the performance of children without disabilities ($n = 1,037$).

Figure 7.2 ■ *Short Sensory Profile Summary*

Interpretations

The SSP Summary was constructed to make it easy for the examiner to determine whether a score is consistent with good sensory processing or is a score that indicates some difficulty with sensory processing.

Interpreting the Total Score

The most important score on the SSP is the total score. It provides the examiner with a clear indication of the child's sensory processing ability. When a child obtains a score in the Definite Difference range, it is likely that this child does not process sensory information like others and may be struggling to keep up on what is going on in the environment or may be disruptive to self and others.

The unusual behaviors that commonly are reported in children who obtain a poor SSP score (e.g., Definite Difference or Probable Difference) represent that child's attempts to manage daily life with inaccurate or insufficient sensory information. Although many of these behaviors are considered weird or maladaptive, it is important to recognize that from a sensory processing perspective, the child is demonstrating coping strategies designed to mediate the distorted or inadequate sensory information available from his or her system.

It is recommended that a follow-up assessment be conducted for children receiving a Definite Difference score on the SSP. It would be appropriate to use the long form of the *Sensory Profile* as part of the follow-up because it provides more detailed information about sensory processing. It is also useful to make a referral to a professional with expertise in sensory processing. Typically, occupational therapists have this expertise as part of their basic professional education; other disciplines also can develop this knowledge during their careers through coursework and mentoring.

If a child receives a Probable Difference score, there is a good chance that sensory processing difficulties are interfering with performance in daily life. Look at this score in combination with other reports, parent comments, observations, and referral concerns to determine the likelihood that sensory processing difficulties are part of the overall picture of this child's performance challenges. If you are unsure, then administer the long form of the *Sensory Profile* to gather additional and more detailed information. A referral to an occupational therapist to investigate further into the relationship between sensory processing and daily life performance also is appropriate. Remember scores in this range represent children in the lower 3–14% of the research sample (i.e., -1 *SD* to -2 *SD*), so in some cases this score alone may be enough to warrant a comprehensive assessment.

Interpreting the Section Scores

If a child receives a score that is within the Definite Difference range on any section of the SSP, it is likely that this child is having difficulty processing sensory stimuli. The safest interpretation is that any score that is in this range is a cause for concern. It is possible that when a child has difficulty with sensory processing, many section scores on the SSP will be low. This is a difference from the *Sensory Profile* in which there are different patterns of scores that are indicative of particular diagnostic groups. The long form of the *Sensory Profile* will provide additional diagnostic and program planning information.

Tactile Sensitivity. When a child has difficulties with this section, he or she may be defensive and uncomfortable with touch. This discomfort may be particularly present with light touch on the skin. Touch is a primary and basic sensory system, so children with sensitivity to touch react negatively to touch input. Their responses can seem primal (e.g., screaming, crying, hitting back) because the nervous system is interpreting the stimulus as potentially harmful or dangerous. When the nervous system is threatened, "fight or flight" reactions emerge to protect the organism from harm. Although we may not think that an event such as brushing up against someone is threatening, when a nervous system has no schemas for interpreting this input properly, it is threatening because it is unrecognizable.

Taste/Smell Sensitivity. When children have difficulty with this section, it is likely that there will be eating challenges, with the child being a picky eater and/or difficult at mealtime. Also the parents might be concerned about nutrition.

Movement Sensitivity. When a child has difficulty with this section, he or she may be insecure and uncomfortable with movement. This discomfort may be particularly present with activities that are unpredictable, such as roughhousing. As with touch sensations, movement sensations are basic and primal to the child's functioning. Children with sensitivity to movement react negatively when they are moving or when there is a suggestion of movement (e.g., when feet leave the ground).

Underresponsive/Seeks Sensation. When a child has difficulty with this section, he or she may have poor modulation (which can be underresponsive or overresponsive), and both situations interfere with daily life. This child may seem unpredictable in the sense that sometimes he or she has overreactions, while other times he or she may seem to let the world pass by.

Auditory Filtering. When a child has difficulties with this section, he or she may be either hyperresponsive (i.e., sensitive to sounds) or hyporesponsive (i.e., oblivious to sounds). You should be looking for modulation of input (i.e., paying enough attention to sounds to notice important stimuli such as calling one's name, but not being so distracted that one cannot complete daily life activities).

Low Energy/Weak. Children need a certain amount of muscle tone and postural control to engage in activities. Children who have poor muscle development will have difficulties with this section and cannot persist in play and daily life rituals because they tire out easily.

Visual/Auditory Sensitivity. When a child has difficulties with this section, it is likely that he or she will need a more controlled environment in order to be productive (e.g., a quieter place to work, less excess clutter). The items in this section represent the child's difficulty with visual and auditory input, which result in behaviors to limit the amount of stimulation.

■ Technical Characteristics of the SSP

Reliability

Internal reliability of the test total and sections was estimated by calculating Cronbach's Alphas. Reliabilities range from .70 to .90 (see Table 7.4).

Table 7.4				
Reliability Coefficients of SSP Sections and Total				
Sections	No. of Items	**Full Sample** alpha (*n* = 117)	**Typical Developing Children** alpha (*n* = 37)	**Children With Disruption of Sensory Modulation** alpha (*n* = 21)
Tactile Sensitivity	7	.8460	.8291	.7027
Taste/Smell Sensitivity	4	.8811	.7787	.9317
Movement Sensitivity	3	.8793	.8433	.8996
Underresponsive/ Seeks Sensation	7	.8922	.8007	.8738
Auditory Filtering	6	.8702	.7233	.8406
Low Energy/Weak	6	.8765	.7905	.8649
Visual/Auditory Sensitivity	5	.8226	.6872	.8273
SSP Total	38	.9551	.9250	.9088

Validity

Internal Validity

One way of validating that the factor structure underlying the *Short Sensory Profile* is an appropriate one is to examine the intercorrelations of the SSP total and section scores. If the factors are measuring unique aspects of sensory modulation, then these intercorrelations should be of a low to moderate range. The correlations range in magnitude from .25 to .76 (see Table 7.5 on page 70), suggesting that the sections of the *Short Sensory Profile* tap relatively unique constructs and support the factor structure developed.

Table 7.6 on page 71 demonstrates the conceptual relationships among the sections of the *Short Sensory Profile* and the sections and factors of the long version of the *Sensory Profile*. Appendix E shows the conceptual relationship of each item on the *Short Sensory Profile* to *Sensory Profile* sections and factors. The seven sections of the short form are hypothesized to represent key sections and factors from the long version of the *Sensory Profile*. This suggests that the *Short Sensory Profile* has the promise to screen for a variety of sensory processing difficulties. The long form of the *Sensory Profile* can then be used to follow up and gather additional information.

Table 7.5							
Intercorrelations of SSP Total and Section Scores							
	Total*	Tactile Sensitivity	Taste/Smell Sensitivity	Movement Sensitivity	Underresponsive/ Seeks Sensation	Auditory Filtering	Low Energy/ Weak
1. Tactile Sensitivity	.80						
2. Taste/Smell Sensitivity	.54	.61					
3. Movement Sensitivity	.48	.47	.34				
4. Underresponsive/ Seeks Sensation	.73	.63	.46	.25			
5. Auditory Filtering	.76	.65	.40	.43	.71		
6. Low Energy/Weak	.62	.56	.39	.44	.53	.48	
7. Visual/Auditory Sensitivity	.78	.72	.37	.44	.69	.76	.50

*All correlations significant at $p < .01$.
Full sample ($n = 117$); 38 items

Table 7.6 ■ Relation of *Short Sensory Profile* Sections to *Sensory Profile* Sections and Factors

| | **Short Sensory Profile** | | **Caregiver Questionnaire** | |
No.	Section	No.	Section	Factor
1	Tactile Sensivity	30	Touch Processing	
2	Tactile Sensivity	31	Touch Processing	
3	Tactile Sensivity	35	Touch Processing	6
4	Tactile Sensivity	36	Touch Processing	
5	Tactile Sensivity	37	Touch Processing	
6	Tactile Sensivity	38	Touch Processing	
7	Tactile Sensivity	39	Touch Processing	
8	Taste/Smell Sensitivity	55	Oral Sensory Processing	4
9	Taste/Smell Sensitivity	56	Oral Sensory Processing	4
10	Taste/Smell Sensitivity	57	Oral Sensory Processing	4
11	Taste/Smell Sensitivity	58	Oral Sensory Processing	4
12	Movement Sensitivity	18	Vestibular Processing	7
13	Movement Sensitivity	77	Modulation Related to Body Position and Movement	7
14	Movement Sensitivity	19	Vestibular Processing	7
15	Underresponsive/Seeks Sensation	8	Auditory Processing	1
16	Underresponsive/Seeks Sensation	24	Vestibular Processing	1
17	Underresponsive/Seeks Sensation	89	Modulation of Movement Affecting Activity Level	1
18	Underresponsive/Seeks Sensation	45	Touch Processing	1
19	Underresponsive/Seeks Sensation	46	Touch Processing	1
20	Underresponsive/Seeks Sensation	123	Items Indicating Thresholds for Response	1
21	Underresponsive/Seeks Sensation	53	Multisensory Processing	
22	Auditory Filtering	4	Auditory Processing	5
23	Auditory Filtering	6	Auditory Processing	5
24	Auditory Filtering	5	Auditory Processing	5
25	Auditory Filtering	3	Auditory Processing	5
26	Auditory Filtering	7	Auditory Processing	5
27	Auditory Filtering	48	Multisensory Processing	5
28	Low Energy/Weak	69	Sensory Processing Related to Endurance/Tone	3
29	Low Energy/Weak	67	Sensory Processing Related to Endurance/Tone	3
30	Low Energy/Weak	70	Sensory Processing Related to Endurance/Tone	3
31	Low Energy/Weak	71	Sensory Processing Related to Endurance/Tone	3
32	Low Energy/Weak	72	Sensory Processing Related to Endurance/Tone	3
33	Low Energy/Weak	73	Sensory Processing Related to Endurance/Tone	3
34	Visual/Auditory Sensitivity	1	Auditory Processing	
35	Visual/Auditory Sensitivity	2	Auditory Processing	
36	Visual/Auditory Sensitivity	14	Visual Processing	
37	Visual/Auditory Sensitivity	98	Modulation of Visual Input Affecting Emotional Responses and Activity Level	
38	Visual/Auditory Sensitivity	15	Visual Processing	

Construct Validity

One way in which researchers can measure sensory processing is through various physiological measures, such as electrodermal responses (EDR). If the *Short Sensory Profile* is truly measuring sensory processing, then we would expect lower scores on the SSP for children with abnormal EDR and higher scores on the SSP for children for normal EDR.

Researchers used skin conductance (i.e., EDR) to capture the physiological responses. The *Sensory Challenge Protocol* was designed to gauge the child's physiological responses to repeated sensory stimulation (i.e., a light flash, a sound) (see Miller et al., in press, for a full description of this protocol). This type of protocol is well established to capture physiological responses and to differentiate among groups. Generally, people can have a typical response, a response higher than expected (i.e., hyperresponsive), or a response lower than expected (i.e., hyporesponsive). Both hyperresponsivity and hyporesponsivity are considered atypical physiological responses.

The EDR testing was conducted with the children with SMD and the typically developing children. As expected, children who had abnormal EDR (i.e., either hyporesponsive or hyperresponsive) scored significantly lower (i.e., had more frequency of the SSP behaviors) ($p = <.05$) on all sections of the *Short Sensory Profile* than did children with normal EDR responses. Figure 7.3 presents the SSP section mean scores for children with typical and atypical EDR responses.

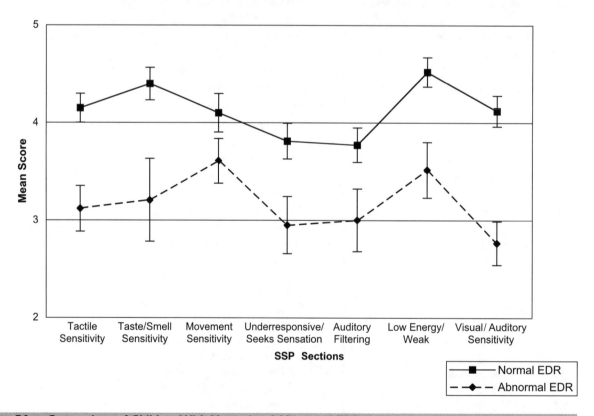

Figure 7.3 ■ **Comparison of Children With Normal and Abnormal EDRs**

Special Group Study

If the *Short Sensory Profile* is to be a useful tool for clinicians, it is also important that it distinguish between children with and without sensory processing difficulties. This was determined by evaluating two groups of children: a typically developing sample (*n* = 19) and a matched sample of children with SMD (*n* = 19) (see Table 7.7 for demographics on the sample). Figure 7.4 illustrates the mean score for each group for each section of the SSP. As you can see, the SMD sample scored lower on average for each section than the typical sample. The *Short Sensory Profile* appears to be able to discriminate between these groups of children.

Table 7.7			
Demographic Characteristics			
Group	***n***	**Age** Mean (*SD*) Range	**Gender** Male/Female
Typically Developing Controls	19	6.6 (1.8) 3–9	14/5
Children With Disruption of Sensory Modulation (SMD)	19	6.0 (1.4) 4–9	14/5

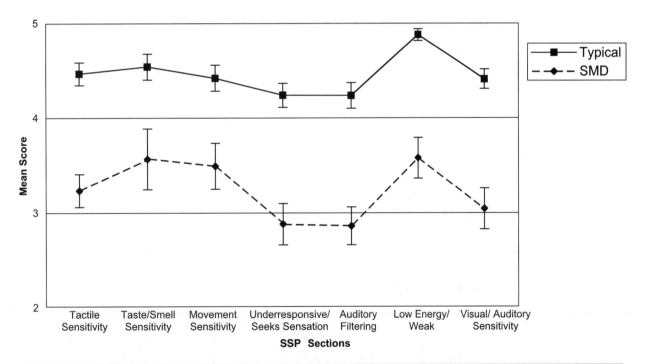

Figure 7.4 ■ **Comparison of Typically Developing Children and Children With SMD**

CHAPTER 8

Case Studies: Interpretations and Interventions

This chapter presents case studies of children who have different performance needs and contexts for performance. Although there are more features to each child's situation, the focus here is on aspects relevant to the *Sensory Profile*. These discussions provide a model for how to use the *Caregiver Questionnaire* and *Summary Score Sheet* to illustrate interpretation strategies and to suggest interventions that might be appropriate in each case.

Framework for Decision Making

Teams using the *Sensory Profile,* a measure of sensory responsiveness in daily life, must consider the daily life context for the child's desired performance when designing interventions. The Ecology of Human Performance (EHP) model offers a framework for constructing a broad range of interventions. This model encourages intervention designs that address the interaction among the person, the task, and the context (Dunn, Brown, & McGuigan, 1994). The five types of interventions are defined in Figure 8.1 on page 76.

Although there are times when it is appropriate to design interventions that address development of better sensory processing, there also are situations that call upon the team to design a more user-friendly environment for the child so that performance can happen. People want to be able to accomplish tasks and participate with others; it would be very unpleasant to have the daily routine designed to address only weak areas of function. The EHP framework acknowledges that there are many ways to solve a performance problem, and illustrates the utility in considering task demands and environmental features in intervention (i.e., adapt/modify, alter, prevent, create interventions). Focusing only on the person's skills and difficulties (i.e., establish/restore interventions) limits the possibilities and is not a best practice approach.

Many of the sensory processing difficulties identified on the *Sensory Profile* might have some effect on the child's performance. Children who have poor registration likely always will be slower to respond to stimuli and may have lower energy levels than other children. Their nervous systems are not designed to be overly excitable. Artful intervention honors these individual differences as part of the planning process to find the best match for each child. Part of best practice, within teams and with families,

Intervention	Focus of Intervention	Definition	Example
Establish/restore	Child's strengths and needs	Interventions that improve the child's skills to perform	Have child push a cart of books to the library to increase proprioceptive input to the trunk and extremities to improve postural control for movements.
Adapt	Task and environmental features	Interventions that change the context or task demands to make performance more possible	Move the child's desk to minimize the number of people bumping into him so that tactile sensitivity doesn't interfere with attention and performance in the classroom.
Alter	Environmental features	Interventions that select a new context in which performance with current skills is possible	Select the classroom that has a teacher whose temperament is best suited to a particular child.
Prevent	Person's strengths and needs, task, and environmental features	Interventions that maintain performance by changing the course of events to keep a possible negative outcome from occurring	Design an oral-motor stimulation ritual before mealtime to prevent the child from having difficult completing the meal within the time constraints.
Create	Environmental features	Interventions that promote optimal performance by all persons in that context	Collaborate in designing the optimal after-school program for all the children.

Figure 8.1 ■ **Ecology of Human Performance: Five Types of Interventions**

includes recognizing these traits and designing interventions with them in mind. You are not abandoning the child's possibility of progress by designing adaptations or changing a placement to a more suitable setting; rather you are making successful performance available to the child. Children do not have to earn the right to participate by demonstrating particular prerequisite skills; professionals have the responsibility to make participation available immediately. Data from the *Sensory Profile* can enhance the possible options for facilitating participation.

■ Overview

Case Study 1: Noah, a boy who needs to be included with peers during school time

This case study illustrates how the parent rated the child's sensory processing abilities and how the therapist scored the *Sensory Profile*. It also demonstrates how to interpret the meaning of pervasive sensory processing needs in a child's performance. In this case, interdisciplinary team members collaborated and used two different frames of reference to analyze the performance problems and identify the best course of action.

Case Study 2: Tim, a third-grader who is becoming more socially isolated

This case study illustrates how to complete the *Summary Score Sheet* and interpret the findings. Tim's therapist, teacher, and mom found ways to adapt tasks and performance environments to provide him with additional input during activities so that he could be more alert and available for interactions. The interventions also provided opportunities for Tim to establish a larger repertoire of adaptive responses to sensory input during daily routines.

Case Study 3: Matine, a 4-year-old who needs to participate in snack time

This case study provides an opportunity to consider the meaning of differences in performance in two settings—home and school. The team had to consider the sensory processing differences to identify the best possible course of action. The team combined several intervention strategies to meet Matine's performance needs in both settings.

Case Study 4: Gretta, a fourth-grader who needs to complete her seatwork efficiently and accurately

This case study illustrates a situation in which the sensory processing needs are less prominent in the overall picture. It shows how the team considered the child's performance in light of this and other factors in designing an intervention plan.

Case Study 1: Noah

Noah is a first-grade boy. He and his family have received supports during his preschool years so that they could learn how to manage family life with Noah's pervasive developmental disorder (he had been diagnosed with autism when he was 3 years old). As they approached the time for Noah to enter public school, they expressed a desire for him to be included with age peers at the neighborhood school.

Autism has distinct characteristics, including qualitative impairments in verbal and nonverbal communication, poor social reciprocity, and restricted repertoire of interests. Poor modulation of sensory input is one of the hallmarks of this disorder. Therefore, the team at the school wanted to identify Noah's patterns of responding to sensory events in daily life so that they could plan for him appropriately. The parents completed the *Caregiver Questionnaire* as part of Noah's comprehensive assessment (see Figure 8.2 on page 78). They also gave the therapist a videotape of Noah at home with his siblings because they wanted the school personnel to "get to know Noah" by seeing how he reacts and behaves in a familiar setting.

Scores

The therapist completed the *Summary Score Sheet* (see Figure 8.3 on page 87) from the answers Noah's parents had given on the *Caregiver Questionnaire*. Because it is common for children who have autism to display very different levels of responses from other children, the therapist was not surprised to see that many of the sections fell outside the Typical Performance range. However, labeling Noah as dysfunctional in all these sections would not help team planning. The therapist had to consider the meaning of the pattern in relation to Noah's rituals. To make sure that all possibilities would be considered, the therapist also completed the Factor Grid and the Factor Summary.

Interpretation

From information on the *Summary Score Sheet*, the therapist developed some hypotheses about Noah. She noted that Noah had more difficulty with auditory processing than visual processing and more difficulty with touch than movement processing. Noah also displayed poor oral sensory processing, consistent with findings reported by Ermer and Dunn (1998), in which children who had autism displayed difficulty with oral sensory processing when compared with children with ADHD and children without disabilities. She also noted that Noah was relatively more capable of modulating sensory input than of processing basic sensory information. Because children who have autism typically lack regard for social cues, the therapist was not surprised that emotional responses were somewhat of a problem also.

SENSORY PROFILE

Winnie Dunn, Ph.D., OTR, FAOTA

Caregiver Questionnaire

Child's Name: **Noah Jones** Birth Date: **7/10/93** Date: **8/16/99**

Completed by: **Sara Jones** Relationship to Child: **mother**

Service Provider's Name: **Pat Flores** Discipline: **Occupational therapist**

INSTRUCTIONS

Please check the box that **best** describes the frequency with which your child does the following behaviors. Please answer all of the statements. If you are unable to comment because you have not observed the behavior or believe that it does not apply to your child, please draw an X through the number for that item. Write any comments at the end of each section. Please do not write in the Section Raw Score Total row.

Use the following key to mark your responses:

ALWAYS	When presented with the opportunity, your child always responds in this manner, 100% of the time.
FREQUENTLY	When presented with the opportunity, your child frequently responds in this manner, about 75% of the time.
OCCASIONALLY	When presented with the opportunity, your child occasionally responds in this manner, about 50% of the time.
SELDOM	When presented with the opportunity, your child seldom responds in this manner, about 25% of the time.
NEVER	When presented with the opportunity, your child never responds in this manner, 0% of the time.

THE
PSYCHOLOGICAL
CORPORATION®
A Harcourt Assessment Company
0761638059

Figure 8.2 ■ **Noah's** *Caregiver Questionnaire*

Sensory Processing

	Item		A. Auditory Processing	ALWAYS	FREQUENTLY	OCCASIONALLY	SELDOM	NEVER
🔊	L	1	Responds negatively to unexpected or loud noises (for example, cries or hides at noise from vacuum cleaner, dog barking, hair dryer)			X₃		
🔊	L	2	Holds hands over ears to protect ears from sound			X₃		
🔊	L	3	Has trouble completing tasks when the radio is on			X₃		
🔊	L	4	Is distracted or has trouble functioning if there is a lot of noise around			X₃		
🔊	L	5	Can't work with background noise (for example, fan, refrigerator)			X₃		
🔊	H	6	Appears to not hear what you say (for example, does not "tune-in" to what you say, appears to ignore you)			X₃		
🔊	H	7	Doesn't respond when name is called but you know the child's hearing is OK				X₄	
🔊	H	8	Enjoys strange noises/seeks to make noise for noise's sake		X₂			
			Section Raw Score Total		24			

Comments

Noah makes a lot of noise and it seems
to calm him.

	Item		B. Visual Processing	ALWAYS	FREQUENTLY	OCCASIONALLY	SELDOM	NEVER
👁	L	9	Prefers to be in the dark			X₃		
👁	L	10	Expresses discomfort with or avoids bright lights (for example, hides from sunlight through window in car)			X₃		
👁	L	11	Happy to be in the dark			X₃		
👁	L	12	Becomes frustrated when trying to find objects in competing backgrounds (for example, a cluttered drawer)				X₄	
👁	L	13	Has difficulty putting puzzles together (as compared to same age children)			X₃		
👁	L	14	Is bothered by bright lights after others have adapted to the light			X₃		
👁	L	15	Covers eyes or squints to protect eyes from light			X₃		
👁	H	16	Looks carefully or intensely at objects/people (for example, stares)				X₄	
👁	H	17	Has a hard time finding objects in competing backgrounds (for example, shoes in a messy room, favorite toy in the "junk drawer")				X₄	
			Section Raw Score Total		30			

Comments

Figure 8.2 ■ **Noah's *Caregiver Questionnaire* (continued)**

Item			C. Vestibular Processing	ALWAYS	FREQUENTLY	OCCASIONALLY	SELDOM	NEVER
→	L	18	Becomes anxious or distressed when feet leave the ground				X4	
→	L	19	Dislikes activities where head is upside down (for example, somersaults, roughhousing)				X4	
→	L	20	Avoids playground equipment or moving toys (for example, swing set, merry-go-round)				X4	
→	L	21	Dislikes riding in a car				X4	
→	L	22	Holds head upright, even when bending over or leaning (for example, maintains a rigid position/posture during activity)				X4	
→	L	23	Becomes disoriented after bending over sink or table (for example, falls or gets dizzy)					X5
→	H	24	Seeks all kinds of movement and this interferes with daily routines (for example, can't sit still, fidgets)				X4	
→	H	25	Seeks out all kinds of movement activities (for example, being whirled by adult, merry-go-rounds, playground equipment, moving toys)				X4	
→	H	26	Twirls/spins self frequently throughout the day (for example, likes dizzy feeling)				X4	
→	H	27	Rocks unconsciously (for example, while watching TV)				X4	
→	H	28	Rocks in desk/chair/on floor				X4	
			Section Raw Score Total			45		

Comments

Figure 8.2 ■ **Noah's *Caregiver Questionnaire* (continued)**

	Item		D. Touch Processing	ALWAYS	FREQUENTLY	OCCASIONALLY	SELDOM	NEVER
	L	29	Avoids getting "messy" (for example, in paste, sand, finger paint, glue, tape)		X2			
	L	30	Expresses distress during grooming (for example, fights or cries during haircutting, face washing, fingernail cutting)		X2			
	L	31	Prefers long-sleeved clothing when it is warm or short sleeves when it is cold		X2			
	L	32	Expresses discomfort at dental work or toothbrushing (for example, cries or fights)	X1				
	L	33	Is sensitive to certain fabrics (for example, is particular about certain clothes or bedsheets)	X1				
	L	34	Becomes irritated by shoes or socks		X2			
	L	35	Avoids going barefoot, especially in sand or grass			X3		
	L	36	Reacts emotionally or aggressively to touch		X2			
	L	37	Withdraws from splashing water		X2			
	L	38	Has difficulty standing in line or close to other people		X2			
	L	39	Rubs or scratches out a spot that has been touched		X2			
	H	40	Touches people and objects to the point of irritating others			X3		
	H	41	Displays unusual need for touching certain toys, surfaces, or textures (for example, constantly touching objects)			X3		
	H	42	Decreased awareness of pain and temperature			X3		
	H	43	Doesn't seem to notice when someone touches arm or back (for example, unaware)			X3		
	H	44	Avoids wearing shoes; loves to be barefoot			X3		
	H	45	Touches people and objects			X3		
	H	46	Doesn't seem to notice when face or hands are messy			X3		
			Section Raw Score Total		*42*			

Comments

Noah does better if we stick to a set routine for personal hygiene.

	Item		E. Multisensory Processing	ALWAYS	FREQUENTLY	OCCASIONALLY	SELDOM	NEVER
		47	Gets lost easily (even in familiar places)			X3		
		48	Has difficulty paying attention				X4	
	L	49	Looks away from tasks to notice all actions in the room				X4	
	H	50	Seems oblivious within an active environment (for example, unaware of activity)			X3		
	H	51	Hangs on people, furniture, or objects even in familiar situations			X3		
	H	52	Walks on toes			X3		
	H	53	Leaves clothing twisted on body			X3		
			Section Raw Score Total		*23*			

Comments

Figure 8.2 ■ **Noah's *Caregiver Questionnaire* (continued)**

Item			F. Oral Sensory Processing	ALWAYS	FREQUENTLY	OCCASIONALLY	SELDOM	NEVER
⚡	L	54	Gags easily with food textures or food utensils in mouth					X5
👄	L	55	Avoids certain tastes or food smells that are typically part of children's diets		X2			
👄	L	56	Will only eat certain tastes (list: _____)			X3		
⚡	L	57	Limits self to particular food textures/temperatures (list: _____)		X2			
⚡	L	58	Picky eater, especially regarding food textures		X2			
👄	H	59	Routinely smells nonfood objects			X3		
👄	H	60	Shows strong preference for certain smells (list: _____)		X2			
👄	H	61	Shows strong preference for certain tastes (list: _____)		X2			
👄	H	62	Craves certain foods (list: _____)			X3		
👄	H	63	Seeks out certain tastes or smells (list: _____)				X4	
👄	H	64	Chews or licks on nonfood objects					X5
⚡	H	65	Mouths objects (for example, pencil, hands)			X3		
			Section Raw Score Total			36		

Comments

Modulation

Item			G. Sensory Processing Related to Endurance/Tone	ALWAYS	FREQUENTLY	OCCASIONALLY	SELDOM	NEVER
🧍		66	Moves stiffly					X5
🧍	H	67	Tires easily, especially when standing or holding particular body position				X4	
🧍	H	68	Locks joints (for example, elbows, knees) for stability					X5
🧍	H	69	Seems to have weak muscles				X4	
🧍	H	70	Has a weak grasp			X3		
🧍	H	71	Can't lift heavy objects (for example, weak in comparison to same age children)				X4	
🧍	H	72	Props to support self (even during activity)			X3		
→	H	73	Poor endurance/tires easily				X4	
→	H	74	Appears lethargic (for example, has no energy, is sluggish)				X4	
			Section Raw Score Total			36		

Comments

Figure 8.2 ■ **Noah's *Caregiver Questionnaire* (continued)**

Item			H. Modulation Related to Body Position and Movement	ALWAYS	FREQUENTLY	OCCASIONALLY	SELDOM	NEVER
♡		75	Seems accident-prone				X₄	
👁		76	Hesitates going up or down curbs or steps (for example, is cautious, stops before moving)				X₄	
→	L	77	Fears falling or heights				X₄	
→	L	78	Avoids climbing/jumping or avoids bumpy/uneven ground				X₄	
→	L	79	Holds onto walls or banisters (for example, clings)				X₄	
→	H	80	Takes excessive risks during play (for example, climbs high into a tree, jumps off tall furniture)				X₄	
→	H	81	Takes movement or climbing risks during play that compromise personal safety				X₄	
→	H	82	Turns whole body to look at you				X₄	
🧍	H	83	Seeks opportunities to fall without regard to personal safety				X₄	
🧍	H	84	Appears to enjoy falling				X₄	
			Section Raw Score Total			*40*		

Comments

Item			I. Modulation of Movement Affecting Activity Level	ALWAYS	FREQUENTLY	OCCASIONALLY	SELDOM	NEVER
🏃	L	85	Spends most of the day in sedentary play (for example, does quiet things)		X₂			
🏃	L	86	Prefers quiet, sedentary play (for example, watching TV, books, computers)			X₃		
→	L	87	Seeks sedentary play options			X₃		
→	L	88	Prefers sedentary activities			X₃		
→	H	89	Becomes overly excitable during movement activity			X₃		
🏃	H	90	"On the go"				X₄	
🏃	H	91	Avoids quiet play activities				X₄	
			Section Raw Score Total			*22*		

Comments

Item			J. Modulation of Sensory Input Affecting Emotional Responses	ALWAYS	FREQUENTLY	OCCASIONALLY	SELDOM	NEVER
♡		92	Needs more protection from life than other children (for example, defenseless physically or emotionally)			X₃		
☝	L	93	Rigid rituals in personal hygiene			X₃		
♡	H	94	Is overly affectionate with others			X₃		
♡	H	95	Doesn't perceive body language or facial expressions (for example, unable to interpret)				X₄	
			Section Raw Score Total			*13*		

Comments

Figure 8.2 ■ **Noah's** *Caregiver Questionnaire (continued)*

	Item		K. Modulation of Visual Input Affecting Emotional Responses and Activity Level	ALWAYS	FREQUENTLY	OCCASIONALLY	SELDOM	NEVER
👁	L	96	Avoids eye contact				X₄	
👁	H	97	Stares intensively at objects or people			X₃		
👁	H	98	Watches everyone when they move around the room			X₃		
👁	H	99	Doesn't notice when people come into the room				X₄	
			Section Raw Score Total			14		

Comments

Behavior and Emotional Responses

	Item		L. Emotional/Social Responses	ALWAYS	FREQUENTLY	OCCASIONALLY	SELDOM	NEVER
♡		100	Seems to have difficulty liking self (for example, low self-esteem)			X₃		
♡		101	Has trouble "growing up" (for example, reacts immaturely to situations)			X₃		
♡		102	Is sensitive to criticisms			X₃		
♡		103	Has definite fears (for example, fears are predictable)			X₃		
♡		104	Seems anxious			X₃		
♡		105	Displays excessive emotional outbursts when unsuccessful at a task			X₃		
♡		106	Expresses feeling like a failure			X₃		
♡		107	Is stubborn or uncooperative			X₃		
♡		108	Has temper tantrums			X₃		
♡		109	Poor frustration tolerance			X₃		
♡		110	Cries easily			X₃		
♡		111	Overly serious			X₃		
♡		112	Has difficulty making friends (for example, does not interact or participate in group play)			X₃		
♡		113	Has nightmares					X₅
♡		114	Has fears that interfere with daily routine					X₅
♡		115	Doesn't have a sense of humor			X₃		
♡		116	Doesn't express emotions				X₄	
			Section Raw Score Total			56		

Comments

Easily upset when his routine
is disrupted.

Figure 8.2 ■ **Noah's Caregiver Questionnaire (continued)**

Item			M. Behavioral Outcomes of Sensory Processing	ALWAYS	FREQUENTLY	OCCASIONALLY	SELDOM	NEVER
👂		117	Talks self through tasks			X₃		
👁		118	Writing is illegible			X₃		
👁		119	Has trouble staying between the lines when coloring or when writing			X₃		
🤍		120	Uses inefficient ways of doing things (for example, wastes time, moves slowly, does things a harder way than is needed)			X₃		
🤍	L	121	Has difficulty tolerating changes in plans and expectations		X₂			
🤍	L	122	Has difficulty tolerating changes in routines			X₃		
			Section Raw Score Total			*17*		

Comments

Item			N. Items Indicating Thresholds for Response	ALWAYS	FREQUENTLY	OCCASIONALLY	SELDOM	NEVER
🏃		123	Jumps from one activity to another so that it interferes with play				X₄	
👄	H	124	Deliberately smells objects			X₃		
👄	H	125	Does not seem to smell strong odors			X₃		
			Section Raw Score Total			*10*		

Comments

Figure 8.2 ■ **Noah's *Caregiver Questionnaire* (continued)**

The therapist, school psychologist, and primary level teacher met to watch the family's videotape. They observed Noah engaging in parallel activities with his siblings; he seemed unaware of their playing. They also observed that Noah had very clear patterns in his play schemas, and if anyone interfered with these rituals, he became very upset. He hummed and lined up small cars and trucks against the open door. If one of the other children moved a car or disrupted the order, Noah screamed, flapped his hands, and began to sway. This seemed to be the only time he was aware of his siblings.

The team invited Noah and his parents to come to the school so that they could observe Noah and talk further. Noah also generated sounds during this visit, but in this new environment, he mouthed objects as he roamed the classroom. The parents explained that Noah commonly acts this way in new places. Later, Noah participated with the therapist in a play pattern in which the therapist copied what Noah did. This led Noah to stop his activity and give momentary eye contact.

The patterns of behavior recorded and observed are consistent with the Sensation Avoiding category described in Dunn (1997a). This category is representative of a person with low neurological thresholds. Because the child reacts to these thresholds as uncomfortable or unpleasant, he or she establishes patterns or rituals to try to control the frequency of meeting these thresholds. Sometimes the behavior patterns of these children are misinterpreted because it appears that they are actively engaging with objects and the environment. However, when the behaviors are rigid and ritual-istic, the activity pattern also might be interpreted "avoiding" because they limit new or unpredictable stimuli from having to be dealt with.

Intervention

As this team planned for Noah, the most important issue from a sensory processing point of view was to honor what Noah was telling them with his behavior. The rituals he has established indicated both what stimuli he could manage and what stimuli might be more difficult. With this information, the team could plan the best ways to introduce learning to Noah. The most common error in serving a child like Noah is that professionals interpret his rigidity as defiance and enter into a power struggle, reasoning that he "needs to get used to the rules like everyone else," or "it's not fair for him to get special consideration." In fact, from a sensory processing point of view, the team must provide Noah with support through his rituals and build slowly and carefully upon this available state in order for learning to occur. Once Noah begins his avoiding behavior patterns, he is unavailable for learning.

Because the therapist was successful at getting a response from Noah by copying his play schemas, team planning emerged from this strategy. They taught several other children in the class to play with Noah in this way, copying what he did during free play in the morning. This provided Noah with familiarity to participate as much as he could with the other children and reduced his withdrawal behaviors (e.g., hiding, screaming, hand flapping). During structured learning small groups, the teacher played a tape of Noah humming during play time at home, and this seemed to enable Noah to stay with the group longer each day. During other times, the teacher let Noah roam around. For example, when she read a book to the class, Noah would stand and roam. His roaming seemed to provide sensory support for remaining "with" the group. He would stay near her and the other children under these conditions, whereas when she tried to get him to sit like the other children, he became agitated and tried to escape.

SENSORY PROFILE
Winnie Dunn, Ph.D., OTR, FAOTA
Summary Score Sheet

Child's Name: **Noah Jones**   Gender: ☒ Male ☐ Female

Questionnaire Completed by: **Sara Jones**

Relationship to Child: **mother**

Service Provider's Name: **Pat Flores**

Discipline: **Occupational therapist**

	YEAR	MONTH	DAY
Date Tested	99	8	16
Date of Birth	93	7	10
Chronological Age	6	1	6

The child receives the following service(s)

☒ Early Intervention/Preschool Services *-previously*   ☐ Physical Therapy

☒ Regular Education *-Parents want him included*   ☒ Speech Therapy

☐ Special Education   ☐ Other (please specify) *see below*

☐ Occupational Therapy

Child's condition(s)

☐ Mental Retardation   ☐ Cerebral Palsy

☐ Specific Learning Disability   ☐ Fragile X

☐ Speech or Language Impairment   ☐ Tic Disorder (e.g., Tourette's)

☒ Autism/Pervasive Developmental Disorder (PDD)   ☐ Multiple Disabilities

☐ Asperger's Syndrome   ☐ Traumatic Brain Injury

☐ Emotional Disturbance or Serious Behavioral Difficulties   ☐ Other Neurological Disorder

☐ Attention Disorder (ADD, ADHD)   ☐ Other Health Conditions (e.g., cardiac disorder, asthma)

☐ Visual Impairment/Blindness   ☐ Other (please specify) _____

☐ Hearing Impairment/Deafness

Other comments

Parents comments: Noah makes a lot of noise and it seems to calm him.

Noah does better if we stick to a set routine for personal hygiene.

Easily upset when his routine is disrupted.

*We are investigating ways to support Noah and the classroom teacher in regular education.

0761638067

Figure 8.3 ■ **Noah's *Summary Score Sheet***

SENSORY PROFILE

Factor Grid

Instructions: Transfer from the *Caregiver Questionnaire* the item raw score that corresponds with each item listed. Add the Raw Score column to get the Factor Raw Score Total for each factor.

FACTOR 1		
Sensory Seeking		
Item		**Raw Score**
👂	8	2
→	24	4
→	25	4
→	26	4
✋	44	3
✋	45	3
✋	46	3
🧍	51	3
→	80	4
→	81	4
→	82	4
🧍	83	4
🧍	84	4
→	89	3
🏃	90	4
♡	94	3
🏃	123	4
Factor Raw Score Total		60

FACTOR 2		
Emotionally Reactive		
Item		**Raw Score**
♡	92	3
♡	100	3
♡	101	3
♡	102	3
♡	103	3
♡	104	3
♡	105	3
♡	106	3
♡	107	3
♡	108	3
♡	109	3
♡	110	3
♡	111	3
♡	112	3
♡	121	2
♡	122	3
Factor Raw Score Total		47

FACTOR 3		
Low Endurance/Tone		
Item		**Raw Score**
🧍	66	5
🧍	67	4
🧍	68	5
🧍	69	4
🧍	70	3
🧍	71	4
🧍	72	3
→	73	4
→	74	4
Factor Raw Score Total		36

FACTOR 4		
Oral Sensory Sensitivity		
Item		**Raw Score**
👄	55	2
👄	56	3
✋	57	2
✋	58	2
👄	59	3
👄	60	2
👄	61	2
👄	62	3
👄	63	4
Factor Raw Score Total		23

FACTOR 5		
Inattention/Distractibility		
Item		**Raw Score**
👂	3	3
👂	4	3
👂	5	3
👂	6	3
👂	7	4
🏃	48	4
👁	49	4
Factor Raw Score Total		24

ICON KEY	
👂	Auditory
👁	Visual
🏃	Activity Level
👄	Taste/Smell
🧍	Body Position
→	Movement
✋	Touch
♡	Emotional/Social

Figure 8.3 ■ **Noah's *Summary Score Sheet* (continued)**

FACTOR 6		
Poor Registration		
Item		Raw Score
✋	35	3
✋	42	3
✋	43	3
♡	95	4
👁	99	4
♡	115	3
♡	116	4
👄	125	3
Factor Raw Score Total		27

FACTOR 7		
Sensory Sensitivity		
Item		Raw Score
→	18	4
→	19	4
→	77	4
→	78	4
Factor Raw Score Total		16

FACTOR 8		
Sedentary		
Item		Raw Score
🏃	85	2
🏃	86	3
→	87	3
→	88	3
Factor Raw Score Total		11

FACTOR 9		
Fine Motor/Perceptual		
Item		Raw Score
👁	13	3
👁	118	3
👁	119	3
Factor Raw Score Total		9

Factor Summary

Instructions: Transfer the child's score for each factor to the column labeled Factor Raw Score Total.
Then plot these totals by marking an X in the appropriate classification column
(Typical Performance, Probable Difference, Definite Difference).*

Factor	Factor Raw Score Total	Typical Performance	Probable Difference	Definite Difference
1. Sensory Seeking	60 /85	85 ---------- 63	62 ---X--- 55	54 ---------- 17
2. Emotionally Reactive	47 /80	80 ---------- 57	56 ---------- 48	47 ---------- 16
3. Low Endurance/Tone	36 /45	45 ---------- 39	38 ---------- 36	35 ---------- 9
4. Oral Sensory Sensitivity	23 /45	45 ---------- 33	32 ---------- 27	26 X --- 9
5. Inattention/Distractibility	24 /35	35 ---------- 25	24 ---------- 22	21 ---------- 7
6. Poor Registration	27 /40	40 ---------- 33	32 ---------- 30	29 X --- 8
7. Sensory Sensitivity	16 /20	20 ---------- 16	15 ---------- 14	13 ---------- 4
8. Sedentary	11 /20	20 ---------- 12	11 ---------- 10	9 ---------- 4
9. Fine Motor/Perceptual	9 /15	15 ---------- 10	9 ---------- 8	7 ---------- 3

*Classifications are based on the performance of children without disabilities (*n* = 1,037).

Figure 8.3 ■ Noah's *Summary Score Sheet (continued)*

Section Summary

Instructions: Transfer the child's score for each section to the Section Raw Score Total column.
Then plot these totals by marking an X in the appropriate classification column
(Typical Performance, Probable Difference, Definite Difference).*

Sensory Processing	Section Raw Score Total	Typical Performance	Probable Difference	Definite Difference
A. Auditory Processing	24 /40	40 --------- 30	29 --------- 26	25 -X- 8
B. Visual Processing	30 /45	45 --------- 32	31 X-- 27	26 --------- 9
C. Vestibular Processing	45 /55	55 --------- 48	47 --------- 46	44 --------- 11
D. Touch Processing	42 /90	90 --------- 73	72 --------- 65	64 -X- 18
E. Multisensory Processing	23 /35	35 --------- 27	26 --------- 24	23 --------- 7
F. Oral Sensory Processing	36 /60	60 --------- 46	45 --------- 40	39 -X- 12
Modulation				
G. Sensory Processing Related to Endurance/Tone	36 /45	45 --------- 39	38 --------- 36	35 --------- 9
H. Modulation Related to Body Position and Movement	40 /50	50 --------- 41	40 --------- 36	35 --------- 10
I. Modulation of Movement Affecting Activity Level	22 /35	35 --------- 23	22 --------- 19	18 --------- 7
J. Modulation of Sensory Input Affecting Emotional Responses	13 /20	20 --------- 16	15 --------- 14	13 --------- 4
K. Modulation of Visual Input Affecting Emotional Responses and Activity Level	14 /20	20 --------- 15	14 --------- 12	11 --------- 4
Behavior and Emotional Responses				
L. Emotional/Social Responses	56 /85	85 --------- 63	62 ----- X 55	54 --------- 17
M. Behavioral Outcomes of Sensory Processing	17 /30	30 --------- 22	21 --------- 19	18 X-- 6
N. Items Indicating Thresholds for Response	10 /15	15 --------- 12	11 --------- 10	9 --------- 3

*Classifications are based on the performance of children without disabilities (n = 1,037).

Figure 8.3 ■ **Noah's *Summary Score Sheet* (continued)**

During the first months, the team slowly increased the sensory features of tasks. For example, they added weights to toys with which Noah played to increase touch pressure and proprioceptive input to skin, joints, and limbs. They added a cart for him to push when the class moved to the library (filled with the books to add weight) and had him wear a backpack as he moved around the classroom and school. Each of these strategies enabled Noah increasingly to receive more sensory processing opportunities within the rituals that made him feel comfortable. By reducing his outbursts, Noah became more available for interactive moments with peers and the teacher.

Outcomes of Intervention

With this intervention plan in place, Noah became more and more comfortable with his classroom situation and transitions to and from school, and school routines got easier. Because the teachers were allowing behaviors that sometimes were unusual in classrooms, they decided to videotape Noah in various situations so that they could introduce him and his rituals to the next set of teachers. Although the therapist attended these briefing meetings, she found that the other teachers had more clout with the new teachers. The questions about classroom disruptions and management of the other children were easy for the current teachers to handle.

The team decided that Noah was ready to have a Circle of Friends group to support him at school. This is a strategy for peers to make particular commitments to Noah as their friend; because the children would be more familiar with Noah's routines when they went to the next grade, this eased the transition to the new environment. The children were able to offer suggestions about how to handle situations with Noah and thereby support the teachers as they learned how to be effective with him and all the children.

Case Study 2: Tim

Tim is a third-grader who completes his work at school, but is a "plodder" according to his teacher. Because he was having increasing trouble developing friendships, his teacher and mother worried that Tim was becoming more isolated and soon would be excluded from peer socialization opportunities, which they both believe is an important part of his school experience. Tim's mom completed the *Sensory Profile* as part of the interdisciplinary team's exploration of Tim's strengths and needs. Figures 8.4 and 8.5 (on page 92 and page 100, respectively) summarize his scores on the *Caregiver Questionnaire* and the *Summary Score Sheet*.

Scores

As the therapist reviewed Tim's scores, he saw that Tim has some strengths and some areas of concern related to sensory processing (see Figure 8.5). He seems to have typical emotional responses to sensory events (Sections J, K, and L), and is processing oral, auditory, and body position sensory input (Sections A, F, and H). He has more difficulty processing visual and vestibular information (Sections B and C). His most serious sensory processing issues seem to be related to touch and multisensory processing, especially as this integrated information is needed to maintain an optimal level of arousal and endurance for tasks (Sections D, E, G, and I).

The therapist wished to learn more about the processing and modulation issues that might be affecting Tim's slowed classroom performance and his deteriorating socialization. By completing the Factor Grid and transferring the totals to the Factor Summary, the therapist gained additional insights about the impact of Tim's sensory processing and modulation patterns on his performance at school (see Figure 8.5).

Sensory Processing

A. Auditory Processing

Item			A. Auditory Processing	ALWAYS	FREQUENTLY	OCCASIONALLY	SELDOM	NEVER
👂	L	1	Responds negatively to unexpected or loud noises (for example, cries or hides at noise from vacuum cleaner, dog barking, hair dryer)				X4	
👂	L	2	Holds hands over ears to protect ears from sound					X5
👂	L	3	Has trouble completing tasks when the radio is on					X5
👂	L	4	Is distracted or has trouble functioning if there is a lot of noise around					X5
👂	L	5	Can't work with background noise (for example, fan, refrigerator)					X5
👂	H	6	Appears to not hear what you say (for example, does not "tune-in" to what you say, appears to ignore you)					X5
👂	H	7	Doesn't respond when name is called but you know the child's hearing is OK					X5
👂	H	8	Enjoys strange noises/seeks to make noise for noise's sake					X5
			Section Raw Score Total		39			

Comments

B. Visual Processing

Item			B. Visual Processing	ALWAYS	FREQUENTLY	OCCASIONALLY	SELDOM	NEVER
👁	L	9	Prefers to be in the dark			X3		
👁	L	10	Expresses discomfort with or avoids bright lights (for example, hides from sunlight through window in car)				X4	
👁	L	11	Happy to be in the dark			X3		
👁	L	12	Becomes frustrated when trying to find objects in competing backgrounds (for example, a cluttered drawer)				X4	
👁	L	13	Has difficulty putting puzzles together (as compared to same age children)				X4	
👁	L	14	Is bothered by bright lights after others have adapted to the light			X3		
👁	L	15	Covers eyes or squints to protect eyes from light				X4	
👁	H	16	Looks carefully or intensely at objects/people (for example, stares)			X3		
👁	H	17	Has a hard time finding objects in competing backgrounds (for example, shoes in a messy room, favorite toy in the "junk drawer")			X3		
			Section Raw Score Total		31			

Comments

Figure 8.4 ■ Tim's *Caregiver Questionnaire*

	Item		C. Vestibular Processing	ALWAYS	FREQUENTLY	OCCASIONALLY	SELDOM	NEVER
→	L	18	Becomes anxious or distressed when feet leave the ground					X5
→	L	19	Dislikes activities where head is upside down (for example, somersaults, roughhousing)					X5
→	L	20	Avoids playground equipment or moving toys (for example, swing set, merry-go-round)				X4	
→	L	21	Dislikes riding in a car				X4	
→	L	22	Holds head upright, even when bending over or leaning (for example, maintains a rigid position/posture during activity)				X4	
→	L	23	Becomes disoriented after bending over sink or table (for example, falls or gets dizzy)				X4	
→	H	24	Seeks all kinds of movement and this interferes with daily routines (for example, can't sit still, fidgets)				X4	
→	H	25	Seeks out all kinds of movement activities (for example, being whirled by adult, merry-go-rounds, playground equipment, moving toys)				X4	
→	H	26	Twirls/spins self frequently throughout the day (for example, likes dizzy feeling)				X4	
→	H	27	Rocks unconsciously (for example, while watching TV)				X4	
→	H	28	Rocks in desk/chair/on floor				X4	
			Section Raw Score Total			*46*		

Comments

Figure 8.4 ■ Tim's *Caregiver Questionnaire (continued)*

	Item		D. Touch Processing	ALWAYS	FREQUENTLY	OCCASIONALLY	SELDOM	NEVER
🖐	L	29	Avoids getting "messy" (for example, in paste, sand, finger paint, glue, tape)			X3		
🖐	L	30	Expresses distress during grooming (for example, fights or cries during haircutting, face washing, fingernail cutting)			X3		
🖐	L	31	Prefers long-sleeved clothing when it is warm or short sleeves when it is cold			X3		
🖐	L	32	Expresses discomfort at dental work or toothbrushing (for example, cries or fights)			X3		
🖐	L	33	Is sensitive to certain fabrics (for example, is particular about certain clothes or bedsheets)			X3		
🖐	L	34	Becomes irritated by shoes or socks			X3		
🖐	L	35	Avoids going barefoot, especially in sand or grass			X3		
🖐	L	36	Reacts emotionally or aggressively to touch			X3		
🖐	L	37	Withdraws from splashing water				X4	
🖐	L	38	Has difficulty standing in line or close to other people					X5
🖐	L	39	Rubs or scratches out a spot that has been touched					X5
🖐	H	40	Touches people and objects to the point of irritating others				X4	
🖐	H	41	Displays unusual need for touching certain toys, surfaces, or textures (for example, constantly touching objects)				X4	
🖐	H	42	Decreased awareness of pain and temperature		X3			
🖐	H	43	Doesn't seem to notice when someone touches arm or back (for example, unaware)		X3			
🖐	H	44	Avoids wearing shoes; loves to be barefoot				X4	
🖐	H	45	Touches people and objects				X4	
🖐	H	46	Doesn't seem to notice when face or hands are messy				X4	
			Section Raw Score Total			64		

Comments

	Item		E. Multisensory Processing	ALWAYS	FREQUENTLY	OCCASIONALLY	SELDOM	NEVER
👁		47	Gets lost easily (even in familiar places)	X1				
🏃		48	Has difficulty paying attention					X5
👁	L	49	Looks away from tasks to notice all actions in the room					X5
❓	H	50	Seems oblivious within an active environment (for example, unaware of activity)	X1				
🧍	H	51	Hangs on people, furniture, or objects even in familiar situations			X3		
🧍	H	52	Walks on toes				X4	
🖐	H	53	Leaves clothing twisted on body				X4	
			Section Raw Score Total			23		

Comments

Figure 8.4 ■ **Tim's _Caregiver Questionnaire_ (continued)**

	Item		F. Oral Sensory Processing	ALWAYS	FREQUENTLY	OCCASIONALLY	SELDOM	NEVER
👋	L	54	Gags easily with food textures or food utensils in mouth				X4	
👄	L	55	Avoids certain tastes or food smells that are typically part of children's diets					X5
👄	L	56	Will only eat certain tastes (list: _____)					X5
👋	L	57	Limits self to particular food textures/temperatures (list: _____)					X5
👋	L	58	Picky eater, especially regarding food textures					X5
👄	H	59	Routinely smells nonfood objects					X5
👄	H	60	Shows strong preference for certain smells (list: _____)					X5
👄	H	61	Shows strong preference for certain tastes (list: _____)					X5
👄	H	62	Craves certain foods (list: _____)					X5
👄	H	63	Seeks out certain tastes or smells (list: _____)					X5
👄	H	64	Chews or licks on nonfood objects					X5
👋	H	65	Mouths objects (for example, pencil, hands)					X5
			Section Raw Score Total			59		

Comments

Modulation

	Item		G. Sensory Processing Related to Endurance/Tone	ALWAYS	FREQUENTLY	OCCASIONALLY	SELDOM	NEVER
🧍		66	Moves stiffly				X4	
🧍	H	67	Tires easily, especially when standing or holding particular body position			X3		
🧍	H	68	Locks joints (for example, elbows, knees) for stability			X3		
🧍	H	69	Seems to have weak muscles				X4	
🧍	H	70	Has a weak grasp			X3		
🧍	H	71	Can't lift heavy objects (for example, weak in comparison to same age children)				X4	
🧍	H	72	Props to support self (even during activity)			X3		
→	H	73	Poor endurance/tires easily			X3		
→	H	74	Appears lethargic (for example, has no energy, is sluggish)			X3		
			Section Raw Score Total			30		

Comments

Figure 8.4 ■ Tim's *Caregiver Questionnaire (continued)*

Item			H. Modulation Related to Body Position and Movement	ALWAYS	FREQUENTLY	OCCASIONALLY	SELDOM	NEVER
♡		75	Seems accident-prone				X₄	
👁		76	Hesitates going up or down curbs or steps (for example, is cautious, stops before moving)					X₅
→	L	77	Fears falling or heights					X₅
→	L	78	Avoids climbing/jumping or avoids bumpy/uneven ground					X₅
→	L	79	Holds onto walls or banisters (for example, clings)					X₅
→	H	80	Takes excessive risks during play (for example, climbs high into a tree, jumps off tall furniture)				X₄	
→	H	81	Takes movement or climbing risks during play that compromise personal safety				X₄	
→	H	82	Turns whole body to look at you				X₄	
🧍	H	83	Seeks opportunities to fall without regard to personal safety				X₄	
🧍	H	84	Appears to enjoy falling				X₄	
			Section Raw Score Total			44		

Comments

Item			I. Modulation of Movement Affecting Activity Level	ALWAYS	FREQUENTLY	OCCASIONALLY	SELDOM	NEVER
🏃	L	85	Spends most of the day in sedentary play (for example, does quiet things)	X₂				
🏃	L	86	Prefers quiet, sedentary play (for example, watching TV, books, computers)	X₂				
→	L	87	Seeks sedentary play options	X₂				
→	L	88	Prefers sedentary activities	X₂				
→	H	89	Becomes overly excitable during movement activity			X₃		
🏃	H	90	"On the go"			X₃		
🏃	H	91	Avoids quiet play activities			X₃		
			Section Raw Score Total			17		

Comments

Item			J. Modulation of Sensory Input Affecting Emotional Responses	ALWAYS	FREQUENTLY	OCCASIONALLY	SELDOM	NEVER
♡		92	Needs more protection from life than other children (for example, defenseless physically or emotionally)				X₄	
☝	L	93	Rigid rituals in personal hygiene				X₄	
♡	H	94	Is overly affectionate with others				X₄	
♡	H	95	Doesn't perceive body language or facial expressions (for example, unable to interpret)				X₄	
			Section Raw Score Total			16		

Comments

Figure 8.4 ■ Tim's *Caregiver Questionnaire (continued)*

Item			K. Modulation of Visual Input Affecting Emotional Responses and Activity Level	ALWAYS	FREQUENTLY	OCCASIONALLY	SELDOM	NEVER
👁	L	96	Avoids eye contact				X₄	
👁	H	97	Stares intensively at objects or people				X₄	
👁	H	98	Watches everyone when they move around the room				X₄	
👁	H	99	Doesn't notice when people come into the room			X₃		
			Section Raw Score Total			*15*		

Comments

Behavior and Emotional Responses

Item			L. Emotional/Social Responses	ALWAYS	FREQUENTLY	OCCASIONALLY	SELDOM	NEVER
♡		100	Seems to have difficulty liking self (for example, low self-esteem)					X₅
♡		101	Has trouble "growing up" (for example, reacts immaturely to situations)					X₅
♡		102	Is sensitive to criticisms					X₅
♡		103	Has definite fears (for example, fears are predictable)					X₅
♡		104	Seems anxious					X₅
♡		105	Displays excessive emotional outbursts when unsuccessful at a task					X₅
♡		106	Expresses feeling like a failure					X₅
♡		107	Is stubborn or uncooperative					X₅
♡		108	Has temper tantrums					X₅
♡		109	Poor frustration tolerance					X₅
♡		110	Cries easily				X₄	
♡		111	Overly serious				X₄	
♡		112	Has difficulty making friends (for example, does not interact or participate in group play)				X₄	
♡		113	Has nightmares				X₄	
♡		114	Has fears that interfere with daily routine				X₄	
♡		115	Doesn't have a sense of humor				X₄	
♡		116	Doesn't express emotions				X₄	
			Section Raw Score Total			*78*		

Comments

Figure 8.4 ■ **Tim's *Caregiver Questionnaire* (continued)**

Item			M. Behavioral Outcomes of Sensory Processing	ALWAYS	FREQUENTLY	OCCASIONALLY	SELDOM	NEVER
👂		117	Talks self through tasks				X4	
👁		118	Writing is illegible		X2			
👁		119	Has trouble staying between the lines when coloring or when writing			X3		
♡		120	Uses inefficient ways of doing things (for example, wastes time, moves slowly, does things a harder way than is needed)			X3		
♡	L	121	Has difficulty tolerating changes in plans and expectations				X4	
♡	L	122	Has difficulty tolerating changes in routines				X4	
			Section Raw Score Total			20		

Comments

Item			N. Items Indicating Thresholds for Response	ALWAYS	FREQUENTLY	OCCASIONALLY	SELDOM	NEVER
🏃		123	Jumps from one activity to another so that it interferes with play			X3		
👄	H	124	Deliberately smells objects				X4	
👄	H	125	Does not seem to smell strong odors				X4	
			Section Raw Score Total			11		

Comments

Figure 8.4 ■ Tim's *Caregiver Questionnaire (continued)*

From a sensory processing perspective, the *Sensory Profile* indicated that Factors 1, 2, 4, 5, and 7 are not problem areas, Factor 9 is questionable, and Factors 3, 6, and 8 are definitely problems for Tim.

Interpretation

When considering the meaning of the data in relation to the concerns expressed by his teacher and mom, the therapist saw that Tim is having difficulty responding to and noticing stimuli around him. The three factors with problem scores all contain items related to a child's unresponsiveness to environmental events and demands. Tim is more sedentary and takes a longer time to respond to requests, noises, and changes in his environment. Remember that all the items on the *Sensory Profile* describe behaviors that indicate difficulty with that form of sensory input. Therefore, a high sensory-seeking score (Factor 1) indicates that Tim is *not* engaging in the seeking behaviors that are present in a more fidgety, distractible child (i.e., scores of 4 and 5 are correlated with "seldom" and "never"). Tim does not engage in behaviors that add information to his life or demonstrate his interest in the activities and people around him. Therefore, this information might be quite helpful when talking with his mom and teacher. Tim's pattern indicated that he lacks the level of responsiveness that children his age need to appear interested and engaged with those around him. His slowness to respond or notice cues could be a growing problem as he moves into third grade, because in this grade, school and socialization tasks become more complex. It would be helpful for his parents, teachers, and other service providers to understand this feature of Tim's behavioral repertoire as a first step in effective planning.

According to the proposed conceptual model for understanding children's responses to sensory events in daily life (see Chapter 2), Tim's responses are consistent with Poor Registration. This is a state in which the child has high neurological thresholds and acts in accordance with those thresholds. These children tend to have a dull affect and appear uninterested in activities around them. It is possible that children with poor registration have less-than-adequate activation of neural pathways for maintaining endurance for tasks or cues about performance expectations.

Intervention

This perspective offers information that can help therapists plan effective intervention. The team needed to enhance or intensify the sensory aspects of the events in Tim's life. This increased the chances for his neurological thresholds to be met so that he could notice and respond as other children already do.

The occupational therapist and teacher discussed the classroom culture and identified ways to enhance Tim's arousal through intensified sensory input during school tasks. For example, they considered adding singing, clapping, and marching to classroom routines such as lining up so that Tim would have a better chance of noticing what is happening and could participate with classmates. The teacher also might adjust Tim's methods for working in the classroom by finding a counter at which he can stand for completing seatwork (increasing proprioceptive input through the weight of his body to his legs and lower joints, and vestibular input through bending over to work). The teacher also might create a schedule to increase the number of times Tim gets up and moves around the room, such as for turning in smaller parts of work, or to hand out books or supplies.

The therapist offered Tim's mom suggestions to enhance sensory input at home, including using contrasting placemats and plates with foods Tim eats during mealtime. Other suggestions for family members included adding strong flavors or smells to foods, such as peppermint in milk or chili powder in stew. These added sensory

Factor Grid

Instructions: Transfer from the *Caregiver Questionnaire* the item raw score that corresponds with each item listed. Add the Raw Score column to get the Factor Raw Score Total for each factor.

FACTOR 1
Sensory Seeking

Item		Raw Score
⟨ear⟩	8	5
→	24	4
→	25	4
→	26	4
⟨touch⟩	44	4
⟨touch⟩	45	4
⟨touch⟩	46	4
⟨body⟩	51	3
→	80	4
→	81	4
→	82	4
⟨body⟩	83	4
⟨body⟩	84	4
→	89	3
⟨activity⟩	90	3
♡	94	4
⟨activity⟩	123	3
Factor Raw Score Total		65

FACTOR 2
Emotionally Reactive

Item		Raw Score
♡	92	4
♡	100	5
♡	101	5
♡	102	5
♡	103	5
♡	104	5
♡	105	5
♡	106	5
♡	107	5
♡	108	5
♡	109	5
♡	110	4
♡	111	4
♡	112	4
♡	121	4
♡	122	4
Factor Raw Score Total		74

FACTOR 3
Low Endurance/Tone

Item		Raw Score
⟨body⟩	66	4
⟨body⟩	67	3
⟨body⟩	68	3
⟨body⟩	69	4
⟨body⟩	70	3
⟨body⟩	71	4
⟨body⟩	72	3
→	73	3
→	74	3
Factor Raw Score Total		30

FACTOR 4
Oral Sensory Sensitivity

Item		Raw Score
⟨taste⟩	55	5
⟨taste⟩	56	5
⟨touch⟩	57	5
⟨touch⟩	58	5
⟨taste⟩	59	5
⟨taste⟩	60	5
⟨taste⟩	61	5
⟨taste⟩	62	5
⟨taste⟩	63	5
Factor Raw Score Total		45

FACTOR 5
Inattention/Distractibility

Item		Raw Score
⟨ear⟩	3	5
⟨ear⟩	4	5
⟨ear⟩	5	5
⟨ear⟩	6	5
⟨ear⟩	7	5
⟨activity⟩	48	5
⟨eye⟩	49	5
Factor Raw Score Total		35

ICON KEY

⟨ear⟩	Auditory
⟨eye⟩	Visual
⟨activity⟩	Activity Level
⟨mouth⟩	Taste/Smell
⟨body⟩	Body Position
→	Movement
⟨hand⟩	Touch
♡	Emotional/Social

Figure 8.5 ■ **Tim's *Summary Score Sheet***

FACTOR 6		
Poor Registration		
Item		Raw Score
☀	35	3
☀	42	3
☀	43	3
♡	95	4
👁	99	3
♡	115	4
♡	116	4
👄	125	4
Factor Raw Score Total		28

FACTOR 7		
Sensory Sensitivity		
Item		Raw Score
→	18	5
→	19	5
→	77	5
→	78	5
Factor Raw Score Total		20

FACTOR 8		
Sedentary		
Item		Raw Score
🏃	85	2
🏃	86	2
→	87	2
→	88	2
Factor Raw Score Total		8

FACTOR 9		
Fine Motor/Perceptual		
Item		Raw Score
👁	13	4
👁	118	2
👁	119	3
Factor Raw Score Total		9

Factor Summary

Instructions: Transfer the child's score for each factor to the column labeled Factor Raw Score Total.
Then plot these totals by marking an X in the appropriate classification column
(Typical Performance, Probable Difference, Definite Difference).*

Factor	Factor Raw Score Total	Typical Performance	Probable Difference	Definite Difference
1. Sensory Seeking	65 /85	85 ----X-- 63	62 ---------- 55	54 ---------- 17
2. Emotionally Reactive	74 /80	80 -X----- 57	56 ---------- 48	47 ---------- 16
3. Low Endurance/Tone	30 /45	45 ---------- 39	38 ---------- 36	35 X---- 9
4. Oral Sensory Sensitivity	45 /45	X5 ---------- 33	32 ---------- 27	26 ---------- 9
5. Inattention/Distractibility	35 /35	X5 ---------- 25	24 ---------- 22	21 ---------- 7
6. Poor Registration	28 /40	40 ---------- 33	32 ---------- 30	29 X---- 8
7. Sensory Sensitivity	20 /20	X0 ---------- 16	15 ---------- 14	13 ---------- 4
8. Sedentary	8 /20	20 ---------- 12	11 ---------- 10	9 X--- 4
9. Fine Motor/Perceptual	9 /15	15 ---------- 10	X9 ---------- 8	7 ---------- 3

*Classifications are based on the performance of children without disabilities (*n* = 1,037).

Figure 8.5 ■ Tim's *Summary Score Sheet (continued)*

Section Summary

Instructions: Transfer the child's score for each section to the Section Raw Score Total column.
Then plot these totals by marking an X in the appropriate classification column
(Typical Performance, Probable Difference, Definite Difference).*

Sensory Processing	Section Raw Score Total		Typical Performance	Probable Difference	Definite Difference
A. Auditory Processing	39	/40	40X-------- 30	29 ---------- 26	25 ---------- 8
B. Visual Processing	31	/45	45 ---------- 32	31X ---------- 27	26 ---------- 9
C. Vestibular Processing	46	/55	55 ---------- 48	47X---------- 45	44 ---------- 11
D. Touch Processing	64	/90	90 ---------- 73	72---------- 65	64X ---------- 18
E. Multisensory Processing	23	/35	35 ---------- 27	26 ---------- 24	23X ---------- 7
F. Oral Sensory Processing	59	/60	60X-------- 46	45 ---------- 40	39 ---------- 12
Modulation					
G. Sensory Processing Related to Endurance/Tone	30	/45	45 ---------- 39	38 ---------- 36	35 X-------- 9
H. Modulation Related to Body Position and Movement	44	/50	50 ----X--- 41	40 ---------- 36	35 ---------- 10
I. Modulation of Movement Affecting Activity Level	17	/35	35 ---------- 23	22 ---------- 19	18X-------- 7
J. Modulation of Sensory Input Affecting Emotional Responses	16	/20	20 ---------- 16X	15 ---------- 14	13 ---------- 4
K. Modulation of Visual Input Affecting Emotional Responses and Activity Level	15	/20	20 ---------- 16X	14 ---------- 12	11 ---------- 4
Behavior and Emotional Responses					
L. Emotional/Social Responses	78	/85	85 X-------- 63	62 ---------- 55	54 ---------- 17
M. Behavioral Outcomes of Sensory Processing	20	/30	30 ---------- 22	21 ---------X19	18 ---------- 6
N. Items Indicating Thresholds for Response	11	/15	15 ---------- 12	11X ---------- 10	9 ---------- 3

*Classifications are based on the performance of children without disabilities (*n* = 1,037).

Figure 8.5 ■ Tim's *Summary Score Sheet (continued)*

features might generate arousal for Tim so that he can be more alert during mealtime. The therapist and Tim's mom also could inventory the textures of Tim's clothing and add close-fitting Lycra clothing and fleece items, both of which provide ongoing touch input as Tim moves about. They could change bath time to mornings, place a water-proof radio in the shower, add a massage showerhead, and create a basket of fabric squares that could become his washcloths so that Tim can have many different sensations as he gets ready for the day.

All of these interventions would provide Tim with many opportunities to meet his neurological thresholds and, therefore, become more responsive to his environment. When Tim is more alert, he is more likely to respond to peers and appear interested in being their friend.

Outcomes of Interventions

By the end of the school year, the teacher was very pleased with Tim's continuing participation in the classroom. She found that Tim began to initiate strategies for himself when he was drifting away from the activities at hand. For example, he began going to get a drink more often during seatwork. The teacher recognized this as an adaptation to the "moving around the room" strategies they had started, so she supported Tim's choice. She saw that Tim also did better during library time when the class was more active just prior to this quiet activity. Tim also began standing regularly in the library while he read, which she saw as a generalization of the counter work they organized in the classroom.

At home, mealtime and self-care got better, too. His mother got creative with smells, textures, and tastes so that the whole family was surprised at mealtime, and it got to be an adventure for all of them. She began to notice differences in Tim's participation related to clothing choices and shifted his wardrobe as he grew to provide more textures. She found very thick textured socks were the most helpful and built a large sock wardrobe for Tim.

Case Study 3: Matine

Matine is 4 years old and attends a community day care and preschool program. The day-care provider said that she "fits in" with the other children during free play and is successful during small-group, teacher-directed activities. However, she was concerned that Matine was very disruptive and unsuccessful during snack times. Martine's parents reported that she does fine at mealtimes at home. They explained that they know what Matine likes to eat, prepare her foods so that she will eat them, and provide a very structured ritual. They also believed that Matine, as an only child, could concentrate on the business of eating.

The team started the data-gathering process by conducting a skilled observation of snack time and an in-depth interview of the parents about the mealtime rituals. The parents completed a *Caregiver Questionnaire,* and the therapist summarized the scores on the *Summary Score Sheet.* Matine's parents added comments in the Oral Processing section to help the therapist determine what the parents were doing at home that might be helpful for school (see Figure 8.6 on page 104).

Sensory Processing

Item			A. Auditory Processing	ALWAYS	FREQUENTLY	OCCASIONALLY	SELDOM	NEVER
👂	L	1	Responds negatively to unexpected or loud noises (for example, cries or hides at noise from vacuum cleaner, dog barking, hair dryer)		X2			
👂	L	2	Holds hands over ears to protect ears from sound		X2			
👂	L	3	Has trouble completing tasks when the radio is on	X1				
👂	L	4	Is distracted or has trouble functioning if there is a lot of noise around	X1				
👂	L	5	Can't work with background noise (for example, fan, refrigerator)	X1				
👂	H	6	Appears to not hear what you say (for example, does not "tune-in" to what you say, appears to ignore you)	X1				
👂	H	7	Doesn't respond when name is called but you know the child's hearing is OK	X1				
👂	H	8	Enjoys strange noises/seeks to make noise for noise's sake		X2			
			Section Raw Score Total			11		

Comments

Item			B. Visual Processing	ALWAYS	FREQUENTLY	OCCASIONALLY	SELDOM	NEVER
👁	L	9	Prefers to be in the dark			X3		
👁	L	10	Expresses discomfort with or avoids bright lights (for example, hides from sunlight through window in car)				X4	
👁	L	11	Happy to be in the dark				X4	
👁	L	12	Becomes frustrated when trying to find objects in competing backgrounds (for example, a cluttered drawer)				X4	
👁	L	13	Has difficulty putting puzzles together (as compared to same age children)			X3		
👁	L	14	Is bothered by bright lights after others have adapted to the light				X4	
👁	L	15	Covers eyes or squints to protect eyes from light				X4	
👁	H	16	Looks carefully or intensely at objects/people (for example, stares)			X3		
👁	H	17	Has a hard time finding objects in competing backgrounds (for example, shoes in a messy room, favorite toy in the "junk drawer")			X3		
			Section Raw Score Total			32		

Comments

Figure 8.6 ■ **Matine's *Caregiver Questionnaire***

	Item		C. Vestibular Processing	ALWAYS	FREQUENTLY	OCCASIONALLY	SELDOM	NEVER
→	L	18	Becomes anxious or distressed when feet leave the ground					X5
→	L	19	Dislikes activities where head is upside down (for example, somersaults, roughhousing)					X5
→	L	20	Avoids playground equipment or moving toys (for example, swing set, merry-go-round)					X5
→	L	21	Dislikes riding in a car					X5
→	L	22	Holds head upright, even when bending over or leaning (for example, maintains a rigid position/posture during activity)					X5
→	L	23	Becomes disoriented after bending over sink or table (for example, falls or gets dizzy)					X5
→	H	24	Seeks all kinds of movement and this interferes with daily routines (for example, can't sit still, fidgets)			X3		
→	H	25	Seeks out all kinds of movement activities (for example, being whirled by adult, merry-go-rounds, playground equipment, moving toys)			X3		
→	H	26	Twirls/spins self frequently throughout the day (for example, likes dizzy feeling)			X3		
→	H	27	Rocks unconsciously (for example, while watching TV)					X5
→	H	28	Rocks in desk/chair/on floor					X5
			Section Raw Score Total			*49*		

Comments

Figure 8.6 ■ Matine's *Caregiver Questionnaire (continued)*

105

	Item		D. Touch Processing	ALWAYS	FREQUENTLY	OCCASIONALLY	SELDOM	NEVER
	L	29	Avoids getting "messy" (for example, in paste, sand, finger paint, glue, tape)			X₃		
	L	30	Expresses distress during grooming (for example, fights or cries during haircutting, face washing, fingernail cutting)			X₃		
	L	31	Prefers long-sleeved clothing when it is warm or short sleeves when it is cold			X₃		
	L	32	Expresses discomfort at dental work or toothbrushing (for example, cries or fights)			X₃		
	L	33	Is sensitive to certain fabrics (for example, is particular about certain clothes or bedsheets)				X₄	
	L	34	Becomes irritated by shoes or socks			X₃		
	L	35	Avoids going barefoot, especially in sand or grass					X₅
	L	36	Reacts emotionally or aggressively to touch			X₃		
	L	37	Withdraws from splashing water			X₃		
	L	38	Has difficulty standing in line or close to other people				X₄	
	L	39	Rubs or scratches out a spot that has been touched				X₄	
	H	40	Touches people and objects to the point of irritating others				X₄	
	H	41	Displays unusual need for touching certain toys, surfaces, or textures (for example, constantly touching objects)				X₄	
	H	42	Decreased awareness of pain and temperature					X₅
	H	43	Doesn't seem to notice when someone touches arm or back (for example, unaware)					X₅
	H	44	Avoids wearing shoes; loves to be barefoot			X₃		
	H	45	Touches people and objects			X₃		
	H	46	Doesn't seem to notice when face or hands are messy			X₃		
			Section Raw Score Total			*65*		

Comments

	Item		E. Multisensory Processing	ALWAYS	FREQUENTLY	OCCASIONALLY	SELDOM	NEVER
		47	Gets lost easily (even in familiar places)				X₄	
		48	Has difficulty paying attention		X₂			
	L	49	Looks away from tasks to notice all actions in the room		X₂			
	H	50	Seems oblivious within an active environment (for example, unaware of activity)				X₄	
	H	51	Hangs on people, furniture, or objects even in familiar situations		X₂			
	H	52	Walks on toes				X₄	
	H	53	Leaves clothing twisted on body				X₄	
			Section Raw Score Total			22		

Comments

Figure 8.6 ■ **Matine's *Caregiver Questionnaire* (continued)**

Item			F. Oral Sensory Processing	ALWAYS	FREQUENTLY	OCCASIONALLY	SELDOM	NEVER
	L	54	Gags easily with food textures or food utensils in mouth	X$_1$				
	L	55	Avoids certain tastes or food smells that are typically part of children's diets		X$_2$			
	L	56	Will only eat certain tastes (list: hates spicy food)		X$_2$			
	L	57	Limits self to particular food textures/temperatures (list: I always mash her food and take the crust off her bread.)		X$_2$			
	L	58	Picky eater, especially regarding food textures		X$_2$			
	H	59	Routinely smells nonfood objects		X$_2$			
	H	60	Shows strong preference for certain smells (list:)		X$_2$			
	H	61	Shows strong preference for certain tastes (list:)		X$_2$			
	H	62	Craves certain foods (list: wants pudding every day)		X$_2$			
	H	63	Seeks out certain tastes or smells (list:)		X$_2$			
	H	64	Chews or licks on nonfood objects			X$_3$		
	H	65	Mouths objects (for example, pencil, hands)			X$_3$		
			Section Raw Score Total		25			

Comments

Matine eats better if I make her plate and let it sit out, while I prepare the rest of the meal.

Modulation				ALWAYS	FREQUENTLY	OCCASIONALLY	SELDOM	NEVER
Item			G. Sensory Processing Related to Endurance/Tone					
		66	Moves stiffly					X$_5$
	H	67	Tires easily, especially when standing or holding particular body position				X$_4$	
	H	68	Locks joints (for example, elbows, knees) for stability				X$_4$	
	H	69	Seems to have weak muscles					X$_5$
	H	70	Has a weak grasp				X$_4$	
	H	71	Can't lift heavy objects (for example, weak in comparison to same age children)				X$_4$	
	H	72	Props to support self (even during activity)					X$_5$
	H	73	Poor endurance/tires easily					X$_5$
	H	74	Appears lethargic (for example, has no energy, is sluggish)					X$_5$
			Section Raw Score Total		41			

Comments

Figure 8.6 ■ **Matine's *Caregiver Questionnaire* (continued)**

Item		H. Modulation Related to Body Position and Movement	ALWAYS	FREQUENTLY	OCCASIONALLY	SELDOM	NEVER
♡		75	Seems accident-prone				X4	
👁		76	Hesitates going up or down curbs or steps (for example, is cautious, stops before moving)					X5
→	L	77	Fears falling or heights				X4	
→	L	78	Avoids climbing/jumping or avoids bumpy/uneven ground				X4	
→	L	79	Holds onto walls or banisters (for example, clings)				X4	
→	H	80	Takes excessive risks during play (for example, climbs high into a tree, jumps off tall furniture)		X3			
→	H	81	Takes movement or climbing risks during play that compromise personal safety		X3			
→	H	82	Turns whole body to look at you		X3			
✶	H	83	Seeks opportunities to fall without regard to personal safety		X3			
✶	H	84	Appears to enjoy falling		X3			
			Section Raw Score Total		36			

Comments

Item		I. Modulation of Movement Affecting Activity Level	ALWAYS	FREQUENTLY	OCCASIONALLY	SELDOM	NEVER
✶	L	85	Spends most of the day in sedentary play (for example, does quiet things)					X5
✶	L	86	Prefers quiet, sedentary play (for example, watching TV, books, computers)					X5
→	L	87	Seeks sedentary play options					X5
→	L	88	Prefers sedentary activities					X5
→	H	89	Becomes overly excitable during movement activity		X3			
✶	H	90	"On the go"		X3			
✶	H	91	Avoids quiet play activities		X3			
			Section Raw Score Total		29			

Comments

Item		J. Modulation of Sensory Input Affecting Emotional Responses	ALWAYS	FREQUENTLY	OCCASIONALLY	SELDOM	NEVER
♡		92	Needs more protection from life than other children (for example, defenseless physically or emotionally)				X4	
☼	L	93	Rigid rituals in personal hygiene					X5
♡	H	94	Is overly affectionate with others				X4	
♡	H	95	Doesn't perceive body language or facial expressions (for example, unable to interpret)					X5
			Section Raw Score Total		18			

Comments

Figure 8.6 ■ **Matine's *Caregiver Questionnaire* (continued)**

	Item		K. Modulation of Visual Input Affecting Emotional Responses and Activity Level	ALWAYS	FREQUENTLY	OCCASIONALLY	SELDOM	NEVER
👁	L	96	Avoids eye contact				X4	
👁	H	97	Stares intensively at objects or people				X4	
👁	H	98	Watches everyone when they move around the room				X4	
👁	H	99	Doesn't notice when people come into the room					X5
			Section Raw Score Total			/7		

Comments

Behavior and Emotional Responses

	Item		L. Emotional/Social Responses	ALWAYS	FREQUENTLY	OCCASIONALLY	SELDOM	NEVER
♡		100	Seems to have difficulty liking self (for example, low self-esteem)			X3		
♡		101	Has trouble "growing up" (for example, reacts immaturely to situations)			X3		
♡		102	Is sensitive to criticisms				X4	
♡		103	Has definite fears (for example, fears are predictable)			X3		
♡		104	Seems anxious			X3		
♡		105	Displays excessive emotional outbursts when unsuccessful at a task			X3		
♡		106	Expresses feeling like a failure				X4	
♡		107	Is stubborn or uncooperative			X3		
♡		108	Has temper tantrums				X4	
♡		109	Poor frustration tolerance			X3		
♡		110	Cries easily			X3		
♡		111	Overly serious			X3		
♡		112	Has difficulty making friends (for example, does not interact or participate in group play)				X4	
♡		113	Has nightmares					X5
♡		114	Has fears that interfere with daily routine				X4	
♡		115	Doesn't have a sense of humor					X5
♡		116	Doesn't express emotions					X5
			Section Raw Score Total			62		

Comments

Figure 8.6 ■ Matine's *Caregiver Questionnaire (continued)*

Item			M. Behavioral Outcomes of Sensory Processing	ALWAYS	FREQUENTLY	OCCASIONALLY	SELDOM	NEVER
?		117	Talks self through tasks					X5
👁		118	Writing is illegible		X3			
👁		119	Has trouble staying between the lines when coloring or when writing		X3			
♡		120	Uses inefficient ways of doing things (for example, wastes time, moves slowly, does things a harder way than is needed)					X5
♡	L	121	Has difficulty tolerating changes in plans and expectations		X3			
♡	L	122	Has difficulty tolerating changes in routines		X3			
			Section Raw Score Total		**22**			

Comments

Item			N. Items Indicating Thresholds for Response	ALWAYS	FREQUENTLY	OCCASIONALLY	SELDOM	NEVER
🏃		123	Jumps from one activity to another so that it interferes with play		X3			
👄	H	124	Deliberately smells objects	X2				
👄	H	125	Does not seem to smell strong odors					X5
			Section Raw Score Total		**10**			

Comments

Figure 8.6 ■ **Matine's *Caregiver Questionnaire* (continued)**

Scores

The *Summary Score Sheet* revealed some possible reasons why snack time was difficult for Matine. She had problems with several areas of sensory processing, including auditory, touch, oral, and multisensory processing (see Figure 8.7). In the parent interview, the therapist determined that Matine's parents have been very intuitive with their daughter. They observed and responded to her sensory-processing difficulties by minimizing particular aspects of the eating experience. For example, with only one child, they could create a quieter, less auditorily challenging environment during mealtime (e.g., no television or radio). They prepared foods Matine likes and came to understand the textures she prefers, so they were able to incorporate this awareness into her food preparation.

Section Summary

Instructions: Transfer the child's score for each section to the Section Raw Score Total column. Then plot these totals by marking an X in the appropriate classification column (Typical Performance, Probable Difference, Definite Difference).*

Sensory Processing	Section Raw Score Total	Typical Performance	Probable Difference	Definite Difference
A. Auditory Processing	11 /40	40 --------- 30	29 --------- 26	25 -----X-- 8
B. Visual Processing	32 /45	45 --------- 3X	31 --------- 27	26 --------- 9
C. Vestibular Processing	49 /55	55 ---------X48	47--------- 45	44 --------- 11
D. Touch Processing	65 /90	90 --------- 73	72---------X5	64 --------- 18
E. Multisensory Processing	22 /35	35 --------- 27	26 --------- 24	23X------- 7
F. Oral Sensory Processing	25 /60	60 --------- 46	45 --------- 40	39 ---X----- 12
Modulation				
G. Sensory Processing Related to Endurance/Tone	41 /45	45 -----X--- 39	38 --------- 36	35 --------- 9
H. Modulation Related to Body Position and Movement	36 /50	50 --------- 41	40 --------- 3X	35 --------- 10
I. Modulation of Movement Affecting Activity Level	29 /35	35 --X------ 23	22 --------- 19	18 --------- 7
J. Modulation of Sensory Input Affecting Emotional Responses	18 /20	20 ----X---- 16	15 --------- 14	13 --------- 4
K. Modulation of Visual Input Affecting Emotional Responses and Activity Level	17 /20	20 -------X- 15	14 --------- 12	11 --------- 4
Behavior and Emotional Responses				
L. Emotional/Social Responses	62 /85	85 --------- 63	6X --------- 55	54 --------- 17
M. Behavioral Outcomes of Sensory Processing	22 /30	30 --------- 2X	21 --------- 19	18 --------- 6
N. Items Indicating Thresholds for Response	10 /15	15 --------- 12	11 --------- X0	9 --------- 3

*Classifications are based on the performance of children without disabilities (*n* = 1,037).

Figure 8.7 ■ **Matine's Section Summary**

It is harder for the day-care center to control noise levels and snack food options. With eight other children at the table, snack time was much louder and more unpredictable. Matine was exposed to unfamiliar tastes and textures, which might have added to her sense of discomfort. If, as her *Sensory Profile* indicated, she has poor ability to process touch stimuli, as well as oral sensitivity to textures and tastes, then snack time was providing a combination of stimuli that are beyond Matine's thresholds. The therapist also wondered about Matine's internal control skills because she performed better when her parents controlled the situation or during free play when distractibility was not so noticeable or disruptive to others. The therapist made a note to include the behavior specialist in discussions to investigate behavior management strategies that might complement the overall intervention plan.

Because the therapist was somewhat concerned about Matine's disruptive behavior (from the observation, the referral information, and the questionable responses in Section L of the *Caregiver Questionnaire)*, she conducted follow-up analyses of the *Sensory Profile* factor structure. She completed the Factor Grid and Factor Summary (see Figure 8.8 on page 114).

Interpretation

The worksheet confirmed the pattern of difficulty revealed in the previous information-gathering strategies and provided the therapist with additional insights for planning intervention. Oral sensitivity also was a problem on the Factor Summary because many of the items in this factor also are in the Oral Sensory Processing (Section E.) The difficulty revealed in Factors 1 (Sensory Seeking) and 5 (Inattention/Distractibility) were helpful in understanding Matine's behavior and performance. Poor performance on these factors suggested that Matine tends to be active, creating more intense sensory experiences for herself (Factor 1), but this pattern of engagement seems to be related to poor performance on Factor 5, which indicates distractibility. While other children are active about interacting in their environments in the preschool years, they learn and profit from these interactions. Matine might have been making attempts to engage in her environment, but because of her difficulties in processing certain types of sensory information, her attempts led to disruptions for both her and her peers.

When the team met, they were anxious for the parents to share their insights and strategies about mealtime. The team members explained their perceptions about Matine's differences in performance from home to school, and brainstormed with the parents about how to help Matine be successful.

Intervention

In a situation such as this, understanding the parameters of performance in different settings becomes important to interpretation and intervention planning. Without having formal training, Matine's parents intuitively decided what she needed, and by doing so, had minimized the effects of her poor sensory processing on her performance at home. The challenge in serving a child like Matine is that the team must make clear decisions about the balance between providing supports to enable successful performance and providing opportunities to experience sensory input and modulation successfully. A good rule of thumb is to provide supports for sensory-processing problems during more difficult tasks while designing other opportunities for the child to discover meaningfulness in sensory input that is hard to process and modulate. Professionals must not fall prey to the outdated idea that because Matine is young, the only appropriate intervention focus would be on her learning how to deal with things.

In Matine's case, the likely reason for her troubles at snack time is that this activity requires modulation of all the sensory inputs that are the most challenging for her. If there is concern about Matine's nutrition, or if her disruptive behavior puts her or others in harm's way, adaptive strategies would be appropriate. To reduce the chances of others bumping into Matine, the teacher could place her at the end of the table (thereby reducing tactile opportunities). Ear plugs or muffs would dampen the effect of ambient noise. Team members would need to experiment with an acceptable item here, because with poor tactile processing, furry muffs, or tight plugs might be irritating. Because Matine is 4 years old, she might find ear muffs with animal heads appealing. By tapping the parents' expertise, the team could prepare snacks that are within Matine's oral sensory tolerances to reduce her outbursts from the unpleasant sensations in her mouth.

At other times during the preschool day, the team could incorporate sensory processing opportunities to help Matine develop more adaptability. Mouth play, such as blowing, sucking, and making faces in the mirror, and self-care routines such as face washing might provide opportunities for Matine to develop oral sensory awareness. Because the family has a successful routine, they could work with the therapist to slowly introduce new textures and tastes into her diet at home. They also could start playing the radio or music in the background, noticing which sounds (e.g., talking, classical music, country music) are easier for her to manage. The behavior specialist suggested that at the day-care center, they can work in groups at the table without eating, incorporating auditory and tactile experiences into the activities (e.g., finger painting, singing, clapping). Then Matine would have opportunities to successfully process sensory input for successful performance.

Outcomes of Intervention

When the teachers tried to introduce the ear muffs, Matine kept pulling them off. At first, the teachers thought this meant she hated the muffs, but upon closer observation, they saw that Matine was not throwing them away as a child might do when irritated. Rather, she was taking them off and then looking at them. She seemed intrigued with the bunny faces and would talk about them. The teachers decided to teach Matine to look in the mirror to see the bunnies, and they took a picture of her wearing the bunny ear muffs and posted it by the snack table. These strategies stopped Matine from removing the muffs and the teachers built them into the snack time ritual.

The therapist was very impressed by the teachers' ability to analyze Matine's overall behaviors and not jump to the wrong conclusion in their frustration to find better snack time strategies. The muffs did seem to help with extra noise at snack time, and sometimes Matine wore them to play outside as well.

Introducing new textures took a little longer for success. Matine continued to be very resistant, but with experimentation the teachers identified several strategies that helped. For example, when foods were a more neutral temperature, she was more likely to accept a new texture (e.g., warm apple sauce rather than cold apple sauce). She also responded well to a cognitive approach in which the teachers asked the children which food was "softer" (e.g., pudding) or "harder" (e.g., cookie). Under these conditions, Matine would join in with the other children more readily.

What was important to the teachers was understanding the parameters of Matine's difficulty. This knowledge helped them to be more accurate observers and to make adjustments within the proper parameters for Matine's needs.

Factor Grid

Instructions: Transfer from the *Caregiver Questionnaire* the item raw score that corresponds with each item listed. Add the Raw Score column to get the Factor Raw Score Total for each factor.

FACTOR 1 — Sensory Seeking		
Item		Raw Score
👂	8	2
→	24	3
→	25	3
→	26	3
✋	44	3
✋	45	3
✋	46	3
🧍	51	2
→	80	3
→	81	3
→	82	3
🧍	83	3
🧍	84	3
→	89	3
🏃	90	3
♡	94	4
🏃	123	3
Factor Raw Score Total		**50**

FACTOR 2 — Emotionally Reactive		
Item		Raw Score
♡	92	4
♡	100	3
♡	101	3
♡	102	4
♡	103	3
♡	104	3
♡	105	3
♡	106	4
♡	107	3
♡	108	4
♡	109	3
♡	110	3
♡	111	3
♡	112	4
♡	121	3
♡	122	3
Factor Raw Score Total		**53**

FACTOR 3 — Low Endurance/Tone		
Item		Raw Score
🧍	66	5
🧍	67	4
🧍	68	4
🧍	69	5
🧍	70	4
🧍	71	4
🧍	72	5
→	73	5
→	74	5
Factor Raw Score Total		**41**

FACTOR 4 — Oral Sensory Sensitivity		
Item		Raw Score
👄	55	2
👄	56	2
✋	57	2
✋	58	2
👄	59	2
👄	60	2
👄	61	2
👄	62	2
👄	63	2
Factor Raw Score Total		**18**

FACTOR 5 — Inattention/Distractibility		
Item		Raw Score
👂	3	1
👂	4	1
👂	5	1
👂	6	1
👂	7	1
🏃	48	2
👁	49	2
Factor Raw Score Total		**9**

ICON KEY	
👂	Auditory
👁	Visual
🏃	Activity Level
👄	Taste/Smell
🧍	Body Position
→	Movement
✋	Touch
♡	Emotional/Social

Figure 8.8 ■ **Matine's Factor Summary**

FACTOR 6		
Poor Registration		
Item		Raw Score
👆	35	5
👆	42	5
👆	43	5
♡	95	5
👁	99	5
♡	115	5
♡	116	5
👄	125	5
Factor Raw Score Total		40

FACTOR 7		
Sensory Sensitivity		
Item		Raw Score
→	18	5
→	19	5
→	77	4
→	78	4
Factor Raw Score Total		18

FACTOR 8		
Sedentary		
Item		Raw Score
🏃	85	5
🏃	86	5
→	87	5
→	88	5
Factor Raw Score Total		20

FACTOR 9		
Fine Motor/Perceptual		
Item		Raw Score
👁	13	3
👁	118	3
👁	119	3
Factor Raw Score Total		9

Factor Summary

Instructions: Transfer the child's score for each factor to the column labeled Factor Raw Score Total. Then plot these totals by marking an X in the appropriate classification column (Typical Performance, Probable Difference, Definite Difference).*

Factor	Factor Raw Score Total	Typical Performance	Probable Difference	Definite Difference
1. Sensory Seeking	50 /85	85 ---------- 63	62 ---------- 55	54 X---------- 17
2. Emotionally Reactive	53 /80	80 ---------- 57	56 ---X---- 48	47 ---------- 16
3. Low Endurance/Tone	41 /45	45 ----X--- 39	38 ---------- 36	35 ---------- 9
4. Oral Sensory Sensitivity	18 /45	45 ---------- 33	32 ---------- 27	26 ---X--- 9
5. Inattention/Distractibility	9 /35	35 ---------- 25	24 ---------- 22	21 ---X--- 7
6. Poor Registration	40 /40	X0 ---------- 33	32 ---------- 30	29 ---------- 8
7. Sensory Sensitivity	18 /20	20 ----X--- 16	15 ---------- 14	13 ---------- 4
8. Sedentary	20 /20	X0 ---------- 12	11 ---------- 10	9 ---------- 4
9. Fine Motor/Perceptual	9 /15	15 ---------- 10	X9 ------- 8	7 ---------- 3

*Classifications are based on the performance of children without disabilities (*n* = 1,037).

Figure 8.8 ■ **Matine's Factor Summary** *(continued)*

115

Case Study 4: Gretta

Gretta is in the fourth grade. The teacher was concerned that Gretta was having trouble organizing her materials and herself to get work completed at the pace consistent with her peers. The teacher brought her concern to the child study team at the school. This team conducts regular meetings to review teachers' concerns and collaborate with them in planning alternative teaching methods prior to referral for comprehensive assessment. (School districts call these teams by different names [e.g., pre-assessment team, classroom support team]; their purpose is to determine whether the problem can be solved as part of regular education). Another classroom teacher on the team agreed to meet with Gretta's teacher to review Gretta's work product and to observe her during seatwork time to gain insights about her work patterns. The parents completed a *Caregiver Questionnaire* to provide the team with additional information about Gretta's performance and to see whether sensory processing issues might be contributing to her inefficiency (see Figure 8.9).

Scores

When the therapist summarized the parents' responses onto the *Summary Score Sheet*, she saw that Gretta was performing within a Typical range on most sections (see Figures 8.9 and 8.10 on pages 117 and 124, respectively). The therapist expected that scores on the Behavioral Outcomes section and Fine Motor/Perceptual Factor would be lower because these groups of items ask about the child's work process and product. The therapist also noted that the only other areas of concern were related to Visual Processing and Endurance/Tone. To follow up with this before the next study-team meeting, the therapist conducted a skilled observation of seatwork time (separate from the other classroom teachers' observations). The therapist noted that during seatwork, Gretta worked for a while, but then put her head down on her desk or propped her head up with one hand. Gretta also positioned her paper in an unusual way for writing and frequently repositioned her pencil in her hand.

Interpretation

Team members shared their insights at their next meeting. The therapist said that generally Gretta's sensory processing and modulation were fine. She then reported her observations during Gretta's seatwork, explaining that the endurance/tone issues she observed might be making it hard for Gretta to keep up with the fourth-grade pace. For example, the therapist linked Gretta's tired look (e.g., laying her head down, propping her head up) with poor endurance and low tone. She also suggested that Gretta's difficulty holding onto her pencil for long periods of time might be caused by a weakness in her hands. The therapist inquired about the teachers' impressions about visual perceptual skills because this was a questionable area on the *Sensory Profile*. The teacher felt that sometimes Gretta got things confused on her worksheets but was more concerned about productivity.

Intervention

Because the team was focused on supporting Gretta in the fourth grade, they decided to try some classroom and task adaptations. The occupational therapist experimented with different angles on Gretta's writing surface along with different seating patterns to try to support her low tone and endurance for sitting. The two teachers decided to try having Gretta work on the computer to complete seatwork because this would give her both a vertical visual surface and would be an alternative to holding a pencil for prolonged periods.

Sensory Processing

Item			A. Auditory Processing	ALWAYS	FREQUENTLY	OCCASIONALLY	SELDOM	NEVER
?	L	1	Responds negatively to unexpected or loud noises (for example, cries or hides at noise from vacuum cleaner, dog barking, hair dryer)				X4	
?	L	2	Holds hands over ears to protect ears from sound					X5
?	L	3	Has trouble completing tasks when the radio is on					X5
?	L	4	Is distracted or has trouble functioning if there is a lot of noise around					X5
?	L	5	Can't work with background noise (for example, fan, refrigerator)					X5
?	H	6	Appears to not hear what you say (for example, does not "tune-in" to what you say, appears to ignore you)					X5
?	H	7	Doesn't respond when name is called but you know the child's hearing is OK					X5
?	H	8	Enjoys strange noises/seeks to make noise for noise's sake					X5
			Section Raw Score Total			39		

Comments

Item			B. Visual Processing	ALWAYS	FREQUENTLY	OCCASIONALLY	SELDOM	NEVER
👁	L	9	Prefers to be in the dark				X4	
👁	L	10	Expresses discomfort with or avoids bright lights (for example, hides from sunlight through window in car)				X4	
👁	L	11	Happy to be in the dark				X4	
👁	L	12	Becomes frustrated when trying to find objects in competing backgrounds (for example, a cluttered drawer)				X4	
👁	L	13	Has difficulty putting puzzles together (as compared to same age children)		X2			
👁	L	14	Is bothered by bright lights after others have adapted to the light			X3		
👁	L	15	Covers eyes or squints to protect eyes from light			X3		
👁	H	16	Looks carefully or intensely at objects/people (for example, stares)		X2			
👁	H	17	Has a hard time finding objects in competing backgrounds (for example, shoes in a messy room, favorite toy in the "junk drawer")		X2			
			Section Raw Score Total			28		

Comments

Figure 8.9 ■ Gretta's Caregiver Questionnaire

	Item		C. Vestibular Processing	ALWAYS	FREQUENTLY	OCCASIONALLY	SELDOM	NEVER
→	L	18	Becomes anxious or distressed when feet leave the ground				X4	
→	L	19	Dislikes activities where head is upside down (for example, somersaults, roughhousing)				X4	
→	L	20	Avoids playground equipment or moving toys (for example, swing set, merry-go-round)					X5
→	L	21	Dislikes riding in a car					X5
→	L	22	Holds head upright, even when bending over or leaning (for example, maintains a rigid position/posture during activity)					X5
→	L	23	Becomes disoriented after bending over sink or table (for example, falls or gets dizzy)					X5
→	H	24	Seeks all kinds of movement and this interferes with daily routines (for example, can't sit still, fidgets)					X5
→	H	25	Seeks out all kinds of movement activities (for example, being whirled by adult, merry-go-rounds, playground equipment, moving toys)					X5
→	H	26	Twirls/spins self frequently throughout the day (for example, likes dizzy feeling)					X5
→	H	27	Rocks unconsciously (for example, while watching TV)					X5
→	H	28	Rocks in desk/chair/on floor					X5
			Section Raw Score Total			53		

Comments

Figure 8.9 ■ **Gretta's *Caregiver Questionnaire* (continued)**

Item			D. Touch Processing	ALWAYS	FREQUENTLY	OCCASIONALLY	SELDOM	NEVER
🖐	L	29	Avoids getting "messy" (for example, in paste, sand, finger paint, glue, tape)					X5
🖐	L	30	Expresses distress during grooming (for example, fights or cries during haircutting, face washing, fingernail cutting)					X5
🖐	L	31	Prefers long-sleeved clothing when it is warm or short sleeves when it is cold					X5
🖐	L	32	Expresses discomfort at dental work or toothbrushing (for example, cries or fights)					X5
🖐	L	33	Is sensitive to certain fabrics (for example, is particular about certain clothes or bedsheets)					X5
🖐	L	34	Becomes irritated by shoes or socks					X5
🖐	L	35	Avoids going barefoot, especially in sand or grass					X5
🖐	L	36	Reacts emotionally or aggressively to touch					X5
🖐	L	37	Withdraws from splashing water					X5
🖐	L	38	Has difficulty standing in line or close to other people					X5
🖐	L	39	Rubs or scratches out a spot that has been touched					X5
🖐	H	40	Touches people and objects to the point of irritating others					X5
🖐	H	41	Displays unusual need for touching certain toys, surfaces, or textures (for example, constantly touching objects)					X5
🖐	H	42	Decreased awareness of pain and temperature				X4	
🖐	H	43	Doesn't seem to notice when someone touches arm or back (for example, unaware)				X4	
🖐	H	44	Avoids wearing shoes; loves to be barefoot					X5
🖐	H	45	Touches people and objects					X5
🖐	H	46	Doesn't seem to notice when face or hands are messy					X5
			Section Raw Score Total			88		

Comments

Item			E. Multisensory Processing	ALWAYS	FREQUENTLY	OCCASIONALLY	SELDOM	NEVER
👁		47	Gets lost easily (even in familiar places)			X3		
🏃		48	Has difficulty paying attention					X5
👁	L	49	Looks away from tasks to notice all actions in the room					X5
❓	H	50	Seems oblivious within an active environment (for example, unaware of activity)				X4	
🧍	H	51	Hangs on people, furniture, or objects even in familiar situations					X5
🧍	H	52	Walks on toes				X4	
🖐	H	53	Leaves clothing twisted on body				X4	
			Section Raw Score Total			30		

Comments

Figure 8.9 ■ *Gretta's Caregiver Questionnaire (continued)*

	Item		F. Oral Sensory Processing	ALWAYS	FREQUENTLY	OCCASIONALLY	SELDOM	NEVER
	L	54	Gags easily with food textures or food utensils in mouth				X4	
	L	55	Avoids certain tastes or food smells that are typically part of children's diets				X4	
	L	56	Will only eat certain tastes (list: _____)				X4	
	L	57	Limits self to particular food textures/temperatures (list: _____)					X5
	L	58	Picky eater, especially regarding food textures				X4	
	H	59	Routinely smells nonfood objects				X4	
	H	60	Shows strong preference for certain smells (list: _____)					X5
	H	61	Shows strong preference for certain tastes (list: _____)					X5
	H	62	Craves certain foods (list: _____)				X4	
	H	63	Seeks out certain tastes or smells (list: _____)				X4	
	H	64	Chews or licks on nonfood objects					X5
	H	65	Mouths objects (for example, pencil, hands)				X4	
			Section Raw Score Total			*52*		

Comments

Modulation

	Item		G. Sensory Processing Related to Endurance/Tone	ALWAYS	FREQUENTLY	OCCASIONALLY	SELDOM	NEVER
		66	Moves stiffly				X4	
	H	67	Tires easily, especially when standing or holding particular body position				X4	
	H	68	Locks joints (for example, elbows, knees) for stability				X4	
	H	69	Seems to have weak muscles				X4	
	H	70	Has a weak grasp				X4	
	H	71	Can't lift heavy objects (for example, weak in comparison to same age children)				X4	
	H	72	Props to support self (even during activity)			X3		
	H	73	Poor endurance/tires easily				X4	
	H	74	Appears lethargic (for example, has no energy, is sluggish)				X4	
			Section Raw Score Total			*35*		

Comments

Figure 8.9 ■ **Gretta's *Caregiver Questionnaire* (continued)**

	Item		H. Modulation Related to Body Position and Movement	ALWAYS	FREQUENTLY	OCCASIONALLY	SELDOM	NEVER
♡		75	Seems accident-prone			X3		
👁		76	Hesitates going up or down curbs or steps (for example, is cautious, stops before moving)			X3		
→	L	77	Fears falling or heights				X4	
→	L	78	Avoids climbing/jumping or avoids bumpy/uneven ground			X3		
→	L	79	Holds onto walls or banisters (for example, clings)			X3		
→	H	80	Takes excessive risks during play (for example, climbs high into a tree, jumps off tall furniture)					X5
→	H	81	Takes movement or climbing risks during play that compromise personal safety					X5
→	H	82	Turns whole body to look at you					X5
大	H	83	Seeks opportunities to fall without regard to personal safety					X5
大	H	84	Appears to enjoy falling					X5
			Section Raw Score Total			*41*		

Comments

	Item		I. Modulation of Movement Affecting Activity Level	ALWAYS	FREQUENTLY	OCCASIONALLY	SELDOM	NEVER
🏃	L	85	Spends most of the day in sedentary play (for example, does quiet things)					X5
🏃	L	86	Prefers quiet, sedentary play (for example, watching TV, books, computers)					X5
→	L	87	Seeks sedentary play options				X4	
→	L	88	Prefers sedentary activities					X5
→	H	89	Becomes overly excitable during movement activity					X5
🏃	H	90	"On the go"					X5
🏃	H	91	Avoids quiet play activities					X5
			Section Raw Score Total			*34*		

Comments

	Item		J. Modulation of Sensory Input Affecting Emotional Responses	ALWAYS	FREQUENTLY	OCCASIONALLY	SELDOM	NEVER
♡		92	Needs more protection from life than other children (for example, defenseless physically or emotionally)					X5
☀	L	93	Rigid rituals in personal hygiene				X4	
♡	H	94	Is overly affectionate with others					X5
♡	H	95	Doesn't perceive body language or facial expressions (for example, unable to interpret)					X5
			Section Raw Score Total			*19*		

Comments

Figure 8.9 ■ *Gretta's Caregiver Questionnaire (continued)*

	Item		K. Modulation of Visual Input Affecting Emotional Responses and Activity Level	ALWAYS	FREQUENTLY	OCCASIONALLY	SELDOM	NEVER
👁	L	96	Avoids eye contact			X3		
👁	H	97	Stares intensively at objects or people			X3		
👁	H	98	Watches everyone when they move around the room			X3		
👁	H	99	Doesn't notice when people come into the room					X5
			Section Raw Score Total			*14*		

Comments

Behavior and Emotional Responses

	Item		L. Emotional/Social Responses	ALWAYS	FREQUENTLY	OCCASIONALLY	SELDOM	NEVER
🤍		100	Seems to have difficulty liking self (for example, low self-esteem)		·			X5
🤍		101	Has trouble "growing up" (for example, reacts immaturely to situations)					X5
🤍		102	Is sensitive to criticisms					X5
🤍		103	Has definite fears (for example, fears are predictable)					X5
🤍		104	Seems anxious					X5
🤍		105	Displays excessive emotional outbursts when unsuccessful at a task					X5
🤍		106	Expresses feeling like a failure					X5
🤍		107	Is stubborn or uncooperative					X5
🤍		108	Has temper tantrums					X5
🤍		109	Poor frustration tolerance		·			X5
🤍		110	Cries easily					X5
🤍		111	Overly serious					X5
🤍		112	Has difficulty making friends (for example, does not interact or participate in group play)					X5
🤍		113	Has nightmares					X5
🤍		114	Has fears that interfere with daily routine				X4	
🤍		115	Doesn't have a sense of humor					X5
🤍		116	Doesn't express emotions					X5
			Section Raw Score Total			*84*		

Comments

Figure 8.9 ■ *Gretta's Caregiver Questionnaire (continued)*

Item			M. Behavioral Outcomes of Sensory Processing	ALWAYS	FREQUENTLY	OCCASIONALLY	SELDOM	NEVER
👂		117	Talks self through tasks		X₂			
👁		118	Writing is illegible		X₂			
👁		119	Has trouble staying between the lines when coloring or when writing		X₂			
♡		120	Uses inefficient ways of doing things (for example, wastes time, moves slowly, does things a harder way than is needed)		X₂			
♡	L	121	Has difficulty tolerating changes in plans and expectations					X₅
♡	L	122	Has difficulty tolerating changes in routines					X₅
			Section Raw Score Total			*18*		

Comments

Item			N. Items Indicating Thresholds for Response	ALWAYS	FREQUENTLY	OCCASIONALLY	SELDOM	NEVER
🏃		123	Jumps from one activity to another so that it interferes with play					X₅
👄	H	124	Deliberately smells objects					X₅
👄	H	125	Does not seem to smell strong odors				X₄	
			Section Raw Score Total			*14*		

Comments

Figure 8.9 ■ Gretta's *Caregiver Questionnaire* (continued)

Factor Grid

Instructions: Transfer from the *Caregiver Questionnaire* the item raw score that corresponds with each item listed. Add the Raw Score column to get the Factor Raw Score Total for each factor.

FACTOR 1 — Sensory Seeking

Item		Raw Score
🦻	8	5
→	24	5
→	25	5
→	26	5
✋	44	5
✋	45	5
✋	46	5
🧍	51	5
→	80	5
→	81	5
→	82	5
🧍	83	5
🧍	84	5
→	89	5
🏃	90	5
♡	94	5
🏃	123	5
Factor Raw Score Total		**85**

FACTOR 2 — Emotionally Reactive

Item		Raw Score
♡	92	5
♡	100	5
♡	101	5
♡	102	5
♡	103	5
♡	104	5
♡	105	5
♡	106	5
♡	107	5
♡	108	5
♡	109	5
♡	110	5
♡	111	5
♡	112	5
♡	121	5
♡	122	5
Factor Raw Score Total		**80**

FACTOR 3 — Low Endurance/Tone

Item		Raw Score
🧍	66	4
🧍	67	4
🧍	68	4
🧍	69	4
🧍	70	4
🧍	71	4
🧍	72	3
→	73	4
→	74	4
Factor Raw Score Total		**35**

FACTOR 4 — Oral Sensory Sensitivity

Item		Raw Score
👄	55	4
👄	56	4
✋	57	5
✋	58	4
👄	59	4
👄	60	5
👄	61	5
👄	62	4
👄	63	4
Factor Raw Score Total		**39**

FACTOR 5 — Inattention/Distractibility

Item		Raw Score
🦻	3	5
🦻	4	5
🦻	5	5
🦻	6	5
🦻	7	5
🏃	48	5
👁	49	5
Factor Raw Score Total		**35**

ICON KEY

🦻	Auditory
👁	Visual
🏃	Activity Level
👄	Taste/Smell
🧍	Body Position
→	Movement
✋	Touch
♡	Emotional/Social

Figure 8.10 ■ **Gretta's *Summary Score Sheet***

FACTOR 6		
Poor Registration		
Item		Raw Score
⚡	35	5
⚡	42	4
⚡	43	4
♡	95	5
👁	99	5
♡	115	5
♡	116	5
👄	125	4
Factor Raw Score Total		37

FACTOR 7		
Sensory Sensitivity		
Item		Raw Score
→	18	4
→	19	4
→	77	4
→	78	3
Factor Raw Score Total		15

FACTOR 8		
Sedentary		
Item		Raw Score
🏃	85	5
🏃	86	5
→	87	4
→	88	5
Factor Raw Score Total		19

FACTOR 9		
Fine Motor/Perceptual		
Item		Raw Score
👁	13	2
👁	118	2
👁	119	2
Factor Raw Score Total		6

Factor Summary

Instructions: Transfer the child's score for each factor to the column labeled Factor Raw Score Total. Then plot these totals by marking an X in the appropriate classification column (Typical Performance, Probable Difference, Definite Difference).*

Factor	Factor Raw Score Total	Typical Performance	Probable Difference	Definite Difference
1. Sensory Seeking	85 /85	X5 ---------- 63	62 ---------- 55	54 ---------- 17
2. Emotionally Reactive	80 /80	X0 ---------- 57	56 ---------- 48	47 ---------- 16
3. Low Endurance/Tone	35 /45	45 ---------- 39	38 ---------- 36	X6 ---------- 9
4. Oral Sensory Sensitivity	39 /45	45 ---X---- 33	32 ---------- 27	26 ---------- 9
5. Inattention/Distractibility	35 /35	X5 ---------- 25	24 ---------- 22	21 ---------- 7
6. Poor Registration	37 /40	40 ---X---- 33	32 ---------- 30	29 ---------- 8
7. Sensory Sensitivity	15 /20	20 ---------- 16	X6 ---------- 14	13 ---------- 4
8. Sedentary	19 /20	20X -------- 12	11 ---------- 10	9 ---------- 4
9. Fine Motor/Perceptual	6 /15	15 ---------- 10	9 --------- 8	7X -------- 3

*Classifications are based on the performance of children without disabilities (*n* = 1,037).

Figure 8.10 ■ **Gretta's *Summary Score Sheet* (continued)**

Section Summary

Instructions: Transfer the child's score for each section to the Section Raw Score Total column. Then plot these totals by marking an X in the appropriate classification column (Typical Performance, Probable Difference, Definite Difference).*

Sensory Processing	Section Raw Score Total		Typical Performance	Probable Difference	Definite Difference
A. Auditory Processing	39	/40	40 X------- 30	29 -------- 26	25 -------- 8
B. Visual Processing	28	/45	45 -------- 32	31 ----X 27	26 -------- 9
C. Vestibular Processing	53	/55	55 -X----- 48	47 -------- 45	44 -------- 11
D. Touch Processing	88	/90	90 -X----- 73	72 -------- 65	64 -------- 18
E. Multisensory Processing	30	/35	35 -----X-- 27	26 -------- 24	23 -------- 7
F. Oral Sensory Processing	52	/60	60 -----X-- 46	45 -------- 40	39 -------- 12
Modulation					
G. Sensory Processing Related to Endurance/Tone	35	/45	45 -------- 39	38 -------- 36	X6 -------- 9
H. Modulation Related to Body Position and Movement	41	/50	50 -------- X1	40 -------- 36	35 -------- 10
I. Modulation of Movement Affecting Activity Level	34	/35	35 X------- 23	22 -------- 19	18 -------- 7
J. Modulation of Sensory Input Affecting Emotional Responses	19	/20	20 -X----- 16	15 -------- 14	13 -------- 4
K. Modulation of Visual Input Affecting Emotional Responses and Activity Level	14	/20	20 -------- 15	X4 -------- 12	11 -------- 4
Behavior and Emotional Responses					
L. Emotional/Social Responses	84	/85	85 -X------ 63	62 -------- 55	54 -------- 17
M. Behavioral Outcomes of Sensory Processing	18	/30	30 -------- 22	21 -------- 19	X6 -------- 6
N. Items Indicating Thresholds for Response	14	/15	15 X------- 12	11 -------- 10	9 -------- 3

*Classifications are based on the performance of children without disabilities (n = 1,037).

Figure 8.10 ■ Gretta's *Summary Score Sheet (continued)*

Outcomes of Intervention

The computer strategies turned out to be very good options for Gretta. She began to use the computer for many activities at school and at home, and developed good mouse skills. The therapist found software for her so that she could enter text by clicking on letters on the screen, and that predicted words as she typed; both these strategies sped up her work product. The team then planned for Gretta to get a laptop to carry along with her when she started middle school and worked with her on organization of her files within this computer. They also got her a cable so that she could plug in and print work from the computer in any class, which increased her overall efficiency. The team of teachers seemed satisfied with this strategy because it increased the number of assignments she turned in.

APPENDIX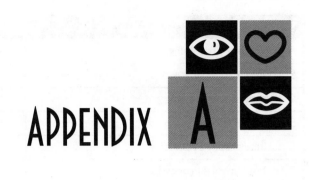

Cut Scores for 3-Year-Old Children

Sections	Typical Performance	Probable Difference	Definite Difference
A. Auditory Processing	40 ---------- 30	29 ---------- 27	26 ---------- 8
B. Visual Processing	45 ---------- 30	29 ---------- 25	24 ---------- 9
C. Vestibular Processing	55 ---------- 46	45 ---------- 42	41 ---------- 11
D. Touch Processing	90 ---------- 70	69 ---------- 62	61 ---------- 18
E. Multisensory Processing	35 ---------- 26	25 ---------- 23	22 ---------- 7
F. Oral Sensory Processing	60 ---------- 45	44 ---------- 39	38 ---------- 12
G. Sensory Processing Related to Endurance/Tone	45 ---------- 40	39 ---------- 38	37 ---------- 9
H. Modulation Related to Body Position and Movement	50 ---------- 39	38 ---------- 35	34 ---------- 10
I. Modulation of Movement Affecting Activity Level	35 ---------- 22	21 ---------- 19	18 ---------- 7
J. Modulation of Sensory Input Affecting Emotional Responses	20 ---------- 16	15 ---------- 14	13 ---------- 4
K. Modulation of Visual Input Affecting Emotional Responses and Activity Level	20 ---------- 13	12 ---------- 11	10 ---------- 4
L. Emotional/Social Responses	85 ---------- 64	63 ---------- 58	57 ---------- 17
M. Behavioral Outcomes of Sensory Processing	30 ---------- 20	19 ---------- 17	16 ---------- 6
N. Items Indicating Thresholds for Response	15 ---------- 11	10 ---------- 9	8 ---------- 3
Factors	**Typical Performance**	**Probable Difference**	**Definite Difference**
1. Sensory Seeking	85 ---------- 59	58 ---------- 50	49 ---------- 17
2. Emotionally Reactive	80 ---------- 58	57 ---------- 52	51 ---------- 16
3. Low Endurance/Tone	45 ---------- 40	39 ---------- 38	37 ---------- 9
4. Oral Sensory Sensitivity	45 ---------- 32	31 ---------- 27	26 ---------- 9
5. Inattention/Distractibility	35 ---------- 26	25 ---------- 23	22 ---------- 7
6. Poor Registration	40 ---------- 33	32 ---------- 29	28 ---------- 8
7. Sensory Sensitivity	20 ---------- 16	15 ---------- 13	12 ---------- 4
8. Sedentary	20 ---------- 12	11 ---------- 10	9 ---------- 4
9. Fine Motor/Perceptual	*	*	*

* not appropriate for 3-year-olds

◼ Cut Scores for 4-Year-Old Children

Sections	Typical Performance	Probable Difference	Definite Difference
A. Auditory Processing	40 ---------- 30	29 ---------- 27	26 ---------- 8
B. Visual Processing	45 ---------- 32	31 ---------- 28	27 ---------- 9
C. Vestibular Processing	55 ---------- 47	46 ---------- 43	42 ---------- 11
D. Touch Processing	90 ---------- 73	72 ---------- 67	66 ---------- 18
E. Multisensory Processing	35 ---------- 27	26 ---------- 24	23 ---------- 7
F. Oral Sensory Processing	60 ---------- 44	43 ---------- 37	36 ---------- 12
G. Sensory Processing Related to Endurance/Tone	45 ---------- 39	38 ---------- 35	34 ---------- 9
H. Modulation Related to Body Position	50 ---------- 39	38 ---------- 35	34 ---------- 10
I. Modulation of Movement Affecting Activity Level and Movement	35 ---------- 23	22 ---------- 20	19 ---------- 7
J. Modulation of Sensory Input Affecting Emotional Responses	20 ---------- 16	15 ---------- 14	13 ---------- 4
K. Modulation of Visual Input Affecting Emotional Responses and Activity level	20 ---------- 15	14 ---------- 13	12 ---------- 4
L. Emotional/Social Responses	85 ---------- 64	63 ---------- 57	56 ---------- 17
M. Behavioral Outcomes of Sensory Processing	30 ---------- 21	20 ---------- 19	18 ---------- 6
N. Items Indicating Thresholds for Response	15 ---------- 11*	10*	9 ---------- 3*
Factors	**Typical Performance**	**Probable Difference**	**Definite Difference**
1. Sensory Seeking	85 ---------- 62	61 ---------- 53	52 ---------- 17
2. Emotionally Reactive	80 ---------- 58	57 ---------- 51	50 ---------- 16
3. Low Endurance/Tone	45 ---------- 39	38 ---------- 35	34 ---------- 9
4. Oral Sensory Sensitivity	45 ---------- 32	31 ---------- 26	25 ---------- 9
5. Inattention/Distractibility	35 ---------- 26	25 ---------- 24	23 ---------- 7
6. Poor Registration	40 ---------- 34	33 ---------- 30	29 ---------- 8
7. Sensory Sensitivity	20 ---------- 16	15 ---------- 13	12 ---------- 4
8. Sedentary	20 ---------- 12	11 ---------- 9	8 ---------- 4
9. Fine Motor/Perceptual	15 ---------- 9	8 ---------- 6	5 ---------- 3

* not appropriate for 4-year-olds

APPENDIX  B

■ Worksheet for Analysis of Visual/Tactile Processing Cluster Related to Children With ADHD

Instructions: Transfer scores from the corresponding *Caregiver Questionnaire* items to the chart below. Then calculate the Raw Score Total by adding the item scores and record them in the Cluster Raw Score Total box.

Visual/Tactile Processing Cluster				Raw Score
Sensory Profile Section Location	Item			
B. Visual Processing	👁	12	Becomes frustrated when trying to find objects in competing backgrounds (for example, a cluttered drawer)	
	👁	17	Has a hard time finding objects in competing backgrounds (for example, shoes in a messy room, favorite toy in the "junk drawer")	
D. Touch Processing	✋	36	Reacts emotionally or aggressively to touch	
	✋	38	Has difficulty standing in line or close to other people	
	✋	40	Touches people and objects to the point of irritating others	
E. Multisensory Processing	👂	50	Seems oblivious within an active environment (for example, unaware of activity)	
H. Modulation Related to Body Position and Movement	♡	75	Seems accident–prone	
I. Modulation of Movement Affecting Activity Level	🏃	91	Avoids quiet play activities	
K. Modulation of Visual Input Affecting Emotional Responses and Activity Level	👁	96	Avoids eye contact	
	👁	97	Stares intensively at objects or people	
	👁	98	Watches everyone when they move around the room	
M. Behavioral Outcomes of Sensory Processing	♡	120	Uses inefficient ways of doing things (for example, wastes time, moves slowly, does things a harder way than is needed)	
			Cluster Raw Score Total	

SUMMARY

Instructions: Transfer the child's score for the cluster and factors to the Raw Score Total column. Then plot these totals by marking an X in the appropriate classification column (Typical Performance, Probable Difference, Definite Difference).

	Raw Score Total	Typical Performance	Probable Difference	Definite Difference
Visual/Tactile Processing Cluster (see above)	/60	60 ---------- 46	45 ---------- 41	40 ---------- 12
Factor 1 Sensory Seeking	/85	85 ---------- 63	62 ---------- 55	54 ---------- 17
Factor 2 Emotionally Reactive	/80	80 ---------- 57	56 ---------- 48	47 ---------- 16
Factor 5 Inattention/Distractibility	/35	35 ---------- 25	24 ---------- 22	21 ---------- 7

APPENDIX

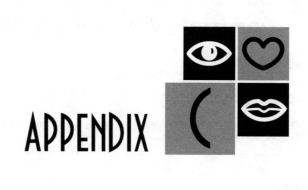

Comparisons of Means and I *SD* Ranges for Children With and Without Disabilities

14 Sections

Sensory Processing

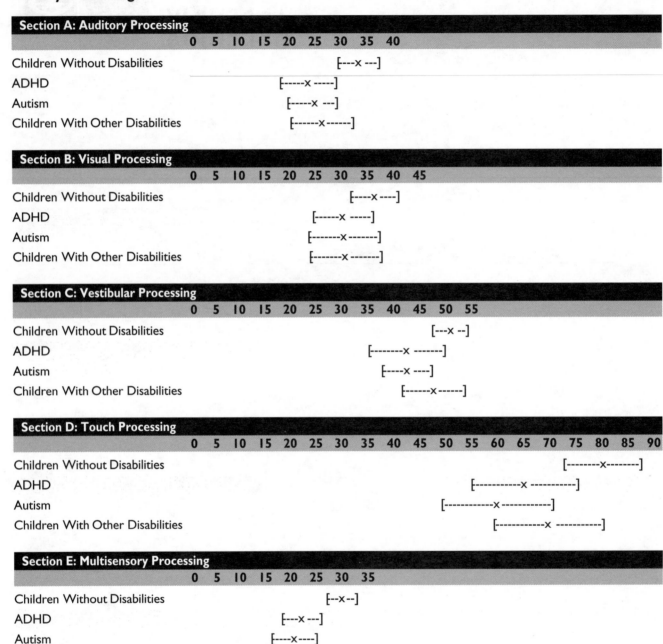

Section A: Auditory Processing

| | 0 | 5 | 10 | 15 | 20 | 25 | 30 | 35 | 40 |
Children Without Disabilities   [---x ---]
ADHD   [-----x -----]
Autism   [-----x ---]
Children With Other Disabilities   [------x ------]

Section B: Visual Processing

0   5   10   15   20   25   30   35   40   45
Children Without Disabilities   [----x ----]
ADHD   [------x -----]
Autism   [-------x -------]
Children With Other Disabilities   [-------x -------]

Section C: Vestibular Processing

0   5   10   15   20   25   30   35   40   45   50   55
Children Without Disabilities   [---x --]
ADHD   [--------x -------]
Autism   [----x ----]
Children With Other Disabilities   [------x ------]

Section D: Touch Processing

0   5   10   15   20   25   30   35   40   45   50   55   60   65   70   75   80   85   90
Children Without Disabilities   [--------x--------]
ADHD   [-----------x -----------]
Autism   [-----------x -----------]
Children With Other Disabilities   [-----------x -----------]

Section E: Multisensory Processing

0   5   10   15   20   25   30   35
Children Without Disabilities   [--x --]
ADHD   [---x ---]
Autism   [----x ----]
Children With Other Disabilities   [-----x -----]

Section F: Oral Sensory Processing

```
                                    0   5   10  15  20  25  30  35  40  45  50  55  60
Children Without Disabilities                                      [-------x ------]
ADHD                                                         [-----------x-----------]
Autism                                           [-----------x -----------]
Children With Other Disabilities                       [-----------x-----------]
```

Modulation

Section G: Sensory Processing Related to Endurance/Tone

```
                                    0   5   10  15  20  25  30  35  40  45
Children Without Disabilities                                   [---x --]
ADHD                                                     [--------x --------]
Autism                                           [---------x ---------]
Children With Other Disabilities                 [----------x ----------]
```

Section H: Modulation Related to Body Position and Movement

```
                                    0   5   10  15  20  25  30  35  40  45  50
Children Without Disabilities                                   [---x ---]
ADHD                                                     [-------x-------]
Autism                                           [-----x -----]
Children With Other Disabilities                    [----x ----]
```

Section I: Modulation of Movement Affecting Activity Level

```
                                    0   5   10  15  20  25  30  35
Children Without Disabilities              [---x --]
ADHD                                    [----x ---]
Autism                                  [--x --]
Children With Other Disabilities            [--x --]
```

Section J: Modulation of Sensory Input Affecting Emotional Response

```
                                    0   5   10  15  20
Children Without Disabilities          [-x ]
ADHD                                 [--x--]
Autism                             [--x --]
Children With Other Disabilities        [--x--]
```

Section K: Modulation of Visual Input Affecting Emotional Resonses and Activity Level

```
                                    0   5   10  15  20
Children Without Disabilities          [-x-]
ADHD                                 [--x--]
Autism                               [-x -]
Children With Other Disabilities        [--x--]
```

Behavioral and Emotional Responses

Section L: Emotional/Social Responses

	0	5	10	15	20	25	30	35	40	45	50	55	60	65	70	75	80	85
Children Without Disabilities														[--------x--------]				
ADHD									[----------x----------]									
Autism									[---------x---------]									
Children With Other Disabilities								[----------------x----------------]										

Section M: Behavioral Outcomes of Sensory Processing

	0	5	10	15	20	25	30
Children Without Disabilities					[--x--]		
ADHD				[---x---]			
Autism				[--x--]			
Children With Other Disabilities				[----x---]			

Section N: Items Indicating Thresholds for Response

	0	5	10	15
Children Without Disabilities			[-x]	
ADHD			[-x -]	
Autism			[--x--]	
Children With Other Disabilities			[-x -]	

Comparisons of Means and 1 *SD* Ranges for Children With and Without Disabilities

9 Factors

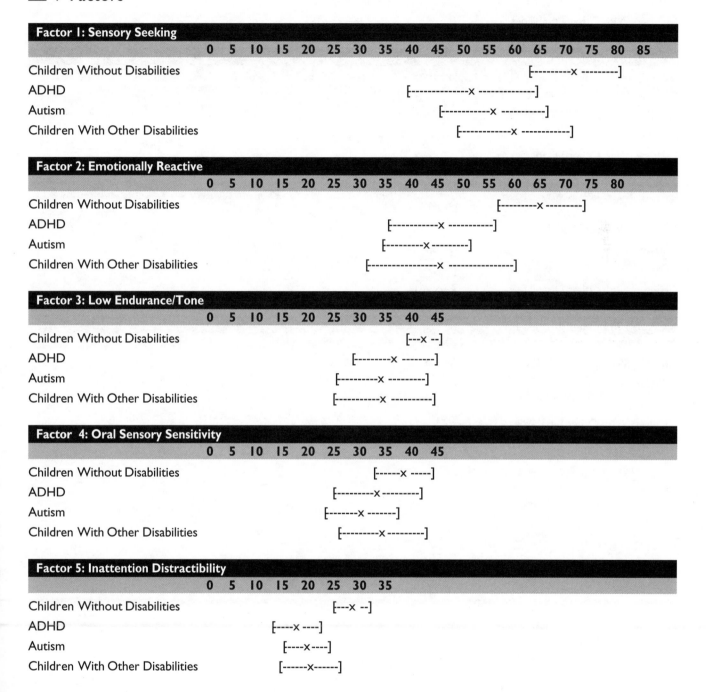

Factor 1: Sensory Seeking

| | 0 | 5 | 10 | 15 | 20 | 25 | 30 | 35 | 40 | 45 | 50 | 55 | 60 | 65 | 70 | 75 | 80 | 85 |

Children Without Disabilities   [--------x --------]

ADHD   [--------------x --------------]

Autism   [-----------x -----------]

Children With Other Disabilities   [------------x ------------]

Factor 2: Emotionally Reactive

| | 0 | 5 | 10 | 15 | 20 | 25 | 30 | 35 | 40 | 45 | 50 | 55 | 60 | 65 | 70 | 75 | 80 |

Children Without Disabilities   [--------x --------]

ADHD   [-----------x -----------]

Autism   [---------x ---------]

Children With Other Disabilities   [---------------x ---------------]

Factor 3: Low Endurance/Tone

| | 0 | 5 | 10 | 15 | 20 | 25 | 30 | 35 | 40 | 45 |

Children Without Disabilities   [---x --]

ADHD   [--------x --------]

Autism   [---------x ---------]

Children With Other Disabilities   [----------x ----------]

Factor 4: Oral Sensory Sensitivity

| | 0 | 5 | 10 | 15 | 20 | 25 | 30 | 35 | 40 | 45 |

Children Without Disabilities   [------x -----]

ADHD   [---------x ---------]

Autism   [-------x -------]

Children With Other Disabilities   [---------x ---------]

Factor 5: Inattention Distractibility

| | 0 | 5 | 10 | 15 | 20 | 25 | 30 | 35 |

Children Without Disabilities   [---x --]

ADHD   [----x ----]

Autism   [----x----]

Children With Other Disabilities   [------x------]

Factor 6: Poor Registration

	0	5	10	15	20	25	30	35	40
Children Without Disabilities							[--x --]		
ADHD						[----x ----]			
Autism					[-----x -----]				
Children With Other Disabilities						[----x ---]			

Factor 7: Sensory Sensitivity

	0	5	10	15	20
Children Without Disabilities			[-x -]		
ADHD			[--x --]		
Autism			[----x ----]		
Children With Other Disabilities			[--x--]		

Factor 8: Sedentary

	0	5	10	15	20
Children Without Disabilities			[--x -]		
ADHD			[---x---]		
Autism			[---x --]		
Children With Other Disabilities			[---x ---]		

Factor 9: Fine Motor/Perceptual

	0	5	10	15
Children Without Disabilities			[-x -]	
ADHD			[--x -]	
Autism		[-x -]		
Children With Other Disabilities			[--x --]	

APPENDIX

Other Research Studies

Using the *Sensory Profile* With Infants and Toddlers

The *Sensory Profile* is not designed to address the unique behaviors of infants and toddlers, although many of its items can be useful for describing the sensory-processing abilities of this age group. There are obvious items that would not be appropriate, such as "writing is illegible" and "has trouble staying between the lines when coloring or when writing." Research is being conducted on a downward extension of *Sensory Profile* for infants and toddlers. For now, use the *Sensory Profile* to stimulate discussion with caregivers, encouraging them to complete any items that they feel characterize their children. This can result in informative data in the interpretation and intervention planning process.

Emerging Knowledge in Studies With Adults With and Without Disabilities

Researchers are conducting studies on adults with and without disabilities for an upward extension of the *Sensory Profile* (Brown, 1999). In a pilot study comparing adults with schizophrenia to adults without disabilities (matched for age and gender), there were significant differences between the groups. Adults who had schizophrenia demonstrated more behaviors in the extremes of responsivity (i.e., both hyperresponsive and hyporesponsive to stimuli), while those without disabilities reported performance in the midrange. This finding suggests that the issue of sensory modulation may be a critical factor in schizophrenia. In initial studies with young adults without disabilities, a factor structure similar to the one in the children's study was identified. The emerging factor structure in the adult sample is consistent with the conceptual model proposed by Dunn (1997a). In subsequent studies, researchers will investigate how adults with schizophrenia and bipolar disorders respond in comparison to this sample of adults without disabilities.

The adult studies are lending additional support to the utility of the *Sensory Profile* for identifying clear phenomena that are relevant for decision making. If these findings are consistent across the life span, consideration of the sensory processing features of performance will become a routine part of comprehensive assessment and intervention planning.

APPENDIX

Comparison of Items From the *Short Sensory Profile* and the *Sensory Profile*

Short Sensory Profile ITEM NUMBER	Caregiver Questionnaire ITEM NUMBER	Item	Caregiver Questionnaire Sections	Sensory Profile Factors
1	30	Expresses distress during grooming (for example, fights or cries during haircutting, face washing, fingernail cutting)	Touch Processing	
2	31	Prefers long-sleeved clothing when it is warm or short sleeves when it is cold	Touch Processing	
3	35	Avoids going barefoot, especially in sand or grass	Touch Processing	6
4	36	Reacts emotionally or aggressively to touch	Touch Processing	
5	37	Withdraws from splashing water	Touch Processing	
6	38	Has difficulty standing in line or close to other people	Touch Processing	
7	39	Rubs or scratches out a spot that has been touched	Touch Processing	
8	55	Avoids certain tastes or food smells that are typically part of children's diets	Oral Sensory Processing	4
9	56	Will only eat certain tastes (list: _____)	Oral Sensory Processing	4
10	57	Limits self to particular food textures/temperatures (list: _____)	Oral Sensory Processing	4
11	58	Picky eater, especially regarding food textures	Oral Sensory Processing	4
12	18	Becomes anxious or distressed when feet leave the ground	Vestibular Processing	7
13	77	Fears falling or heights	Modulation Related to Body Position and Movement	7
14	19	Dislikes activities where head is upside down (for example, somersaults, roughhousing)	Vestibular Processing	7
15	8	Enjoys strange noises/seeks to make noise for noise's sake	Auditory Processing	1
16	24	Seeks all kinds of movement and this interferes with daily routines (for example, can't sit still, fidgets)	Vestibular Processing	1
17	89	Becomes overly excitable during movement activity	Modulation of Movement Affecting Activity Level	1
18	45	Touches people and objects	Touch Processing	1
19	46	Doesn't seem to notice when face or hands are messy	Touch Processing	1
20	123	Jumps from one activity to another so that it interferes with play	Items Indicating Thresholds for Response	1
21	53	Leaves clothing twisted on body	Multisensory Processing	

Short Sensory Profile ITEM NUMBER	Caregiver Questionnaire ITEM NUMBER	Item	Caregiver Questionnaire Sections	Sensory Profile Factors
22	4	Is distracted or has trouble functioning if there is a lot of noise around	Auditory Processing	5
23	6	Appears to not hear what you say (for example, does not "tune-in" to what you say, appears to ignore you)	Auditory Processing	5
24	5	Can't work with background noise (for example, fan, refrigerator)	Auditory Processing	5
25	3	Has trouble completing tasks when the radio is on	Auditory Processing	5
26	7	Doesn't respond when name is called but you know the child's hearing is OK	Auditory Processing	5
27	48	Has difficulty paying attention	Multisensory Processing	5
28	69	Seems to have weak muscles	Sensory Processing Related to Endurance/Tone	3
29	67	Tires easily, especially when standing or holding particular body position	Sensory Processing Related to Endurance/Tone	3
30	70	Has a weak grasp	Sensory Processing Related to Endurance/Tone	3
31	71	Can't lift heavy objects (for example, weak in comparison to same age children)	Sensory Processing Related to Endurance/Tone	3
32	72	Props to support self (even during activity)	Sensory Processing Related to Endurance/Tone	3
33	73	Poor endurance/tires easily	Sensory Processing Related to Endurance/Tone	3
34	1	Responds negatively to unexpected or loud noises (for example, cries or hides at noise from vacuum cleaner, dog barking, hair dryer)	Auditory Processing	
35	2	Holds hands over ears to protect ears from sound	Auditory Processing	
36	14	Is bothered by bright lights after others have adapted to the light	Visual Processing	
37	98	Watches everyone when they move around the room	Modulation of Visual Input Affecting Emotional Responses and Activity Level	
38	15	Covers eyes or squints to protect eyes from light	Visual Processing	

References

Achenbach, T. (1991). *Manual for the Child Behavior Checklist/4-18 and 1991 Profile.* Burlington: University of Vermont, Department of Psychiatry.

Ayres, A. J. (1975). *Southern California Postrotary Nystagmus Test manual.* Los Angeles: Western Psychological Services.

Ayres, A. J. (1980). *Sensory integration and the child.* Los Angeles: Western Psychological Services.

Ayres, A. J., & Maillouix, Z. (1981). Influence of sensory integration procedures on language development. *American Journal of Occupational Therapy, 35,* 383–390.

Bennett, D., & Dunn, W. (1997). *Performance of children with attention deficit hyperactivity disorder on the Sensory Profile.* Manuscript submitted for publication.

Brown, C. (1999). *Patterns of sensory processing in schizophrenia.* Unpublished doctoral dissertation, University of Kansas.

Clarke, A. M., & Clarke, A. D. B. (1976). *Early experience: Myth and evidence.*, New York: Free Press.

Coster, W., Deeney, T., Haltiwanger, J., & Haley, S. (1998). *School Function Assessment.* San Antonio, TX: The Psychological Corporation.

Cox, J. (1996). Functional assessment in context: Observations of children during mealtime. (master's thesis, University of Kansas).

Cox, J., & Dunn, W. (1994). *Assessment of children's functional performance in context.* Poster presented at the Combined Annual Conference of the American Occupational Therapy Association, Boston.

Dunn, W. (1991). The sensorimotor systems: A framework for assessment and intervention. In F. Orelove & D. Sobsey (Eds.), *Educating children with multiple disabilities: A transdisciplinary approach.* (2nd ed., pp. 35–78). Baltimore: Brookes.

Dunn, W. (1994). Performance of typical children on the Sensory Profile: An item analysis. *American Journal of Occupational Therapy. 48*(11), 967–974.

Dunn, W. (1997a). The impact of sensory processing abilities on the daily lives of young children and their families: A conceptual model. *Infants and Young Children, 9*(4), 23–35.

Dunn, W. (1997b). Implementing neuroscience principles to support habitation and recovery. In C. Christiansen. & C. Baum (Eds.), *Occupational therapy: Enabling function and well being.* (p. 182–232). Thorofare, NJ: Slack.

Dunn, W., & Brown, C. (1997). Factor analysis on the Sensory Profile from a national sample of children without disabilities. *American Journal of Occupational Therapy, 51*(7), 490–495.

Dunn, W., Brown, C., & McGuigan, A. (1994). The ecology of human performance: a framework for considering the effect of context. *American Journal of Occupational Therapy, 48,* 595–607.

Dunn, W., & Westman, K. (1997). The Sensory Profile: The performance of a national sample of children without disabilities. *American Journal of Occupational Therapy, 51*(1), 25–34.

Education for All Handicapped Children Act, Public Law 94-142. U.S. Congress. Senate, 94th Congress. 1975.

Ermer, J., & Dunn, W. (1998). The Sensory Profile: A discriminant analysis of children with and without disabilities. *American Journal of Occupational Therapy, 52*(4), 283–290.

Fisher, A. G., & Murray, E. A. (1991). Introduction to sensory integration theory. In A. G. Fisher, E. A. Murray, & A. C. Bundy (Eds.), *Sensory integration: Theory and practice* (pp. 3–26). Philadelphia: F. A. Davis.

Fisher, A. G., Murray, E. A., & Bundy, A. C. (Eds.) (1994). *Sensory integration: Theory and practice*. Philadelphia: F. A. Davis.

Gorsuch, R. (1983). *Factor analysis*. Hillsdale, NJ: Erlbaum.

Hagerman, R. J. (1996). Physical and behavioral phenotype. In R. J. Hagerman & A. Cronister (Eds.), *Fragile X syndrome: Diagnosis, treatment, and research* (2nd ed.) (pp. 3–87). Baltimore, MD: John Hopkins University Press.

Individuals with Disabilities Education Act (IDEA), Public Law 101-476 (Chapter 33). U.S. Congress. Senate, 20th Congress. 1990.

Kandel, E. (1993). Cellular mechanisms of learning and the biological basis of individuality. In E. Kandel, J. Schwartz, & T. Jessell (Eds.) *The principles of neural science*. (3rd ed.). (pp. 1,009–1,031). New York: Elsevier.

Kandel, E., Schwartz, J., & Jessell, T. (Eds.) (1993). *The principles of neural science*. (3rd ed.). New York: Elsevier.

Kemmis, B., & Dunn, W. (1996). Collaborative consultation: The efficacy of remedial and compensatory interventions in school contexts. *American Journal of Occupational Therapy, 50*(9), 709–717.

Kientz, M. A., & Dunn, W. (1997). A comparison of the performance of children with and without autism on the Sensory Profile. *American Journal of Occupational Therapy, 51*(7), 530–537.

Larson, K. A. (1982). The sensory history of developmentally delayed children: With and without tactile defensiveness. *American Journal of Occupational Therapy, 36*(9), 590–596.

Magrun, W. M., McCue, S., Ottenbacher, K., & Keefe, R. (1981). Effects of vestibular stimulation on spontaneous use of verbal language in developmentally delayed children. *American Journal of Occupational Therapy, 35*, 101–104.

McIntosh, D. N., Miller, L. J., Shyu, V., & Hagerman, R. J. (1998). *Sensory modulation disruption, electrodermal responses, and functional behaviors*. Manuscript submitted for publication.

Miller, L. J., McIntosh, D. N., McGrath, J., Shyu, V., Lampe, M., Taylor, A. K., Tassone, F., Neitzel, K., Stackhouse, T., & Hagerman, R. (in press). Electrodermal responses to sensory stimuli in individuals with fragile X syndrome: A preliminary report. *American Journal of Medical Genetics*.

Moorhouse, J. (Director), (1995). *How to make an American quilt*. [videocassette].

Ottenbacher, K., Scoggins, A., & Wayland, J. (1981). The effectiveness of a program of oral sensory-motor therapy with the severely and profoundly developmentally disabled. *Occupational Therapy Journal of Research, 1*, 147–160.

Parham, L. D., & Mallioux, Z. (1996). Sensory integration. In J. Case-Smith, A. S. Allen, & P. N. Pratt (Eds.), *Occupational therapy for children* (3rd ed.) (pp. 307–355). St. Louis, MO: Mosby-Year Book.

Royeen, C. B., & Fortune, J. C. (1990). Touch Inventory for elementary-school-aged children. *American Journal of Occupational Therapy, 44*(2), 155–159.

Schaughency, E. A. (1986). Neuropsychological functioning of children diagnosed as attention deficit disorder with and without hyperactivity. *Dissertation Abstracts International, 47*(6), 2632b. (University of Georgia).

studysync®

Reading & Writing Companion

The Human Condition

studysync®

studysync.com

Send all inquiries to:
BookheadEd Learning, LLC
610 Daniel Young Drive
Sonoma, CA 95476

5 6 7 8 9 LMN 22

G12U2

STUDENT GUIDE

GETTING STARTED

Welcome to the StudySync Reading and Writing Companion! In this booklet, you will find a collection of readings based on the theme of the unit you are studying. As you work through the readings, you will be asked to answer questions and perform a variety of tasks designed to help you closely analyze and understand each text selection. Read on for an explanation of

CORE ELA TEXTS

In each Core ELA Unit you will read texts and text excerpts that share a common theme, despite their different genres, time periods, and authors. Each reading encourages a closer look with questions and a short writing assignment.

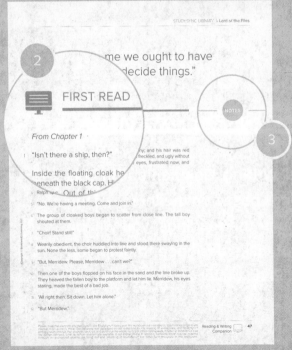

INTRODUCTION

An Introduction to each text provides historical context for your reading as well as information about the author. You will also learn about the genre of the excerpt and the year in which it was written.

FIRST READ

During your first reading of each excerpt, you should just try to get a general idea of the content and message of the reading. Don't worry if there are parts you don't understand or words that are unfamiliar to you. You'll have an opportunity later to dive deeper into the text.

NOTES

Many times, while working through the activities after each text, you will be asked to **annotate** or **make annotations** about what you are reading. This means that you should highlight or underline words in the text and use the "Notes" column to make comments or jot down any questions you may have. You may also want to note any unfamiliar vocabulary words here.

4 THINK QUESTIONS

These questions will ask you to start thinking critically about the text, asking specific questions about its purpose, and making connections to your prior knowledge and reading experiences. To answer these questions, you should go back to the text and draw upon specific evidence that you find there to support your responses. You will also begin to explore some of the more challenging vocabulary words used in the excerpt.

5 CLOSE READ & FOCUS QUESTIONS

After you have completed the First Read, you will then be asked to go back and read the excerpt more closely and critically. Before you begin your Close Read, you should read through the Focus Questions to get an idea of the concepts you will want to focus on during your second reading. You should work through the Focus Questions by making annotations, highlighting important concepts, and writing notes or questions in the "Notes" column. Depending on instructions from your teacher, you may need to respond online or use a separate piece of paper to start expanding on your thoughts and ideas.

6 WRITING PROMPT

Your study of each excerpt or selection will end with a writing assignment. To complete this assignment, you should use your notes, annotations, and answers to both the Think and Focus Questions. Be sure to read the prompt carefully and address each part of it in your writing assignment.

ENGLISH LANGUAGE DEVELOPMENT TEXTS

The English Language Development texts and activities take a closer look at the language choices that authors make to communicate their ideas. Individual and group activities will help develop your understanding of each text.

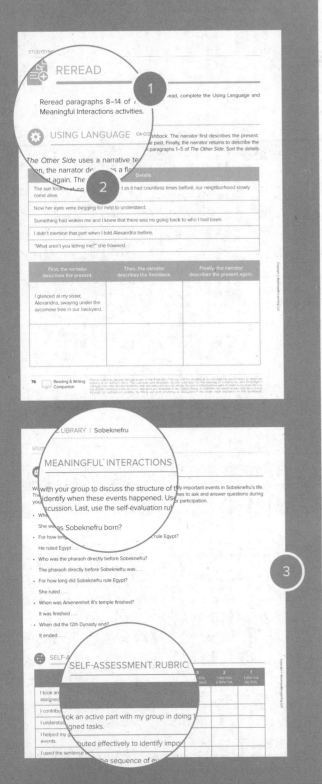

1 REREAD

After you have completed the First Read, you will have two additional opportunities to revisit portions of the excerpt more closely. The directions for each reread will specify which paragraphs or sections you should focus on.

2 USING LANGUAGE

These questions will ask you to analyze the author's use of language and conventions in the text. You may be asked to write in sentence frames, fill in a chart, or you may simply choose between multiple-choice options. To answer these questions, you should read the exercise carefully and go back in the text as necessary to accurately complete the activity.

3 MEANINGFUL INTERACTIONS & SELF-ASSESSMENT RUBRIC

After each reading, you will participate in a group activity or discussion with your peers. You may be provided speaking frames to guide your discussions or writing frames to support your group work. To complete these activities, you should revisit the excerpt for textual evidence and support. When you finish, use the Self-Assessment Rubric to evaluate how well you participated and collaborated.

EXTENDED WRITING PROJECT

The Extended Writing Project is your opportunity to explore the theme of each unit in a longer written work. You will draw information from your readings, research, and own life experiences to complete the assignment.

1 WRITING PROJECT

After you have read all of the unit text selections, you will move on to a writing project. Each project will guide you through the process of writing an argumentative, narrative, informative, or literary analysis essay. Student models and graphic organizers will provide guidance and help you organize your thoughts as you plan and write your essay. Throughout the project, you will also study and work on specific writing skills to help you develop different portions of your writing.

2 WRITING PROCESS STEPS

There are five steps in the writing process: **Prewrite**, **Plan**, **Draft**, **Revise**, and **Edit, Proofread, and Publish**. During each step, you will form and shape your writing project so that you can effectively express your ideas. Lessons focus on one step at a time, and you will have the chance to receive feedback from your peers and teacher.

3 WRITING SKILLS

Each Writing Skill lesson focuses on a specific strategy or technique that you will use during your writing project. The lessons begin by analyzing a student model or mentor text, and give you a chance to learn and practice the skill on its own. Then, you will have the opportunity to apply each new skill to improve the writing in your own project.

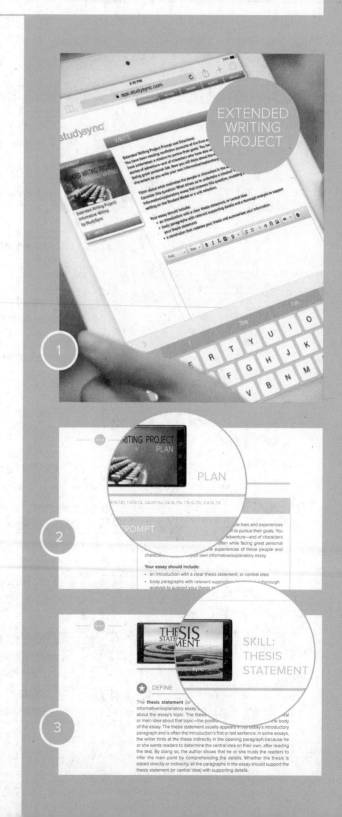

UNIT 2   How do we express the complexities of being human?

The Human Condition

TEXTS

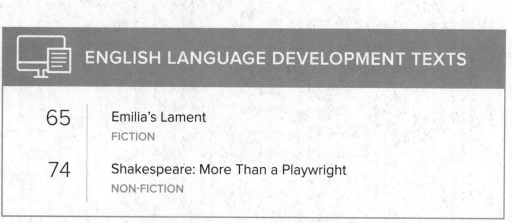

ENGLISH LANGUAGE DEVELOPMENT TEXTS

EXTENDED WRITING PROJECT

Copyright © BookheadEd Learning, LLC

SONNET 29

POETRY
William Shakespeare
1609

INTRODUCTION

Widely considered the world's greatest playwright, William Shakespeare was also an accomplished poet. A deep thinker and learned man, Shakespeare composed over 150 sonnets, which generally consists of fourteen lines organized into three rhyming quatrains and a rhyming couplet, written in iambic pentameter. As you read Sonnet 29, ask yourself how Shakespeare uses the form of the sonnet to express his ideas about love.

"For thy sweet love remember'd such wealth brings..."

FIRST READ

1 When, in disgrace with fortune and men's eyes,
2 I all alone **beweep** my outcast state,
3 And trouble deaf heaven with my **bootless** cries,
4 And look upon myself, and curse my fate,
5 Wishing me like to one more rich in hope,
6 Featur'd like him, like him with friends possess'd,
7 Desiring this man's art and that man's **scope,**
8 With what I most enjoy **contented** least;
9 Yet in these thoughts myself almost despising,
10 Haply I think on thee, and then my state,
11 Like to the lark at break of day arising
12 From sullen earth, sings hymns at heaven's gate;
13 For thy sweet love remember'd such wealth brings
14 That then I **scorn** to change my state with kings.

THINK QUESTIONS   CA-CCSS: CA.RL.11-12.1, CA.RL.11-12.3, CA.L.11-12.4a, CA.L.11-12.4b

1. What is the speaker's state of mind at the beginning of the poem? Support your response with evidence from the poem.

2. Who is the "him" referred to in lines 6 and 7? How do you know? What is the speaker's attitude toward "him"? Support your answer with textual evidence.

3. Where in the poem does the speaker's mood change? What causes this change? Support your response with evidence from the text.

4. Use context to determine the meaning of the word **contented** as it is used in "Sonnet 29." Write your definition of "contented" here and tell how you got it.

5. Use context to determine the meaning of the word **bootless** as it is used in "Sonnet 29." Write your definition of "bootless" here and explain how you got it.

CLOSE READ

CA-CCSS: CA.RL.11-12.1, CA.RL.11-12.2, CA.RL.11-12.4, CA.RL.11-12.5, CA.W.11-12.4, CA.W.11-12.5, CA.W.11-12.6, CA.W.11-12.9a, CA.W.11-12.10, CA.L.11-12.5a

Reread the poem "Sonnet 29." As you reread, complete the Focus Questions below. Then use your answers and annotations from the questions to help you complete the Writing Prompt.

 FOCUS QUESTIONS

1. Reread "Sonnet 29" and focus on the poem's tone. What is the tone at the beginning of the poem, and how is it expressed? How does the tone change over the course of the poem? What is the effect of this change on the meaning of the poem? Highlight evidence in the text, and use the annotation tool to explain how the lines you've chosen reveal the tone.

2. Shakespeare breaks from traditional Elizabethan sonnet form by repeating the same rhyming word in the first quatrain and the third quatrain. What effect does this repetition have? Where else is that word repeated? Highlight evidence to support your ideas and write annotations to explain your response.

3. The sonnet makes two mentions of heaven in different figures of speech. Identify and explain each instance. Then analyze the role of "heaven" in the poem. Highlight your evidence and annotate to explain your ideas.

4. What role does the second quatrain play in the overall sonnet? In what ways is it similar or different to the rest of the poem? Highlight evidence from the text that will help support your ideas.

5. Provide a close reading of the sonnet's final couplet. How does the speaker use figures of speech to sum up the poem? Explain the two figures of speech used in your response. Highlight your evidence and make annotations to explain your ideas.

6. Recall the unit's Essential Question: How do we express the complexities of being human? How does Shakespeare use figures of speech to express the speaker's complex feelings? What makes this strategy effective? Highlight evidence from the text and make annotations to explain your ideas.

WRITING PROMPT

Explain how Shakespeare uses poetic structure, tone, and figurative language in "Sonnet 29" to show the speaker's emotions. What is each element's role, and how do the elements work together? Base your analysis on your understanding of tone, sonnet structure, and figures of speech. Support your writing with evidence from the text.

HAMLET
(SCENES FROM ACTS I, II AND III)

DRAMA
William Shakespeare
1601

INTRODUCTION

The *Tragedy of Hamlet, Prince of Denmark*, by William Shakespeare, is a vivid portrayal of madness, rich with themes of treachery and revenge. His father the King's death and his mother's virtually immediate remarriage to his uncle throws Hamlet into existential turmoil—a struggle for personal meaning and grueling internal strife that threatens to consume him. In this state a ghost, a character once played in Globe productions by Shakespeare himself in around 1602, visits the Prince. Hamlet's soliloquies, exemplifying the best of Shakespeare's eloquent and clever language, raise unanswerable questions and explore the reality of being human in one of the greatest plays ever written.

"To be, or not to be, that is the question..."

FIRST READ

1   *Hamlet has returned home from studying in Wittenberg to attend his father's funeral. Still in deep mourning, Hamlet is appalled by his mother's hasty remarriage to the dead King's brother, who has assumed the throne and persists in calling him "son." The circumstances drive Hamlet to voice his first passionate soliloquy.*

From Act I, Scene ii:

Hamlet: son to the late King Hamlet, and nephew to the present King
Claudius: King of Denmark
Gertrude: Queen of Denmark, and mother to Hamlet
Polonius: Lord Chamberlain
Laertes: son to Polonius

Location: Elsinore, the castle

2   KING: Take thy fair hour, Laertes, time be thine,
3   And thy best graces spend it at thy will!
4   But now, my cousin Hamlet, and my son—

5   HAMLET: *[Aside]* A little more than kin, and less than kind.

6   KING: How is it that the clouds still hang on you?

7   HAMLET: Not so, my lord, I am too much in the sun.

8   QUEEN: Good Hamlet, cast thy nighted color off,
9   And let thine eye look like a friend on Denmark.
10 Do not for ever with thy vailed lids
11 Seek for thy noble father in the dust.
12 Thou know'st 'tis common, all that lives must die,
13 Passing through nature to eternity.

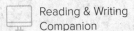

NOTES

14 HAMLET: Ay, madam, it is common.

15 QUEEN: If it be,
16 Why seems it so particular with thee?

17 HAMLET: Seems, madam? Nay, it is, I know not "seems."
18 'Tis not alone my inky cloak, good mother,
19 Nor customary suits of solemn black,
20 Nor windy suspiration of forc'd breath,
21 No, nor the fruitful river in the eye,
22 Nor the dejected havior of the visage,
23 Together with all forms, moods, shapes of grief,
24 That can denote me truly. These indeed seem,
25 For they are actions that a man might play,
26 But I have that within which passes show,
27 These but the **trappings** and the suits of woe.

28 KING: 'Tis sweet and commendable in your nature, Hamlet,
29 To give these mourning duties to your father.
30 But you must know your father lost a father,
31 That father lost, lost his, and the survivor bound
32 In **filial** obligation for some term
33 To do obsequious sorrow. But to persever
34 In **obstinate** condolement is a course
35 Of **impious** stubbornness, 'tis unmanly grief,
36 It shows a will most incorrect to heaven,
37 A heart unfortified, or mind impatient,
38 An understanding simple and unschool'd:
39 For what we know must be, and is as common
40 As any the most vulgar thing to sense,
41 Why should we in our peevish opposition
42 Take it to heart? Fie, 'tis a fault to heaven,
43 A fault against the dead, a fault to nature,
44 To reason most absurd, whose common theme
45 Is death of fathers, and who still hath cried,
46 From the first corse till he that died to-day,
47 "This must be so." We pray you, throw to earth
48 This unprevailing woe, and think of us
49 As of a father, for let the world take note
50 You are the most immediate to our throne,
51 And with no less nobility of love
52 Than that which dearest father bears his son
53 Do I impart toward you. For your intent
54 In going back to school in Wittenberg,
55 It is most **retrograde** to our desire,

Please note that excerpts and passages in the StudySync® library and this workbook are intended as touchstones to generate interest in an author's work. The excerpts and passages do not substitute for the reading of entire texts, and StudySync® strongly recommends that students seek out and purchase the whole literary or informational work in order to experience it as the author intended. Links to online resellers are available in our digital library. In addition, complete works may be ordered through an authorized reseller by filling out and returning to StudySync® the order form enclosed in this workbook.

Reading & Writing
Companion

9

56 And we beseech you, bend you to remain
57 Here in the cheer and comfort of our eye,
58 Our chiefest courtier, cousin, and our son.

59 QUEEN: Let not thy mother lose her prayers, Hamlet,
60 I pray thee stay with us, go not to Wittenberg.

61 HAMLET: I shall in all my best obey you, madam.

62 KING: Why, 'tis a loving and a fair reply.
63 Be as ourself in Denmark. Madam, come.
64 This gentle and unforc'd accord of Hamlet
65 Sits smiling to my heart, in grace whereof,
66 No jocund health that Denmark drinks to-day,
67 But the great cannon to the clouds shall tell,
68 And the King's rouse the heaven shall bruit again,
69 Respeaking earthly thunder. Come away.

70 *[Flourish. Exeunt all but HAMLET.]*

71 HAMLET: O that this too too solid flesh would melt,
72 Thaw and resolve itself into a dew!
73 Or that the Everlasting had not fix'd
74 His canon 'gainst self-slaughter! O God, God,
75 How weary, stale, flat and unprofitable
76 Seem to me all the uses of this world!
77 Fie on't, ah fie! 'tis an unweeded garden
78 That grows to seed, things rank and gross in nature
79 Possess it merely. That it should come to this!
80 But two months dead, nay, not so much, not two.
81 So excellent a king, that was to this
82 Hyperion—to a satyr, so loving to my mother
83 That he might not beteem the winds of heaven
84 Visit her face too roughly. Heaven and earth,
85 Must I remember? Why, she would hang on him
86 As if increase of appetite had grown
87 By what it fed on, and yet, within a month—
88 Let me not think on't! Frailty, thy name is woman!—
89 A little month, or ere those shoes were old
90 With which she followed my poor father's body,
91 Like Niobe, all tears—why, she, even she—
92 O, God, a beast that wants discourse of reason
93 Would have mourn'd longer—married with my uncle,
94 My father's brother, but no more like my father
95 Than I to Hercules. Within a month,

Reading & Writing
Companion

96 Ere yet the salt of most unrighteous tears

97 Had left the flushing in her **galled** eyes,

98 She married—O most wicked speed: to post

99 With such **dexterity** to incestuous sheets,

100 It is not, nor it cannot come to good,

101 But break my heart, for I must hold my tongue.

From Act II, Scene ii

102 *Hamlet has been visited by an apparition claiming to be the ghost of his father, who urges Hamlet to avenge his father's murder. Hamlet swears he will obey, but hesitates. Watching a group of traveling players perform the murder of Priam, king of Troy, Hamlet compares one actor's passionate portrayal of Hecuba, Priam's grieving widow, to his own inaction.*

103 HAMLET: O, what a rogue and peasant slave am I!

104 Is it not monstrous that this player here,

105 But in a fiction, in a dream of passion,

106 Could force his soul so to his own conceit

107 That from her working all his visage wann'd,

108 Tears in his eyes, distraction in his aspect,

109 A broken voice, an' his whole function suiting

110 With forms to his conceit? And all for nothing,

111 For Hecuba!

112 What's Hecuba to him, or he to Hecuba,

113 That he should weep for her? What would he do

114 Had he the motive and the cue for passion

115 That I have? He would drown the stage with tears,

116 And cleave the general ear with horrid speech,

117 Make mad the guilty, and appall the free,

118 Confound the ignorant, and amaze indeed

119 The very faculties of eyes and ears. Yet I,

120 A dull and muddy-mettled rascal, peak

121 Like John-a-dreams, unpregnant of my cause,

122 And can say nothing; no, not for a king,

123 Upon whose property and most dear life

124 A damn'd defeat was made. Am I a coward?

125 Who calls me villain, breaks my pate across,

126 Plucks off my beard, and blows it in my face,

127 Tweaks me by the nose, gives me the lie i' the throat

128 As deep as to the lungs? Who does me this?

129 Hah, 'swounds, I should take it; for it cannot be

130 But I am pigeon-liver'd, and lack gall

131 To make oppression bitter, or ere this

132 I should 'a' fatted all the region kites

NOTES

133 With this slave's offal. Bloody, bawdy villain!

134 Remorseless, treacherous, lecherous, kindless villain!

135 Why, what an ass am I! This is most brave,

136 That I, the son of a dear father murthered,

137 Prompted to my revenge by heaven and hell,

138 Must, like a whore unpack my heart with words,

139 And fall a-cursing like a very drab,

140 A stallion. Fie upon't, foh!

141 About, my brains! Hum—I have heard

142 That guilty creatures sitting at a play

143 Have by the very cunning of the scene

144 Been struck so to the soul, that presently

145 They have proclaim'd their malefactions:

146 For murther, though it have no tongue, will speak

147 With most miraculous organ. I'll have these players

148 Play something like the murther of my father

149 Before mine uncle. I'll observe his looks,

150 I'll tent him to the quick. If 'a do blench,

151 I know my course. The spirit that I have seen

152 May be the dev'l, and the dev'l hath power

153 T' assume a pleasing shape, yea, and perhaps,

154 Out of my weakness and my melancholy,

155 As he is very potent with such spirits,

156 Abuses me to damn me. I'll have grounds

157 More relative than this—the play's the thing

158 Wherein I'll catch the conscience of the King.

From Act III, Scene i

159 *Hamlet has been acting mad in front of his family and the court. The King and Polonius hope that Hamlet's strange behavior stems from his love for Polonius's daughter, Ophelia, and they spy on the young couple in order to confirm their suspicions. While hidden, they catch Hamlet in a private moment of anguished contemplation.*

160 HAMLET: To be, or not to be, that is the question:

161 Whether 'tis nobler in the mind to suffer

162 The slings and arrows of outrageous fortune,

163 Or to take arms against a sea of troubles,

164 And by opposing, end them. To die, to sleep—

165 No more, and by a sleep to say we end

166 The heart-ache and the thousand natural shocks

167 That flesh is heir to; 'tis a consummation

168 Devoutly to be wish'd. To die, to sleep—

169 To sleep, perchance to dream—ay, there's the rub,

170 For in that sleep of death what dreams may come,
171 When we have shuffled off this mortal coil,
172 Must give us pause; there's the respect
173 That makes **calamity** of so long life:
174 For who would bear the whips and scorns of time,
175 Th' oppressor's wrong, the proud man's contumely,
176 The pangs of despis'd love, the law's delay,
177 The **insolence** of office, and the spurns
178 That patient merit of th' unworthy takes,
179 When he himself might his quietus make
180 With a bare bodkin; who would fardels bear,
181 To grunt and sweat under a weary life,
182 But that the dread of something after death,
183 The undiscover'd country, from whose bourn
184 No traveller returns, puzzles the will,
185 And makes us rather bear those ills we have,
186 Than fly to others that we know not of?
187 Thus conscience does make cowards of us all,
188 And thus the native hue of resolution
189 Is sicklied o'er with the pale cast of thought,
190 And enterprises of great pith and moment
191 With this regard their currents turn awry,
192 And lose the name of action.

Act III, Scene iii

A room in the Castle.

193 *[Enter KING, ROSENCRANTZ, and GUILDENSTERN.]*

194 KING: I like him not; nor stands it safe with us
195 To let his madness range. Therefore prepare you;
196 I your commission will forthwith dispatch,
197 And he to England shall along with you:
198 The terms of our estate may not endure
199 Hazard so near us as doth hourly grow
200 Out of his lunacies.

201 GULIDENSTERN: We will ourselves provide:
202 Most holy and religious fear it is
203 To keep those many many bodies safe
204 That live and feed upon your majesty.

205 ROSENCRANTZ: The single and peculiar life is bound,
206 With all the strength and armour of the mind,
207 To keep itself from 'noyance; but much more

208 That spirit upon whose weal depend and rest
209 The lives of many. The cease of majesty
210 Dies not alone; but like a gulf doth draw
211 What's near it with it: it is a massy wheel,
212 Fix'd on the summit of the highest mount,
213 To whose huge spokes ten thousand lesser things
214 Are mortis'd and adjoin'd; which, when it falls,
215 Each small annexment, petty consequence,
216 Attends the **boisterous** ruin. Never alone
217 Did the king sigh, but with a general groan.

218 KING: Arm you, I pray you, to this speedy voyage;
219 For we will fetters put upon this fear,
220 Which now goes too free-footed.

221 ROSENCRANTZ and GULIDENSTERN: We will haste us.

222 *[Exeunt ROSENCRANTZ and GULIDENSTERN.]*

223 *[Enter POLONIUS.]*

224 POLONIUS: My lord, he's going to his mother's closet:
225 Behind the arras I'll convey myself
226 To hear the process; I'll warrant she'll tax him home:
227 And, as you said, and wisely was it said,
228 'Tis meet that some more audience than a mother,
229 Since nature makes them partial, should o'erhear
230 The speech, of vantage. Fare you well, my liege:
231 I'll call upon you ere you go to bed,
232 And tell you what I know.

233 KING: Thanks, dear my lord.

234 [Exit POLONIUS.]

235 O, my offence is rank, it smells to heaven;
236 It hath the primal eldest curse upon't,—
237 A brother's murder!—Pray can I not,
238 Though inclination be as sharp as will:
239 My stronger guilt defeats my strong intent;
240 And, like a man to double business bound,
241 I stand in pause where I shall first begin,
242 And both neglect. What if this cursed hand
243 Were thicker than itself with brother's blood,—
244 Is there not rain enough in the sweet heavens
245 To wash it white as snow? Whereto serves mercy

246 But to confront the visage of offence?
247 And what's in prayer but this twofold force,—
248 To be forestalled ere we come to fall,
249 Or pardon'd being down? Then I'll look up;
250 My fault is past. But, O, what form of prayer
251 Can serve my turn? Forgive me my foul murder!—
252 That cannot be; since I am still possess'd
253 Of those effects for which I did the murder,—
254 My crown, mine own ambition, and my queen.
255 May one be pardon'd and retain the offence?
256 In the corrupted currents of this world
257 Offence's gilded hand may shove by justice;
258 And oft 'tis seen the wicked prize itself
259 Buys out the law; but 'tis not so above;
260 There is no shuffling;—there the action lies
261 In his true nature; and we ourselves compell'd,
262 Even to the teeth and forehead of our faults,
263 To give in evidence. What then? what rests?
264 Try what repentance can: what can it not?
265 Yet what can it when one cannot repent?
266 O wretched state! O bosom black as death!
267 O limed soul, that, struggling to be free,
268 Art more engag'd! Help, angels! Make assay:
269 Bow, stubborn knees; and, heart, with strings of steel,
270 Be soft as sinews of the new-born babe!
271 All may be well.

272 [Retires and kneels.]

273 [Enter Hamlet.]

274 HAMLET: Now might I do it pat, now he is praying;
275 And now I'll do't;—and so he goes to heaven;
276 And so am I reveng'd.—that would be scann'd:
277 A villain kills my father; and for that,
278 I, his sole son, do this same villain send
279 To heaven.
280 O, this is hire and salary, not revenge.
281 He took my father grossly, full of bread;
282 With all his crimes broad blown, as flush as May;
283 And how his audit stands, who knows save heaven?
284 But in our circumstance and course of thought,
285 'Tis heavy with him: and am I, then, reveng'd,
286 To take him in the purging of his soul,
287 When he is fit and season'd for his passage?

288 No.
289 Up, sword, and know thou a more horrid hent:
290 When he is drunk asleep; or in his rage;
291 Or in the incestuous pleasure of his bed;
292 At gaming, swearing; or about some act
293 That has no relish of salvation in't;—
294 Then trip him, that his heels may kick at heaven;
295 And that his soul may be as damn'd and black
296 As hell, whereto it goes. My mother stays:
297 This physic but prolongs thy sickly days.

298 *[Exit.]*

299 *[The King rises and advances.]*

300 KING: My words fly up, my thoughts remain below:
301 Words without thoughts never to heaven go.

302 *[Exit.]*

THINK QUESTIONS CA-CCSS: CA.RL.11-12.1, CA.L.11-12.4a, CA.L.11-12.4d

1. In Act I, how do King Claudius and Queen Gertrude try to reason with Hamlet? What does Hamlet's soliloquy suggest about his response to their reasoning? Cite textual evidence in your response.

2. In Act II, what key comparison does Hamlet draw between himself and the players confirming that he is a coward? What inference can you make about the power of words versus actions from this comparison? Cite evidence from the text.

3. In Act III, Scene i, what does Hamlet mean when he says "to be, or not to be, that is the question"? Citing textual evidence from his soliloquy, explain the determination Hamlet makes on this question. What can you infer about the human condition from this speech?

4. Review the King's lines in Act I, scene ii that begin with "'Tis sweet and commendable..." Use context to determine the meaning of the word **filial** as used in the fifth line. Explain how context helped you determine the meaning of the word.

5. Use context clues to determine a preliminary definition of **trappings** as used in Act I, scene ii. Verify your preliminary definition by checking a dictionary. Write down the definition of *trappings*, identify the part of speech used in the text, and describe the context clue in the text.

CLOSE READ

CA-CCSS: CA.RL.11-12.1, CA.RL.11-12.3, CA.RL.11-12.4, CA.W.11-12.5, CA.W.11-12.6, CA.W.11-12.9a, CA.W.11-12.10, CA.L.11-12.5b

Reread the scenes from *Hamlet*. As you reread, complete the Focus Questions below. Then use your answers and annotations from the questions to help you complete the Writing Prompt.

 FOCUS QUESTIONS

1. How does Hamlet's soliloquy in Act I develop his attitude toward the world? How does Hamlet's soliloquy in Act II compare or contrast with his speech in Act I? What character development does this show? Highlight and explain textual evidence, noting how the evidence relates to both the specific situation at hand and to Hamlet's overall outlook on humanity.

2. What does Hamlet do in Act III, scene iii, when he encounters the King? What positive and negative traits does it reveal, and how does this develop his character? How does it relate to his role as an archetypal character? Highlight textual evidence and use the annotation tool to explain your choices.

3. In Act I, what does Hamlet mean when he describes the "trappings and the suits of woe"? Provide textual evidence that supports the idea that the "trappings" he describes are only the so-called tip of the iceberg for him.

4. In the final excerpt from Act III, the King kneels in prayer. He says:

   > O wretched state! O bosom black as death!
   > O limed soul, that, struggling to be free,
   > Art more engag'd! Help, angels! Make assay:
   > Bow, stubborn knees; and, heart, with strings of steel,
   > Be soft as sinews of the new-born babe!

   Knowing that *limed* refers to a bird trapped with a lime-based paste, what do you think Shakespeare suggests, denotatively and connotatively, through the phrase "limed soul" in this passage?

5. What words with a similar denotation could Shakespeare have used in place of question in the line "To be or not to be, that is the question"? Describe three such words and explain how each would change the meaning of the line.

6. How does Hamlet's "To be or not to be" soliloquy in Act III, scene i reveal the complexities of being human? Highlight textual evidence and use the annotation tool to explain your choices.

Please note that excerpts and passages in the StudySync® library and this workbook are intended as touchstones to generate interest in an author's work. The excerpts and passages do not substitute for the reading of entire texts, and StudySync® strongly recommends that students seek out and purchase the whole literary or informational work in order to experience it as the author intended. Links to online resellers are available in our digital library. In addition, complete works may be ordered through an authorized reseller by filling out and returning to StudySync® the order form enclosed in this workbook.

Reading & Writing Companion

17

WRITING PROMPT

Recall from the Unit 2 Introduction "The English Renaissance" that the intellectual currents behind humanism brought the focus of literature away from the afterlife and toward the affairs of earthly life—including politics, love, and philosophy. In Hamlet's "To be or not to be" soliloquy in Act II, scene i, how does Hamlet blend a discussion of the afterlife with introspection that reflects Renaissance humanism? Look closely at how Hamlet describes the challenges of life with the type of deep thought that marked Renaissance humanism. In your response, provide a summary of Renaissance humanism as you understand it from the Unit 2 Introduction, and provide an inference about Hamlet's attitude toward such deep thought and his interest in human affairs. Provide textual evidence to support your response.

SHAKESPEARE: THE WORLD AS STAGE

NON-FICTION
Bill Bryson
2007

INTRODUCTION

Known for his distinctly humorous writing style, Bill Bryson is a highly regarded American author of various non-fiction books on travel, science, language, and other topics. Bryson's biography of William Shakespeare, *Shakespeare: The World As Stage*, focuses on what little is known conclusively about the famous playwright and poet. The excerpt here discusses the Shakespeare authorship debate.

"...the writer might just as well have suggested that Shakespeare never owned a pair of shoes or pants."

FIRST READ

Excerpt from Chapter 9: Claimants

1 There is an extraordinary—seemingly an **insatiable**—urge on the part of quite a number of people to believe that the plays of William Shakespeare were written by someone other than William Shakespeare. The number of published books suggesting—or more often insisting—as much is estimated now to be well over five thousand.

2 Shakespeare's plays, it is held, so brim with expertise—on law, medicine, statesmanship, court life, military affairs, the bounding main, antiquity, life abroad—that they cannot possibly be the work of a single lightly educated **provincial**. The presumption is that William Shakespeare of Stratford was, at best, an amiable **stooge,** an actor who lent his name as cover for someone of greater talent, someone who could not, for one reason or another, be publicly identified as a playwright.

3 The controversy has been given respectful airing in the highest quarters. PBS, the American television network, in 1996 produced an hour-long documentary **unequivocally** suggesting that Shakespeare probably wasn't Shakespeare. *Harper's Magazine* and the *New York Times* have both devoted generous amounts of space to sympathetically considering the anti-Stratford arguments. The Smithsonian Institution in 2002 held a seminar titled "Who Wrote Shakespeare?" The best-read article in the British magazine *History Today* was one examining the authorship question. Even *Scientific American* entered the fray with an article proposing that the person portrayed in the famous Martin Droeshout engraving might actually be—I weep to say it—Elizabeth I. Perhaps the most extraordinary development of all is that Shakespeare's Globe Theater in London—built as a monument for his plays and with aspirations to be a world-class study center—became, under the stewardship of the artistic director Mark Rylance, a kind of clearinghouse for anti-Stratford sentiment.

Reading & Writing Companion

NOTES

4   So it needs to be said that nearly all of the anti-Shakespeare sentiment—actually all of it, every bit—involves manipulative scholarship or sweeping misstatements of fact. Shakespeare "never owned a book," a writer for the *New York Times* gravely informed readers in one doubting article in 2002. The statement cannot actually be refuted, for we know nothing about his incidental possessions. But the writer might just as well have suggested that Shakespeare never owned a pair of shoes or pants. For all the evidence tells us, he spent his life unclothed as well as bookless, but it is probable that what is lacking is the evidence, not the apparel or the books.

5   Daniel Wright, a professor at Concordia University in Portland, Oregon, and an active anti-Stratfordian, wrote in *Harper's Magazine* that Shakespeare was "a simple, untutored wool and grain merchant" and "a rather ordinary man who had no connection to the literary world." Such statements can only be characterized as wildly imaginative. Similarly, in the normally **unimpeachable** *History Today,* William D. Rubinstein, a professor at the University of Wales at Aberystwyth, stated in the opening paragraph of his anti-Shakespeare survey: "Of the seventy-five known contemporary documents in which Shakespeare is named, not one concerns his career as an author."

6   That is not even close to being so. In the Master of the Revels' accounts for 1604–1605—that is, the record of plays performed before the king, about as official a record as a record can be—Shakespeare is named seven times as the author of plays performed before James I. He is identified on the title pages as the author of the sonnets and in the dedications of two poems. He is named as author on several quarto editions of his plays, by Francis Meres in *Palladis Tamia,* and by Robert Greene in the *Groat's-Worth of Wit.* John Webster identifies him as one of the great playwrights of the age in his preface to *The White Devil.*

7   The only absence among contemporary records is not of documents connecting Shakespeare to his works but of documents connecting any other human being to them. As the Shakespeare scholar Jonathan Bate has pointed out, virtually no one "in Shakespeare's lifetime or for the first two hundred years after his death expressed the slightest doubt about his authorship."

Excerpted *from Shakespeare: The World As Stage* by Bill Bryson, published by HarperCollins Publishers.

THINK QUESTIONS   CA-CCSS: CA.RI.11-12.1, CA.L.11-12.4a

1. For what purpose does the author list sources of media coverage of the authorship controversy at the beginning of the selection? Cite textual evidence to support your answer.

2. What is the author's response to the claim that Shakespeare "never owned a book"? What tone does he use in his response? Support your response with evidence from the text.

3. How does the author conclude this excerpt? What does that tell you about Bryson's view of the authorship debate? Support your inference with textual evidence.

4. Use context to determine the meaning of the word **provincial** as it is used in *Shakespeare: The World as Stage*. Write your definition of "provincial" here and tell how you found it.

5. Use your knowledge of word parts and the context clues provided in the passage to determine the meaning of **unimpeachable**. Write your definition of *unimpeachable* here and tell how you got it.

CLOSE READ

CA-CCSS: CA.RI.11-12.1, CA.RI.11-12.2, CA.W.11-12.4, CA.W.11-12.5, CA.W.11-12.6, CA.W.11-12.9b, CA.W.11-12.10

Reread the excerpt from *Shakespeare: The World as Stage*. As you reread, complete the Focus Questions below. Then use your answers and annotations from the questions to help you complete the Writing Prompt.

FOCUS QUESTIONS

1. In the second paragraph, what does Bryson mean when he refers to Shakespeare as a "lightly educated provincial"? What connotation does that phrase have, and what does it tell you about Bryson's viewpoint? Highlight evidence in the text and use the annotation tool to explain the phrase.

2. Why does Bryson list the professions of Daniel Wright and William D. Rubinstein in Paragraph 5? What is his purpose for including the long list of media outlets in Paragraph 3? How do these details support his central idea? Highlight evidence from the text and make annotations to support your ideas.

3. What is Bryson's central idea in Paragraph 4? How does Bryson's tone in the paragraph help develop the central idea? Highlight evidence to support your ideas and use the annotation tool to write your response.

4. Use your understanding of tone and supporting details to determine the central idea of the excerpt. Highlight evidence from the text to support your ideas.

5. Recall the unit's Essential Question: How do we express the complexities of being human? What does the Shakespearean authorship debate reveal about human nature? What does it say about Shakespeare's critics? Support your response with evidence from the text.

WRITING PROMPT

What is Bill Bryson's central idea in the excerpt from *Shakespeare: The World as Stage*? How does Bryson's tone or bias contribute to the development of this central idea? Which key details support the central idea? Cite textual evidence to support your response.

THE LOVE SONG OF J. ALFRED PRUFROCK

POETRY
T.S. Eliot
1915

INTRODUCTION

T.S. Eliot's pedigree is impeccable. Born in St. Louis to an old New England family, he was educated at Harvard, the Sorbonne, and Oxford, and received the Nobel Prize for Literature in 1948 for his boldly innovative and influential style. "Prufrock" demonstrates Eliot's characteristic stream of consciousness and versatility with diction. His narrator seems to be struggling with middle age, but

"And would it have been worth it, after all...?"

FIRST READ

"The Love Song of J. Alfred Prufrock"

1   *S'io credesse che mia risposta fosse*
2   *A persona che mai tornasse al mondo,*
3   *Questa fiamma staria senza piu scosse.*
4   *Ma perciocche giammai di questo fondo*
5   *Non torno vivo alcun, s'l'odo il vero,*
6   *Senza tema d'infamia ti rispondo.*

7   Let us go then, you and I,
8   When the evening is spread out against the sky
9   Like a patient **etherized** upon a table;
10   Let us go, through certain half-deserted streets,
11   The muttering retreats
12   Of restless nights in one-night cheap hotels
13   And sawdust restaurants with oyster-shells:
14   Streets that follow like a **tedious** argument
15   Of **insidious** intent
16   To lead you to an overwhelming question....
17   Oh, do not ask, "What is it?"
18   Let us go and make our visit.

19   In the room the women come and go
20   Talking of Michelangelo.

21   The yellow fog that rubs its back upon the window-panes,
22   The yellow smoke that rubs its muzzle on the window-panes
23   Licked its tongue into the corners of the evening,
24   Lingered upon the pools that stand in drains,
25   Let fall upon its back the soot that falls from chimneys,
26   Slipped by the terrace, made a sudden leap,

Please note that excerpts and passages in the StudySync® library and this workbook are intended as touchstones to generate interest in an author's work. The excerpts and passages do not substitute for the reading of entire texts, and StudySync® strongly recommends that students seek out and purchase the whole literary or informational work in order to experience it as the author intended. Links to online resellers are available in our digital library. In addition, complete works may be ordered through an authorized reseller by filling out and returning to StudySync® the order form enclosed in this workbook.

Reading & Writing Companion   **25**

NOTES

27 And seeing that it was a soft October night,
28 Curled once about the house, and fell asleep.

29 And indeed there will be time
30 For the yellow smoke that slides along the street,
31 Rubbing its back upon the window panes;
32 There will be time, there will be time
33 To prepare a face to meet the faces that you meet
34 There will be time to murder and create,
35 And time for all the works and days of hands
36 That lift and drop a question on your plate;
37 Time for you and time for me,
38 And time yet for a hundred indecisions,
39 And for a hundred visions and revisions,
40 Before the taking of a toast and tea.

41 In the room the women come and go
42 Talking of Michelangelo.

43 And indeed there will be time
44 To wonder, "Do I dare?" and, "Do I dare?"
45 Time to turn back and descend the stair,
46 With a bald spot in the middle of my hair—
47 (They will say: "How his hair is growing thin!")
48 My morning coat, my collar mounting firmly to the chin,
49 My necktie rich and modest, but asserted by a simple pin—
50 (They will say: "But how his arms and legs are thin!")
51 Do I dare
52 Disturb the universe?
53 In a minute there is time
54 For decisions and revisions which a minute will reverse.

55 For I have known them all already, known them all:
56 Have known the evenings, mornings, afternoons,
57 I have measured out my life with coffee spoons;
58 I know the voices dying with a dying fall
59 Beneath the music from a farther room.
60   So how should I presume?

61 And I have known the eyes already, known them all—
62 The eyes that fix you in a formulated phrase,
63 And when I am formulated, sprawling on a pin,
64 When I am pinned and wriggling on the wall,
65 Then how should I begin
66 To spit out all the butt-ends of my days and ways?
67   And how should I presume?

68   And I have known the arms already, known them all—
69   Arms that are braceleted and white and bare
70   (But in the lamplight, downed with light brown hair!)
71   Is it perfume from a dress
72   That makes me so digress?
73   Arms that lie along a table, or wrap about a shawl.
74   And should I then presume?
75   And how should I begin?

...

76   Shall I say, I have gone at dusk through narrow streets
77   And watched the smoke that rises from the pipes
78   Of lonely men in shirt-sleeves, leaning out of windows?

79   I should have been a pair of ragged claws
80   Scuttling across the floors of silent seas.

...

81   And the afternoon, the evening, sleeps so peacefully!
82   Smoothed by long fingers,
83   Asleep... tired... or it **malingers**.
84   Stretched on the floor, here beside you and me.
85   Should I, after tea and cakes and ices,
86   Have the strength to force the moment to its crisis?
87   But though I have wept and fasted, wept and prayed,
88   Though I have seen my head (grown slightly bald) brought in upon a platter,
89   I am no prophet—and here's no great matter;
90   I have seen the moment of my greatness flicker,
91   And I have seen the eternal Footman hold my coat, and snicker,
92   And in short, I was afraid.

93   And would it have been worth it, after all,
94   After the cups, the marmalade, the tea,
95   Among the porcelain, among some talk of you and me,
96   Would it have been worth while,
97   To have bitten off the matter with a smile,
98   To have squeezed the universe into a ball
99   To roll it toward some overwhelming question,
100   To say: "I am Lazarus, come from the dead,
101   Come back to tell you all, I shall tell you all"—
102   If one, settling a pillow by her head,
103   Should say: "That is not what I meant at all;
104   That is not it, at all."

Please note that excerpts and passages in the StudySync® library and this workbook are intended as touchstones to generate interest in an author's work. The excerpts and passages do not substitute for the reading of entire texts, and StudySync® strongly recommends that students seek out and purchase the whole literary or informational work in order to experience it as the author intended. Links to online resellers are available in our digital library. In addition, complete works may be ordered through an authorized reseller by filling out and returning to StudySync® the order form enclosed in this workbook.

Reading & Writing
Companion

27

105 And would it have been worth it, after all,

106 Would it have been worth while,

107 After the sunsets and the dooryards and the sprinkled streets,

108 After the novels, after the teacups, after the skirts that trail along the

109   floor—

110 And this, and so much more?—

111 It is impossible to say just what I mean!

112 But as if a magic lantern threw the nerves in patterns on a screen:

113 Would it have been worth while

114 If one, settling a pillow or throwing off a shawl,

115 And turning toward the window, should say:

116   "That is not it at all,

117   That is not what I meant, at all."

    ...

118 No! I am not Prince Hamlet, nor was meant to be;

119 Am an attendant lord, one that will do

120 To swell a progress, start a scene or two,

121 Advise the prince; no doubt, an easy tool,

122 **Deferential,** glad to be of use,

123 Politic, cautious, and meticulous;

124 Full of high sentence, but a bit obtuse;

125 At times, indeed, almost ridiculous—

126 Almost, at times, the Fool.

127 I grow old... I grow old...

128 I shall wear the bottoms of my trousers rolled.

129 Shall I part my hair behind? Do I dare to eat a peach?

130 I shall wear white flannel trousers, and walk upon the beach.

131 I have heard the mermaids singing, each to each.

132 I do not think that they will sing to me.

133 I have seen them riding seaward on the waves

134 Combing the white hair of the waves blown back

135 When the wind blows the water white and black.

136 We have lingered in the chambers of the sea

137 By sea-girls wreathed with seaweed red and brown

138 Till human voices wake us, and we drown.

THINK QUESTIONS CA-CCSS: CA.RL.11-12.1, CA.L.11-12.4a

1. What phrases or lines are repeated in the poem? What do these repetitions tell you about the speaker of the poem? Cite textual evidence to support your answer.

2. What physical descriptions of the speaker does "The Love Song of J. Alfred Prufrock" provide? What inferences can you make about Prufrock using the direct descriptions and his actions? Support your response with textual evidence.

3. Write two or three sentences summarizing the events of the poem. What is the speaker's goal or purpose in the poem? Does he achieve his purpose? What seems to occur in the time span of the poem? Use textual evidence to support your response.

4. Use context to determine the meaning of the word **deferential** as it is used in "The Love Song of J. Alfred Prufrock." Write your definition of *deferential* here and explain how you arrived at this definition.

5. Use context to determine the meaning of the word **malingers** as it is used in "The Love Song of J. Alfred Prufrock." Write your definition of *malingers* here and explain how you arrived at this definition.

Please note that excerpts and passages in the StudySync® library and this workbook are intended as touchstones to generate interest in an author's work. The excerpts and passages do not substitute for the reading of entire texts, and StudySync® strongly recommends that students seek out and purchase the whole literary or informational work in order to experience it as the author intended. Links to online resellers are available in our digital library. In addition, complete works may be ordered through an authorized reseller by filling out and returning to StudySync® the order form enclosed in this workbook.

Reading & Writing Companion   **29**

CLOSE READ

CA-CCSS: CA.RL.11-12.1, CA.RL.11-12.2, CA.RL.11-12.4, CA.W.11-12.4, CA.W.11-12.5, CA.W.11-12.6, CA.W.11-12.9a, CA.W.11-12.10, CA.L.11-12.5a

Reread the poem "The Love Song of Alfred J. Prufrock." As you reread, complete the Focus Questions below. Then use your answers and annotations from the questions to help you complete the Writing Prompt.

 ## FOCUS QUESTIONS

1. In the first stanza, Prufrock tells his audience that this poem is leading to "an overwhelming question." Highlight the questions Prufrock asks in the text. Are any of these questions likely to be the "overwhelming question" he promised? Use the annotation tool to draw conclusions about Prufrock from the questions you identified.

2. The title tells a reader that this poem is a "love song." What is the role of women in the poem? What seems to be Prufrock's relationship to them? How does the author use figures of speech to describe women, and how do those choices imply a theme? Highlight evidence to support your ideas and write annotations to explain your responses.

3. What is the role of the ocean imagery in "The Love Song of J. Alfred Prufrock"? How does it relate to other figures of speech in the poem? Highlight examples of ocean imagery and annotate to explain how this imagery might contribute to theme.

4. What is the speaker's tone in the first four stanzas of the poem? What kinds of words and phrases does the speaker use, and what connotations do those words have? What effect does the tone have on the reader? Highlight textual evidence and write annotations to explain your ideas.

5. Choose one allusion in the poem and explain its meaning. What is the role of the allusion in the poem? What inferences about theme can be made from the allusion? Highlight textual evidence to support your answer.

6. Throughout "The Love Song of J. Alfred Prufrock," there are repeated references to food and eating and drinking. What do these references say about Prufrock? What might they say about the complexity of human lives in general, and how do these ideas contribute to a theme of the poem? Highlight your evidence and make annotations to explain your response.

WRITING PROMPT

Determine two or more themes in "The Love Song of J. Alfred Prufrock" and analyze how they are developed over the course of the text. How does T. S. Eliot use figures of speech—including hyperbole, understatement, metaphors, and allusions—to develop theme in the poem? How do the themes interact with or support each other? Support your response with textual evidence.

ON MONSIEUR'S DEPARTURE

POETRY
Elizabeth I
1582

INTRODUCTION

Elizabeth I was the queen of England from 1558 until her death in 1603. Her reign was known as the Elizabethan era, which is famous for the emergence of the English Renaissance. While serving as queen, the well-educated Elizabeth I wrote numerous poems that seem to be about her life, including "On Monsieur's Departure," in which the speaker expresses the pain of unrequited love.

"I love, and yet am forced to seem to hate..."

 FIRST READ

1   I grieve and dare not show my **discontent;**
2   I love, and yet am forced to seem to hate;
3   I do, yet dare not say I ever meant;
4   I seem **stark mute,** but inwardly do prate.
5   I am, and not; I freeze and yet am burned,
6   Since from myself another self I turned.

7   My care is like my shadow in the sun—
8   Follows me flying, flies when I pursue it,
9   Stands, and lies by me, doth what I have done;
10 His too familiar care doth make me **rue** it.
11 No means I find to rid him from my breast,
12 Till by the end of things it be **supprest.**

13 Some gentler passion slide into my mind,
14 For I am soft, and made of melting snow;
15 Or be more cruel, Love, and so be kind.
16 Let me float or sink, be high or low;
17 Or let me live with some more sweet content,
18 Or die, and so forget what love e'er meant.

THINK QUESTIONS CA-CCSS: CA.RL.11-12.1, CA.L.11-12.4a

1. What contrasts does the speaker set up in the first stanza? What is the effect of these contrasts? Cite textual evidence to support your response.

2. In the second stanza, to what does the speaker compare her feelings? What feeling does this stanza give the reader? Support your response with textual evidence.

3. What is the speaker asking for in the third stanza? Support your answer with evidence from the text.

4. The word *prate* as used in the poem means "chatter." Knowing that and the structure of the first stanza, what does the word **mute** mean as it is used in "On Monsieur's Departure"? Write your definition of *mute* here and tell how you got it.

5. Remembering that the prefix *dis-* means "not" or "opposite of," use the context clues provided in the passage to determine the meaning of **discontent**. Write your definition of *discontent* here, and explain how you found it.

Please note that excerpts and passages in the StudySync® library and this workbook are intended as touchstones to generate interest in an author's work. The excerpts and passages do not substitute for the reading of entire texts, and StudySync® strongly recommends that students seek out and purchase the whole literary or informational work in order to experience it as the author intended. Links to online resellers are available in our digital library. In addition, complete works may be ordered through an authorized reseller by filling out and returning to StudySync® the order form enclosed in this workbook.

Reading & Writing Companion   **33**

CLOSE READ
CA-CCSS: CA.RL.11-12.1, CA.RL.11-12.4, CA.W.11-12.4, CA.W.11-12.6, CA.W.11-12.9a, CA.W.11-12.10, CA.L.11-12.5a

Reread the poem "On Monsieur's Departure." As you reread, complete the Focus Questions below. Then use your answers and annotations from the questions to help you complete the Writing Prompt.

FOCUS QUESTIONS

1. Examine the speaker's use of similes and metaphors in the poem. What does the speaker compare using these figures of speech? What purpose do they serve? Highlight similes and metaphors in the text and use the annotation tool to explain their purpose.

2. What point does the speaker make using the hyperbole in the second stanza? How is that different from the point she makes at the end of the third stanza? Highlight your evidence and annotate to explain your ideas.

3. Compare the third stanza with the first stanza. What inference can you make about the speaker's changing state of mind? Highlight your evidence and annotate to explain your ideas.

4. Whom is the speaker addressing in the poem? What inference can be made about the speaker based on this information? Highlight your evidence and make annotations to explain your choices.

5. What option does the speaker leave out of the third stanza? What does this tell the reader about the speaker? What does it reveal about the complexity of being human? Highlight evidence from the text that will help support your ideas.

WRITING PROMPT

What can you infer about the speaker based on what is not said in the poem? How do the figures of speech shape your view of the speaker? What do the emotions of the speaker tell you about the human condition? Support your writing with textual evidence.

SPEECH TO THE TROOPS AT TILBURY

NON-FICTION
Elizabeth I
1588

INTRODUCTION

studysync tv

I n August, 1588, King Philip II of Spain sent the huge fleet of warships known as the Spanish Armada to attack and invade England. As ground troops and others assembled at Tilbury, on the bank of the Thames River, in preparation for the expected attack, Elizabeth I, the queen of England, delivered this speech. The Armada was ultimately defeated at sea and never reached England's shores.

"Let tyrants fear."

FIRST READ

1 My loving people,

2 We have been persuaded by some that are careful of our safety, to take heed how we commit ourselves to armed multitudes, for fear of **treachery;** but I assure you I do not desire to live to distrust my faithful and loving people.

3 Let **tyrants** fear. I have always so behaved myself that, under God, I have placed my chiefest strength and safeguard in the loyal hearts and good-will of my subjects; and therefore I am come amongst you, as you see, at this time, not for my recreation and **disport,** but being resolved, in the midst and heat of the battle, to live and die amongst you all; to lay down for my God, and for my kingdom, and my people, my honour and my blood, even in the dust.

4 I know I have the body of a weak, feeble woman; but I have the heart and stomach of a king, and of a king of England too, and think foul scorn that Parma or Spain, or any prince of Europe, should dare to invade the borders of my realm; to which rather than any dishonour shall grow by me, I myself will take up arms, I myself will be your general, judge, and rewarder of every one of your virtues in the field.

5 I know already, for your forwardness you have deserved rewards and crowns; and We do assure you on a word of a prince, they shall be duly paid. In the mean time, my lieutenant general shall be in my stead, than whom never prince commanded a more noble or worthy subject; not doubting but by your obedience to my general, by your **concord** in the camp, and your **valour** in the field, we shall shortly have a famous victory over these enémies of my God, of my kingdom, and of my people.

THINK QUESTIONS CA-CCSS: CA.RI.11-12.1, CA.L.11-12.4a, CA.L.11-12.4d

1. Who is Queen Elizabeth addressing with this text? How do you know? Support your response with textual evidence.

2. What reason would Queen Elizabeth have for saying that she does not fear for her safety? Support your response with textual evidence.

3. What does Queen Elizabeth promise to her audience? What reason would she have for making such a promise? Cite textual evidence to support your answer.

4. Use context as a clue to the meaning of the word **disport** as it is used in "Speech to the Troops at Tilbury." Then look up "disport" in a print or online dictionary to verify your definition and explain how you found it.

5. Use context to determine the meaning of **tyrants** as used in "Speech to the Troops at Tilbury." Write your definition of "tyrants" here and tell how you found it.

CLOSE READ
CA-CCSS: CA.RI.11-12.1, CA.RI.11-12.6, CA.W.11-12.4, CA.W.11-12.5, CA.W.11-12.6, CA.W.11-12.9b, CA.W.11-12.10

Reread the text "Speech to the Troops at Tilbury." Then use your answers and annotations from the questions to help you complete the Writing Prompt.

 ## FOCUS QUESTIONS

1. In the third paragraph of her speech, why does Elizabeth say, "Let tyrants fear"? How does this statement support her purpose for the speech? Highlight evidence in the text that shows why Elizabeth uses this phrase, and use the annotation tool to explain her purpose.

2. Why does Elizabeth call out her gender in paragraph 4 of the speech? What purpose does it serve? Highlight evidence and write annotations to support and explain your ideas.

3. What qualities does Elizabeth praise her soldiers for having? How will those qualities bring victory for the English army? What rhetorical device does Elizabeth use in praising her soldiers? Highlight your evidence and annotate to explain your ideas.

4. In the Unit 2 Introduction "The English Renaissance," you read that Elizabeth supported the Protestant Reformation. Using this knowledge, what purpose do Elizabeth's invocations of God in the speech serve? What phrase does Elizabeth use with her references to God to strengthen this purpose? Highlight your evidence and make annotations to explain your choices.

5. Use your understanding of point of view and rhetoric to determine Elizabeth's overall purpose in this speech. Highlight evidence from the text that will help support your ideas.

6. Recall the unit's Essential Question: How do we express the complexities of being human? What complexities about herself does Elizabeth reveal in the speech? How does discussing these complexities aid her purpose? Support your response with textual evidence.

WRITING PROMPT

How does Elizabeth's point of view in "Speech to the Troops at Tilbury" support her purpose for giving the speech? How does she use rhetorical devices to show her point of view and reveal her purpose? Support your writing with textual evidence.

Copyright © BookheadEd Learning, LLC

THE PASSIONATE SHEPHERD TO HIS LOVE

POETRY

Christopher Marlowe

1599

INTRODUCTION

Considered by many critics to be the father of English drama, Christopher Marlowe not only had an illustrious literary career as a playwright and poet, he also engaged in covert and dangerous political operations. Marlowe's plays called attention to corruption of those in power, the danger of greed, the darkness of individual suffering, and the need for social responsibility. In contrast to those themes, Marlowe's pastoral poem "The Passionate Shepherd to His Love" is a romantic and idealized celebration of "natural life."

"Come live with me and be my love..."

 FIRST READ

1 Come live with me and be my love,
2 And we will all the pleasures prove
3 That valleys, groves, hills, and fields,
4 Woods, or steepy mountain yields.

5 And we will sit upon the rocks,
6 Seeing the shepherds feed their flocks
7 By shallow rivers to whose falls
8 **Melodious** birds sing **madrigals.**

9 And I will make thee beds of roses
10 And a thousand fragrant posies;
11 A cap of flowers and a **kirtle**
12 Embroidered all with leaves of **myrtle;**

13 A gown made of the finest wool
14 Which from our pretty lambs we pull;
15 Fair lined slippers for the cold,
16 With buckles of the purest gold;

17 A belt of straw and ivy buds,
18 With coral clasps and amber studs.
19 And if these pleasures may thee move,
20 Come live with me, and be my Love.

21 The shepherds' **swains** shall dance and sing
22 For thy delight each May morning.
23 If these delights thy mind may move,
24 Then live with me and be my Love.

THINK QUESTIONS   CA-CCSS: CA.RL.11-12.1, CA.L.11-12.4a

1. What does the shepherd promise to give his love? What do these promises tell you about the speaker? Support your response with textual evidence.

2. What is the speaker's goal in this poem? Do his promises seem realistic? Why or why not? Support your answer with textual evidence.

3. What words or phrases are repeated in the poem? What effect does this repetition have?

4. Use context to determine the meaning of the word **madrigals** as it is used in "The Passionate Shepherd to His Love." Write your definition of "madrigals" here and tell how you found it.

5. Use context to determine the meaning of the word **myrtle** as it is used in "The Passionate Shepherd to His Love." Write your definition of "myrtle" here and explain how you found it.

Please note that excerpts and passages in the StudySync® library and this workbook are intended as touchstones to generate interest in an author's work. The excerpts and passages do not substitute for the reading of entire texts, and StudySync® strongly recommends that students seek out and purchase the whole literary or informational work in order to experience it as the author intended. Links to online resellers are available in our digital library. In addition, complete works may be ordered through an authorized reseller by filling out and returning to StudySync® the order form enclosed in this workbook.

Reading & Writing Companion   **41**

CLOSE READ
CA-CCSS: CA.RL.11-12.1, CA.RL.11-12.2, CA.RL.11-12.4, CA.W.11-12.4, CA.W.11-12.5, CA.W.11-12.6, CA.W.11-12.9a, CA.W.11-12.10, CA.L.11-12.5a

Reread the poem "The Passionate Shepherd to His Love." As you reread, complete the Focus Questions below. Then use your answers and annotations from the questions to help you complete the Writing Prompt.

FOCUS QUESTIONS

1. What types of figurative language do the first two stanzas contain? What is the effect of this language on the opening of the poem? Highlight evidence in the text and use the annotation tool to explain the language's effect.

2. In what way is the imagery in stanzas 3–5 different from the imagery in the rest of the poem? What effect does this change have? Highlight evidence and write annotations to support your ideas.

3. What message does the alliteration in the final lines of the fifth and sixth stanzas convey to the reader? Highlight your evidence and annotate to explain your ideas.

4. What symbolic meaning might the poem's repeated references to flowers, shepherds, and the month of May represent? Highlight your evidence and make annotations to explain your ideas.

5. Use your understanding of figurative language to identify the central message, or theme, of the poem. Highlight evidence from the text that will help support your ideas.

6. Recall the unit's Essential Question: How do we express the complexities of being human? Does the speaker of "The Passionate Shepherd to His Love" express the complexities of being human? If so, how? If not, what purpose might that serve? Support your response with textual evidence.

WRITING PROMPT

How does the speaker of "The Passionate Shepherd to His Love" use figurative language and hyperbole to attempt to convince his beloved to run away with him? What message does the speaker send about love and his beloved? Support your writing with textual evidence.

THE NYMPH'S REPLY TO THE SHEPHERD

POETRY
Sir Walter Raleigh
1596

INTRODUCTION

Sir Walter Raleigh was an English poet, writer, soldier, politician and explorer—perhaps the best example of a Renaissance man to emerge from the Elizabethan Age. He was described as "the most romantic figure of the most romantic age in the annals of English history" by biographer Hugh de Selincourt. Raleigh's poem "The Nymph's Reply to the Shepherd" was a response to Christopher Marlowe's pastoral "The Passionate Shepherd to His Love."

"All these in me no means can move..."

NOTES

FIRST READ

1   If all the world and love were young,
2   And truth in every shepherd's tongue,
3   These pretty pleasures might me move
4   To live with thee and be thy Love.

5   But Time drives flocks from field to fold;
6   When rivers rage and rocks grow cold;
7   And **Philomel** becometh dumb;
8   The rest complains of cares to come.

9   The flowers do fade, and **wanton** fields
10   To wayward Winter reckoning yields;
11   A honey tongue, a heart of **gall,**
12   In fancy's spring, but sorrow's fall.

13   Thy gowns, thy shoes, thy beds of roses,
14   Thy cap, thy kirtle, and thy posies,
15   Soon break, soon **wither**—soon forgotten,
16   In folly ripe, in reason rotten.

17   Thy belt of straw and ivy-buds,
18   Thy coral clasps and amber studs,—
19   All these in me no means can move
20   To come to thee and be thy Love.

21   But could youth last, and love still breed,
22   Had joys no date, nor age no need,
23   Then these delights my mind might move
24   To live with thee, and be thy Love.

THINK QUESTIONS   CA-CCSS: CA.RL.11-12.1, CA.L.11-12.4a

1. What hypothetical situation ("if-then") does the speaker set up in the first stanza and build throughout the poem? Support your answer with textual evidence.

2. Identify two or three ways the speaker badmouths the offerings from "The Passionate Shepherd to His Love." Support your answer with textual evidence.

3. How does the poem end? Does the speaker give a definite answer to the shepherd's advances? Support your answer with evidence from the poem.

4. Use context to determine the meaning of the word **gall** as it is used in "The Nymph's Reply to the Shepherd." Write your definition of "gall" here and tell how you found it.

5. Use context to determine the meaning of the word **wither** as it is used in "The Nymph's Reply to the Shepherd." Write your definition of "wither" here and tell how you got it.

CLOSE READ
CA-CCSS: CA.RL.11-12.1, CA.RL.11-12.2, CA.RL.11-12.4, CA.RL.11-12.7, CA.W.11-12.4, CA.W.11-12.5, CA.W.11-12.6, CA.W.11-12.9a, CA.W.11-12.10

Reread the poem "The Nymph's Reply to the Shepherd." As you reread, complete the Focus Questions below. Then use your answers and annotations from the questions to help you complete the Writing Prompt.

FOCUS QUESTIONS

1. The speaker—the nymph—begins and ends the poem with a conditional "If." What could the shepherd do or change to get the nymph to come live with him? What can you infer about the nymph based on her request? Highlight evidence in the text and use the annotation tool to explain your answer.

2. The lines "In fancy's spring, but sorrow's fall" and "In folly ripe, in reason rotten" sound almost like idioms or common sayings. Why might the nymph use language that sounds like an idiom? Why is the placement of these lines important? Highlight evidence to support your ideas.

3. Look back at "The Passionate Shepherd to His Love." How is the imagery in Marlowe's poem different from the imagery in Raleigh's reply? Highlight your evidence and make annotations to explain your choices.

4. Look back at "The Passionate Shepherd to His Love." Compare stanzas 3–5 from that poem with stanzas 3–5 of "The Nymph's Reply to the Shepherd." What is the tone of each section of the poem? What key point does each make? Highlight your evidence and annotate to explain your ideas.

5. What is the theme, or central message, of "The Nymph's Reply to the Shepherd"? Highlight evidence from the poem that will help support your ideas.

6. Recall the unit's Essential Question: How do we express the complexities of being human? Who more accurately expresses the complexities of being human, the nymph in Raleigh's poem or the shepherd in "The Passionate Shepherd to His Love"? Highlight textual evidence to support your response.

WRITING PROMPT

Analyze how Christopher Marlowe and Sir Walter Raleigh created different interpretations of the same story in each of their poems. How does Raleigh's poem challenge the meaning and tone of Marlowe's poem? Evaluate which poem is a more effective interpretation. Support your writing with textual evidence from both poems.

Reading & Writing Companion

UTOPIA

FICTION
Sir Thomas More
1516

INTRODUCTION

Originally published in Latin, *Utopia* is a work of political philosophy by Thomas More, a sixteenth-century English politician and lawyer greatly influenced by the ideas of Renaissance humanism. The book describes a fictional island society called Utopia, where all customs and policies are based on humanistic and rational thought. While the residents of Utopia enjoy communal property, lack of class distinctions and poverty, religious tolerance, and strict control over crime and immoral behavior, the narrative also presents the absurdities in such a near-perfect society. Most scholars view More's depiction of Utopia as a

"...those that relapse after they are once pardoned are punished with death."

FIRST READ

Excerpt from: Of Their Slaves, and of Their Marriages

1   Their women are not married before eighteen nor their men before two-and-twenty, and if any of them run into forbidden embraces before marriage they are severely punished, and the privilege of marriage is denied them unless they can obtain a special warrant from the Prince. Such disorders cast a great reproach upon the master and mistress of the family in which they happen, for it is supposed that they have failed in their duty. The reason of punishing this so severely is, because they think that if they were not strictly restrained from all vagrant appetites, very few would engage in a state in which they venture the quiet of their whole lives, by being confined to one person, and are obliged to endure all the inconveniences with which it is accompanied. In choosing their wives they use a method that would appear to us very absurd and ridiculous, but it is constantly observed among them, and is accounted perfectly consistent with wisdom. Before marriage some grave matron presents the bride, naked, whether she is a virgin or a widow, to the bridegroom, and after that some grave man presents the bridegroom, naked, to the bride. We, indeed, both laughed at this, and condemned it as very indecent. But they, on the other hand, wondered at the folly of the men of all other nations, who, if they are but to buy a horse of a small value, are so cautious that they will see every part of him, and take off both his saddle and all his other tackle, that there may be no secret ulcer hid under any of them, and that yet in the choice of a wife, on which depends the happiness or unhappiness of the rest of his life, a man should venture upon trust, and only see about a handsbreadth of the face, all the rest of the body being covered, under which may lie hid what may be contagious as well as loathsome. All men are not so wise as to choose a woman only for her good qualities, and even wise men consider the body as that which adds not a little to the mind, and it is certain there may be some such deformity covered with clothes as may totally **alienate** a man from his wife, when it is too late to part with her; if such a thing is discovered after marriage a man has no remedy but patience;

they, therefore, think it is reasonable that there should be good provision made against such mischievous frauds.

2   There was so much the more reason for them to make a regulation in this matter, because they are the only people of those parts that neither allow of **polygamy** nor of divorces, except in the case of adultery or insufferable **perverseness,** for in these cases the Senate dissolves the marriage and grants the injured person leave to marry again; but the guilty are made infamous and are never allowed the privilege of a second marriage. None are suffered to put away their wives against their wills, from any great **calamity** that may have fallen on their persons, for they look on it as the height of cruelty and treachery to abandon either of the married persons when they need most the tender care of their consort, and that chiefly in the case of old age, which, as it carries many diseases along with it, so it is a disease of itself. But it frequently falls out that when a married couple do not well agree, they, by mutual consent, separate, and find out other persons with whom they hope they may live more happily; yet this is not done without obtaining leave of the Senate, which never admits of a divorce but upon a strict **inquiry** made, both by the senators and their wives, into the grounds upon which it is desired, and even when they are satisfied concerning the reasons of it they go on but slowly, for they imagine that too great easiness in granting leave for new marriages would very much shake the kindness of married people. They punish severely those that defile the marriage bed; if both parties are married they are divorced, and the injured persons may marry one another, or whom they please, but the adulterer and the adulteress are condemned to slavery, yet if either of the injured persons cannot shake off the love of the married person they may live with them still in that state, but they must follow them to that labour to which the slaves are condemned, and sometimes the repentance of the condemned, together with the unshaken kindness of the innocent and injured person, has prevailed so far with the Prince that he has taken off the sentence; but those that relapse after they are once pardoned are punished with death.

THINK QUESTIONS CA-CCSS: CA.RL.11-12.1, CA.L.11-12.4b, CA.L.11-12.4c

1. More's *Utopia* describes the social rules of a perfect society. What is the purpose of this excerpt from *Utopia*? Support your answer with evidence from the text.

2. To what does the writer compare the process of examining the bodies of the bride and bridegroom before marriage? What does this comparison reveal about the author and the society? Support your answer with evidence from the text.

3. When a married couple in Utopia wishes to divorce, by mutual consent, who makes an inquiry into the matter? What does this tell you about the author's view of the role of women in society? Support your answer with evidence from the text.

4. Remembering that the suffix -*y* can refer to the instance of an action, use context to determine the meaning of the word **inquiry** as used in *Utopia*. Write your definition of *inquiry* here and tell how you found it.

5. Remembering that the Middle English prefix *poly-* means "many," and the Greek verb *gamos* means "marriage," consult a dictionary to determine the meaning of the word **polygamy.**

CLOSE READ

CA-CCSS: CA.RL.11-12.1, CA.RL.11-12.6, CA.W.11-12.3a, CA.W.11-12.4, CA.W.11-12.5, CA.W.11-12.6, CA.W.11-12.9a, CA.W.11-12.10

Reread the excerpt from the text *Utopia*. As you reread, complete the Focus Questions below. Then use your answers and annotations from the questions to help you complete the Writing Prompt.

 FOCUS QUESTIONS

1. What topics related to marriage are discussed in the excerpt from *Utopia*? Highlight evidence to support each topic you identify and use the annotation tool to explain your choices.

2. Verbal irony is when a person says one thing and means another. There is verbal irony in the rules of Utopia involving marriage. The rules are very strict, yet many of the rules have exceptions. Highlight one strict rule that has an exception in the passage. Explain both the rule and the exception using the annotation tool.

3. In the Unit 2 introduction "The English Renaissance" you read about humanism, an intellectual movement that emphasized the ability of individuals to think and act independently, without guidance from higher authorities. Which actions of the leaders of Utopia in this excerpt might have been frowned on by European religious authorities of the time?

4. What goals might the leaders of Utopia have in mind with these rules involving marriage? What sort of society might they be trying to create? Highlight evidence that supports your answers.

5. Recall the unit's Essential Question: How do we express the complexities of being human? What do the strict rules regarding marriage suggest about the complexities of human relationships? Highlight textual evidence to support your answer.

WRITING PROMPT

The word *inquiry* refers to the process of gathering information by asking questions. Write a narrative in which the Senate in Utopia conducts an inquiry into a divorce for two spouses who are not able to get along. Include questions from both the senators and their wives, as well as answers from the people seeking the divorce. Use the excerpt from *Utopia* to inform your understanding of the country's laws about marriage and divorce. Include an example of verbal irony and an example of situational irony in your narrative.

BRAVE NEW WORLD

FICTION
Aldous Huxley
1932

INTRODUCTION

English author and philosopher Aldous Huxley is considered one of the premier intellectuals of his time, and was nominated seven times for the Nobel Prize in Literature. His dystopian page-turner *Brave New World* is more than literature—it's a warning about what the future might hold. In this excerpt, the Director of Hatcheries and Conditioning proudly explains Bokanovsky's Process, which creates up to 96 clones from a single egg.

"The principle of mass production at last applied to biology."

 FIRST READ

Excerpt from Chapter 1

1   A squat grey building of only thirty-four stories. Over the main entrance the words, Central London Hatchery and Conditioning Centre, and, in a shield, the World State's motto, Community, Identity, Stability.

2   The enormous room on the ground floor faced towards the north. Cold for all the summer beyond the panes, for all the tropical heat of the room itself, a harsh thin light glared through the windows, hungrily seeking some draped lay figure, some **pallid** shape of academic goose-flesh, but finding only the glass and nickel and bleakly shining porcelain of a laboratory. Wintriness responded to wintriness. The overalls of the workers were white, their hands gloved with a pale corpse-coloured rubber. The light was frozen, dead, a ghost. Only from the yellow barrels of the microscopes did it borrow a certain rich and living substance, lying along the polished tubes like butter, streak after luscious streak in long recession down the work tables.

3   "And this," said the Director opening the door, "is the Fertilizing Room."

4   Bent over their instruments, three hundred Fertilizers were plunged, as the Director of Hatcheries and Conditioning entered the room, in the scarcely breathing silence, the absentminded, **soliloquizing** hum or whistle, of absorbed concentration. A troop of newly arrived students, very young, pink and **callow,** followed nervously, rather abjectly, at the Director's heels. Each of them carried a note-book, in which, whenever the great man spoke, he desperately scribbled. Straight from the horse's mouth. It was a rare privilege. The DHC for Central London always made a point of personally conducting his new students round the various departments.

5   "Just to give you a general idea," he would explain to them. For of course some sort of general idea they must have, if they were to do their work

intelligently—though as little of one, if they were to be good and happy members of society, as possible. For particulars, as everyone knows, make for virtue and happiness; generalities are intellectually necessary evils. Not philosophers, but fret-sawyers and stamp collectors compose the backbone of society.

6 "Tomorrow," he would add, smiling at them with a slightly menacing geniality, "you'll be settling down to serious work. You won't have time for generalities. Meanwhile . . ."

7 Meanwhile, it was a privilege. Straight from the horse's mouth into the note-book. The boys scribbled like mad.

8 Tall and rather thin but upright, the Director advanced into the room. He had a long chin and big, rather prominent teeth, just covered, when he was not talking, by his full, floridly curved lips. Old, young? Thirty? fifty? fifty-five? It was hard to say. And anyhow the question didn't arise; in this year of stability, a.f. 632, it didn't occur to you to ask it.

9 "I shall begin at the beginning," said the DHC, and the more zealous students recorded his intention in their note-books: Begin at the beginning. "These," he waved his hand, "are the incubators." And opening an insulated door he showed them racks upon racks of numbered test-tubes. "The week's supply of ova. Kept," he explained, "at blood heat; whereas the male gametes," and here he opened another door, "they have to be kept at thirty-five instead of thirty-seven. Full blood heat sterilizes." Rams wrapped in thermogene beget no lambs.

10 Still leaning against the incubators he gave them, while the pencils scurried illegibly across the pages, a brief description of the modern fertilizing process; spoke first, of course, of its surgical introduction — "the operation undergone voluntarily for the good of Society, not to mention the fact that it carries a bonus amounting to six months' salary"; continued with some account of the technique for preserving the excised ovary alive and actively developing; passed on to a consideration of optimum temperature, salinity, viscosity; referred to the liquor in which the detached and ripened eggs were kept; and, leading his charges to the work tables, actually showed them how the liquor was drawn off from the test-tubes; how it was let out drop by drop on to the specially warmed slides of the microscopes; how the eggs which it contained were inspected for abnormalities, counted and transferred to a porous receptacle; how (and he now took them to watch the operation) this receptacle was immersed in a warm bouillon containing free-swimming spermatozoa—at a minimum concentration of one hundred thousand per cubic centimetre, he insisted; and how, after ten minutes, the container was lifted out of the liquor and its contents re-examined; how, if any of the eggs remained unfertilized, it was again immersed, and, if necessary, yet again;

how the fertilized ova went back to the incubators; where the Alphas and Betas remained until definitely bottled; while the Gammas, Deltas and Epsilons were brought out again, after only thirty-six hours, to under-go Bokanovsky's Process.

11   "Bokanovsky's Process," repeated the Director, and the students underlined the words in their little note-books.

12   One egg, one embryo, one adult—normality. But a bokanovskified egg will bud, will **proliferate,** will divide. From eight to ninety-six buds, and every bud will grow into a perfectly formed embryo, and every embryo into a full-sized adult. Making ninety-six human beings grow where only one grew before. Progress.

13   "Essentially," the DHC concluded, "bokanovskification consists of a series of arrests of development. We check the normal growth and, paradoxically enough, the egg responds by budding."

14   Responds by budding. The pencils were busy.

15   He pointed. On a very slowly moving band a rack-full of test-tubes was entering a large metal box, another rack-full was emerging. Machinery faintly purred. It took eight minutes for the tubes to go through, he told them. Eight minutes of hard X-rays being about as much as an egg can stand. A few died; of the rest, the least susceptible divided into two; most put out four buds; some eight; all were returned to the incubators, where the buds began to develop; then, after two days, were suddenly chilled, chilled and checked. Two, four, eight, the buds in their turn budded; and having budded were dosed almost to death with alcohol; consequently burgeoned again and having budded—bud out of bud out of bud were thereafter—further arrest being generally fatal—left to develop in peace. By which time the original egg was in a fair way to becoming anything from eight to ninety-six embryos—a **prodigious** improvement, you will agree, on nature. Identical twins—but not in piddling twos and threes as in the old viviparous days, when an egg would sometimes accidentally divide; actually by dozens, by scores at a time.

16   "Scores," the Director repeated and flung out his arms, as though he were distributing **largesse**. "Scores."

17   But one of the students was fool enough to ask where the advantage lay.

18   "My good boy!" The Director wheeled sharply round on him. "Can't you see? Can't you see?" He raised a hand; his expression was solemn. "Bokanovsky's Process is one of the major instruments of social stability!"

19   Major instruments of social stability.

20 Standard men and women; in uniform batches. The whole of a small factory staffed with the products of a single bokanovskified egg.

21 "Ninety-six identical twins working ninety-six identical machines!" The voice was almost tremulous with enthusiasm.

22 "You really know where you are. For the first time in history." He quoted the planetary motto. "Community, Identity, Stability." Grand words. "If we could bokanovskify indefinitely the whole problem would be solved."

23 Solved by standard Gammas, unvarying Deltas, uniform Epsilons. Millions of identical twins. The principle of mass production at last applied to biology.

Excerpted from Brave New World by Aldous Huxley, published by HarperCollins Publishers.

THINK QUESTIONS CA-CCSS: CA.RL.11-12.1, CA.L.11-12.4a

1. Describe the setting of the first chapter of *Brave New World*. Remember that setting includes details such as the time period, not just the physical locations. Support your response with textual evidence.

2. What happens in the Fertilizing Room shown on the tour? What does this room tell you about the world in which *Brave New World* is set? Cite textual evidence to support your answer.

3. What is Bokanovsky's Process? Why does the Hatchery and Conditioning Centre use this process? How is the process related to the World State's motto? Support your response with textual evidence.

4. The Latin root *sol* means "alone." Use that information and the context clues provided in the passage to determine the meaning of **soliloquizing.** Write your definition of "soliloquizing" here and explain how you found it.

5. Use the context clues provided in the passage to determine the meaning of **proliferate**. Write your definition of "proliferate" here and explain how you arrived at it.

CLOSE READ

CA-CCSS: CA.RL.11-12.1, CA.RL.11-12.3, CA.RL.11-12.6, CA.W.11-12.4, CA.W.11-12.5, CA.W.11-12.6, CA.W.11-12.9a, CA.W.11-12.10

Reread the excerpt from *Brave New World*. As you reread, complete the Focus Questions below. Then use your answers and annotations from the questions to help you complete the Writing Prompt.

 ## FOCUS QUESTIONS

1. As you reread the first chapter of *Brave New World*, pay attention to the characterization, or the descriptions, of the workers in the Central London Hatchery and Conditioning Centre and the characterization of the new students touring the facility. How is each group described? How are the descriptions different, and what might that difference imply? Highlight evidence in the text and use the annotation tool to explain the meaning of these differences.

2. In paragraph 5, the author explains the difference between knowing "particulars" and knowing "generalities." What difference does the author set up? What does this distinction say about the World State's priorities? Highlight evidence and write annotations to explain your ideas.

3. *Irony* is when an author writes one thing but means another. What is the World State's motto? Based on the description of the work at the Central London Hatchery and Conditioning Centre, how is this motto ironic? What other examples of irony does this excerpt contain? Highlight your evidence and annotate to explain your ideas.

4. Much of the excerpt is a detailed explanation of how human eggs are fertilized and of Bokanovsky's Process. What is the role of the technical language and long descriptions of this process? What does it tell the reader about the World State? Highlight your evidence and make annotations to explain your ideas.

5. Chapter 1 contains several references to animals. What purpose do these elements serve? How do they support the development of story elements? Highlight evidence from the text that will help support your ideas.

6. The Essential Question for this unit is "How do we express the complexities of being human?" How does the society in *Brave New World* view complexity in people? What is ironic, in light of this view, about the students' treatment of the Director? Highlight textual evidence from the selection to support your ideas.

WRITING PROMPT

Analyze how Huxley's choices regarding setting and characterization affect the reader's experience with *Brave New World*. How are characters introduced and described? How does Huxley use description to relate the setting to the characters? How do these story elements contribute to the overall message, or theme, of the selection? Explain any use of irony in Huxley's development of theme. Support your writing with textual evidence.

Please note that excerpts and passages in the StudySync® library and this workbook are intended as touchstones to generate interest in an author's work. The excerpts and passages do not substitute for the reading of entire texts, and StudySync® strongly recommends that students seek out and purchase the whole literary or informational work in order to experience it as the author intended. Links to online resellers are available in our digital library. In addition, complete works may be ordered through an authorized reseller by filling out and returning to StudySync® the order form enclosed in this workbook.

Reading & Writing Companion

57

A VALEDICTION FORBIDDING MOURNING

POETRY
John Donne
1633

INTRODUCTION

Born in 1572, English clergyman John Donne is considered to be the leader of the metaphysical school of poetry, which is known in part for its use of complex and unusual metaphors to meld the sensory and the abstract. Donne's poem "A Valediction Forbidding Mourning" relies on one ingenious simile—that of the drafting compass—to beautifully evoke the sense of two people separated physically but deeply connected emotionally.

"Care less, eyes, lips, and hands to miss."

FIRST READ

1   As virtuous men pass mildly away,
2   And whisper to their souls to go,
3   Whilst some of their sad friends do say
4   The breath goes now, and some say, no;

5   So let us melt, and make no noise,
6   No tear floods, nor sigh-**tempests** move,
7   'Twere **profanation** of our joys
8   To tell the **laity** our love.

9   Moving of th' earth brings harms and fears,
10   Men reckon what it did and meant;
11   But trepidation of the spheres,
12   Though greater far, is innocent.

13   Dull sublunary lovers' love
14   (Whose soul is sense) cannot admit
15   Absence, because it doth remove
16   Those things which elemented it.

17   But we by a love so much refined
18   That our selves know not what it is,
19   Inter-assured of the mind,
20   Care less, eyes, lips, and hands to miss.

21   Our two souls therefore, which are one,
22   Though I must go, endure not yet
23   A **breach,** but an expansion,
24   Like gold to airy thinness beat.

Please note that excerpts and passages in the StudySync® library and this workbook are intended as touchstones to generate interest in an author's work. The excerpts and passages do not substitute for the reading of entire texts, and StudySync® strongly recommends that students seek out and purchase the whole literary or informational work in order to experience it as the author intended. Links to online resellers are available in our digital library. In addition, complete works may be ordered through an authorized reseller by filling out and returning to StudySync® the order form enclosed in this workbook.

Reading & Writing Companion   **59**

25 If they be two, they are two so
26 As stiff twin compasses are two;
27 Thy soul, the fixed foot, makes no show
28 To move, but doth, if th' other do.

29 And though it in the center sit,
30 Yet when the other far doth roam,
31 It leans and hearkens after it,
32 And grows erect, as that comes home.

33 Such wilt thou be to me, who must
34 Like th' other foot, **obliquely** run.
35 Thy firmness makes my circle just,
36 And makes me end where I begun.

THINK QUESTIONS CA-CCSS: CA.RL.11-12.1, CA.L.11-12.4a, CA.L.11-12.4b

1. "A Valediction Forbidding Mourning" consists of a series of comparisons. What is the first comparison that appears in lines 1–8? Support your answer with textual evidence.

2. The second comparison in lines 9–16 equates earthquakes with "sublunary lovers" and planetary movements with the speaker's relationship. How is this connected with physical love and spiritual love?

3. Why might the speaker be concerned about the future of the relationship with the beloved? Support your answer with textual evidence.

4. Use context to determine the meaning of the word **breach** as it is used in "A Valediction Forbidding Mourning." Write your definition of breach here and tell how you got it.

5. Remembering that the Middle English suffix *-ly* is used to create adverbs, look for context clues provided in "A Valediction Forbidding Mourning" to determine the meaning of **obliquely**. Write your definition of *obliquely* here and explain how you found it.

CLOSE READ

CA-CCSS: CA.RL.11-12.1, CA.RL.11-12.2, CA.RL.11-12.4, CA.RL.11-12.5, CA.W.11-12.4, CA.W.11-12.5, CA.W.11-12.6, CA.W.11-12.9a, CA.W.11-12.10

Reread the poem "A Valediction Forbidding Mourning." As you reread, complete the Focus Questions below. Then use your answers and annotations from the questions to help you complete the Writing Prompt.

FOCUS QUESTIONS

1. As you reread the text of "A Valediction Forbidding Mourning," think about the ways in which the poem is structured as an argument. The speaker is trying to convince the speaker's beloved that they can continue to feel close to each other even when they are far apart. Summarize the sections of the argument, and explain how the sections are related.

2. Two themes in the poem are separation and spirituality. Which theme do you think is more prominent? Highlight textual evidence to support your answer and use the annotation tool to record your ideas.

3. Although Donne's poem is highly structured and formal in tone, he is still able to instill powerful feelings and musical language in these lines of verse. How can a poem with a formal structure avoid being emotionless and dull? Cite textual evidence to support your statements.

4. How does Donne's word choice contribute to the formal tone of the poem? Use the annotation tool to highlight evidence from the text, taking into account other words he might have chosen.

5. One of the themes in "A Valediction Forbidding Mourning" is the pain of one person going away from another person. How does Donne use this theme to explore the complexities of being human? Cite textual evidence to support your statements.

WRITING PROMPT

How would the impact of "A Valediction Forbidding Mourning" be affected if Donne rewrote it with an open form? Which aspects of the original poem would be difficult to retain, and which would be easy to retain? Use your understanding of poetic structure and figurative language to support your analysis. Support your response with textual evidence.

TO LUCASTA, GOING TO THE WARS

POETRY
Richard Lovelace
1649

INTRODUCTION

Born into a distinguished military and legal family, the cavalier poet Richard Lovelace embroiled himself in the political affairs of 17th century England and was twice thrown in prison. While incarcerated, Lovelace wrote his most acclaimed poetry, including "To Lucasta, Going to the Wars." Some scholars believe that the "Lucasta" of the poem refers to Lucy Sacherevell, who after wrongly hearing that Lovelace had died of wounds in battle, married another man.

"To war and arms I fly."

FIRST READ

NOTES

1　Tell me not, Sweet, I am unkind,
2　　That from the **nunnery**
3　Of thy **chaste** breast and quiet mind
4　　To war and arms I fly.

5　True, a new **mistress** now I chase,
6　　The first **foe** in the field;
7　And with a stronger faith embrace
8　　A sword, a horse, a shield.

9　Yet this **inconstancy** is such
10　　As you too shall adore;
11　I could not love thee, Dear, so much,
12　　Loved I not Honor more.

THINK QUESTIONS CA-CCSS: CA.RL.11-12.1, CA.L.11-12.4a, CA.L.11-12.4d

1. In "To Lucasta, Going to the Wars," where is the speaker starting from, and where is he going? Support your answer with evidence from the text.

2. What does the speaker mean by the phrase in Stanza 1, "That from the nunnery / of thy chaste breast and quiet mind"?

3. What does the speaker hope to accomplish in the poem? Use textual evidence to support your response.

4. Use context to determine the meaning of the word **chaste** as it is used in the first stanza of "To Lucasta, Going to the Wars." Write your definition of *chaste* here and explain how you arrived at this definition.

5. Use the context to identify the meaning of **mistress** as it is used in Stanza 2 of "To Lucasta, Going to the Wars." Then use a dictionary to check your definition and explain how you arrived at this definition.

CLOSE READ
CA-CCSS: CA.RL.11-12.1, CA.RL.11-12.4, CA.W.11-12.3a, CA.W.11-12.3d, CA.W.11-12.4, CA.W.11-12.5, CA.W.11-12.6, CA.W.11-12.9a, CA.W.11-12.10, CA.L.11-12.4d, CA.L.11-12.5a

Reread the poem "To Lucasta, Going to the Wars." As you reread, complete the Focus Questions below. Then use your answers and annotations from the questions to help you complete the Writing Prompt.

FOCUS QUESTIONS

1. Remember that in any poem, the poet uses language economically to pack as much meaning as he into his words. This is especially true of a short poem, like "To Lucasta, Going to the Wars," where every word counts. As you look back at the text, identify words that are particularly vivid or meaningful. Highlight any unfamiliar words and look them up in the dictionary. Use the annotation tool to note the effect of your selected words.

2. Write a short summary of what is happening in Stanza 1. Identify the connotation evoked by words like "sweet," "chaste," and "quiet." How do these words influence the theme and tone of the stanza? Use the annotation tool to record your response.

3. How does the poet use the words "Sweet" and "Dear" in the poem? What are the dictionary definitions—denotations—of these words, and how do those definitions compare to their connotative meanings? What prior knowledge do you have that allows you to understand the emotional context of these terms?

4. Recall that paradox is a figure of speech in which a statement appears to contradict itself yet expresses a truth. Use the highlighter tool to identify the paradox in lines 11–12. How do denotation and connotation work to create the paradox?

5. Use your understanding of connotation, denotation, and figurative language, such as paradox, to identify the theme and deeper meaning of the poem. Highlight evidence from the poem that will help support your ideas and use the annotation tool to record your response.

6. Recall the unit's Essential Question: How do we express the complexities of being human? How does the speaker of "To Lucasta, Going to the Wars" express the complexity of having to choose between love and duty? Highlight evidence from the poem that supports your ideas.

WRITING PROMPT

Using the events and emotions of the poem as a guide, write a letter from the speaker of "To Lucasta, Going to the Wars" to Lucasta. Assume that the speaker has now left for the war and is writing about his experiences. Compare the realities of battle to the speaker's expectations of what "war and arms" would be like. Remember to clearly describe the setting and the speaker's emotions using vivid language with precise connotations. Conclude the letter with the speaker's hopes about the future of their relationship.

EMILIA'S LAMENT

English Language Development

FICTION

INTRODUCTION

This work of historical fiction is set in medieval Spain. It tells the story of a young woman named Emilia who looks out at the Mediterranean Sea and confesses her anxieties about her upcoming arranged marriage. Emilia reveals that her older sister's arranged marriage turned out differently than planned, and hopes she can avoid the same outcome.

"...today she wanted the still waters to turn into angry waves to mirror the turbulence she felt within her heart."

NOTES

FIRST READ

1   Emilia gazed out her window at the sapphire waters of the Mediterranean Sea. On most days, looking out onto the sea and thinking about the world beyond their waves made her feel **exhilarated,** but today she wanted the still waters to turn into angry waves to mirror the **turbulence** she felt within her heart. Tomorrow she would be wed. She knew she was supposed to feel happy and grateful. She remembered the joy her older sister felt the day before she was married in 1427, just a few years ago. On the other hand, she also knew the despair Maria had felt since her wedding day. She ranted at the sea.

2   "I do not understand why I have to do this. Didn't Mama and Papa learn anything from the mistake they made with Maria? Don't they see how unhappy she is? Maria and I stood together at this same window, staring out at the sea and dreaming about her future. We had not yet met Alfonzo, Maria's **betrothed,** but Papa and Mama told us he was a wealthy merchant from a respected family. They heard he was very handsome, generous, and kind to his mother. They swore he would be a perfect match for Maria.

3   "I feel so foolish to think about how **giddy** we felt imagining what Maria's life would be like once she was married. She would be the lady of her own household, free to do as she pleased. That is to say, she would finally have the chance to do what we both desired more than anything else. She would finally be able to see what lay beyond the vast Mediterranean Sea as she traveled the world at her new husband's side. But, in reality, after Maria became Alfonzo's wife, her world became smaller. Yes, Alfonzo travels all the time, but he never takes Maria with him. Instead, he leaves her to care for his mother. Maria has to do everything according to the old woman's rules. It was not the life our parents had been promised for their daughter, but it was too late."

Copyright © BookheadEd Learning, LLC

4   After the family had learned the truth about Alfonzo, Emilia begged her father to let her choose a husband for herself, but he rejected her plea. "That is not how the world works," he explained. "Although your happiness means everything to me, I have no sons to carry on our family name. It is the responsibility of my daughters to make connections with the right people so that our family tree can continue to blossom and thrive."

5   Emilia did not think her sister was thriving. On the contrary, Maria was wilting in front of their eyes. Every time Emilia saw her sister, she seemed smaller and quieter. When her father announced that Emilia, too, would marry a man she had never met, her heart shrank with fear that her life would turn out like Maria's had.

6   Meanwhile, Emilia's wedding day was almost here, and there was nothing she could do to change her future. Emilia **mused** to the sea air. "Mama and Papa have promised that Diego is different than Alfonzo. For instance, Diego makes his swords nearby. He must stay in town to run his shop, so he will not sail away and leave me alone. But how am I to know that he will not invent another reason to abandon me with our children? They say that he is kind. As an illustration, they recall tales told by his apprentices about his patience and generosity, but that does not prove that he will be kind and patient with a woman. There is so much about this arrangement that I do not understand, yet there is nothing I can do to stop it. I must send my fears out into the sea and accept my fate as Diego's wife. I do not know if Diego will be a good husband, but he may be. I must remember that I am not Maria, and he is not Alfonzo."

7   At the end of this declaration, Emilia closed her eyes, bowed her head, and stepped away from the window. She needed to get some rest. Her new life would begin tomorrow.

USING LANGUAGE CA-CCSS: ELD.PII.11-12.2.b.Ex

Read each sentence pair and consider the type of transitional, or connecting, word or phrase it might need. Complete the second column with the correct type of connecting word or phrase and the third column with the connecting word or phrase that completes the sentence.

Type of Connecting Word or Phrase Options			Connecting Word or Phrase Options		
contrast	example	sequence	Then	As a result	For instance
effect	addition		In addition	However	

Sentence	Type of Connecting Word or Phrase	Connecting Word or Phrase
Emilia had to marry a man she had never met. _____, she was feeling nervous.		
Emilia usually liked looking out at the calm sea. _____, that day she wished for a storm.		
First, Emilia remembered how happy Maria felt before her wedding. _____, Emilia remembered how unhappy Maria is now.		
Maria's marriage to Alfonzo did not turn out as expected. _____, Maria is never allowed to travel with him.		
Emilia is comforted when she realizes that she and her sister are different people. _____, so are Diego and Alfonzo.		

MEANINGFUL INTERACTIONS CA-CCSS: ELD.PI.11-12.1.Ex, ELD.PI.11-12.6.a.Ex

Work with your partner or group to paraphrase key details from the text using the writing frames below. Then, use those paraphrases to discuss the internal and external conflicts and theme of the story. Use the self-assessment rubric to evaluate your participation in the activity.

- A sentence that shows Emilia's internal conflict is _____

  _____ .

  In other words, Emilia feels _____ because _____

  _____ .

- A sentence that shows a conflict Emilia has with someone else is _____

  _____ .

  In other words, Emilia and _____ are in conflict because _____

  _____ .

- A sentence that shows the theme of the story is _____

  _____ .

  In other words, the central message of the story is _____ because _____

  _____ .

- Another key detail that supports this theme is _____ .

 ## SELF-ASSESSMENT RUBRIC CA-CCSS: ELD.PI.11-12.1.Ex, ELD.PI.11-12.6.a.Ex

	4 I did this well.	3 I did this pretty well.	2 I did this a little bit.	1 I did not do this.
I took an active part with others in doing the activity.				
I paraphrased key ideas from the text accurately.				
I used details from the text to discuss an internal conflict.				
I used details from the text to discuss an external conflict.				
I used details from the text to discuss the theme.				

REREAD

Reread paragraphs 1–3 of "Emilia's Lament." After you reread, complete the Using Language and Meaningful Interactions activities.

USING LANGUAGE   CA-CCSS: ELD.PI.11-12.7.Ex

Read each quotation from the text and consider the order in which information is given. Then determine the effect each section of the speech has on the reader and write the correct answer in each row.

This shows readers . . . Options		
the high hopes the family had	how Emilia's feelings have changed	a sense of powerlessness
the value of a person's reputation	how their expectations were not met	

Quotation	This shows readers . . .
"We had not yet met Alfonzo, Maria's betrothed, but Papa and Mama told us he was a wealthy merchant from a respected family."	
"They heard he was very handsome, generous, and kind to his mother. They swore he would be a perfect match for Maria."	
"I feel so foolish to think about how giddy we felt imagining what Maria's life would be like once she was married."	
"She would finally be able to see what lay beyond the vast Mediterranean Sea as she traveled the world at her new husband's side. But, in reality, after Maria became Alfonzo's wife, her world became smaller."	
"It was not the life our parents had been promised for their daughter, but it was too late."	

Reading & Writing Companion

MEANINGFUL INTERACTIONS CA-CCSS: ELD.PI.11-12.1.Ex , ELD.PI.11-12.6.b.Ex

Based on what you have read in "Emilia's Lament," make inferences about the main character. What kind of person is she? What are her motivations? What are her fears? Work in a small group to practice sharing coherent and well-articulated comments and adding relevant information, using the speaking frames. Then, use the self-assessment rubric to evaluate your participation in the discussion.

- The text says, " . . . "
  As a result, I can infer that Emilia is . . . because . . .

- Textual evidence suggests that Emilia is motivated by . . . because . . .
  This suggests that she . . .

- Textual evidence suggests that Emilia is afraid of . . . because . . .
  This suggests that she . . .

- I agree with what you said about . . . , but I would add . . .

- More textual evidence that supports your inference includes . . .

SELF-ASSESSMENT RUBRIC CA-CCSS: ELD.PI.11-12.1.Ex, ELD.PI.11-12.6.b.Ex

	4 I did this well.	3 I did this pretty well.	2 I did this a little bit.	1 I did not do this.
I made inferences about the main character of the story.				
I used textual evidence to support inferences.				
I made coherent and well-articulated comments.				
I added relevant information.				

REREAD

Reread paragraphs 4–7 of "Emilia's Lament." After you reread, complete the Using Language and Meaningful Interactions activities.

⚙ **USING LANGUAGE** CA-CCSS: ELD.PI.11-12.7.Ex

Read each passage from the text in the first column, and note the boldfaced words and phrases. Then complete the chart by writing the emotion readers will feel after reading each passage in the second column and the reason readers are likely to feel that way in the third column.

Emotion Options	Because Options
anxious confident sad hopeful uncertain	the character thinks her situation might be different. the character is faced with a frightening situation. the character is compared to a dying plant. the character has come to terms with her situation. the character does not know what will happen.

Passages	Emotion	Because
On the contrary, Maria was **wilting in front of their eyes**. Every time Emilia saw her sister, she seemed smaller and quieter.		
When her father announced that Emilia, too, would marry a man she had never met, **her heart shrank with fear** that her life would turn out like Maria's had.		
"He must stay in town to run his shop, so he will not sail away and leave me alone. But **how am I to know** that he will not invent another reason to abandon me with our children?"		
"I do not know if Diego will be a good husband, but he may be. I must remember that **I am not Maria, and he is not Alfonzo**."		
At the end of this **declaration**, Emilia closed her eyes, bowed her head, and stepped away from the window. She needed to get some rest. Her **new life** would begin tomorrow.		

MEANINGFUL INTERACTIONS   CA-CCSS: ELD.PI.11-12.3.Ex, ELD.PI.11-12.6.a.Ex

What do you think Emilia should do? Is she trapped by destiny, or does she have a choice? Explain your thoughts and opinions using the speaking frames below.

- My opinion is that Emilia should . . .

- My opinion is based on . . .

- You made a good point about . . . , but what about . . . ?

- I agree / disagree with what you said about . . . because . . .

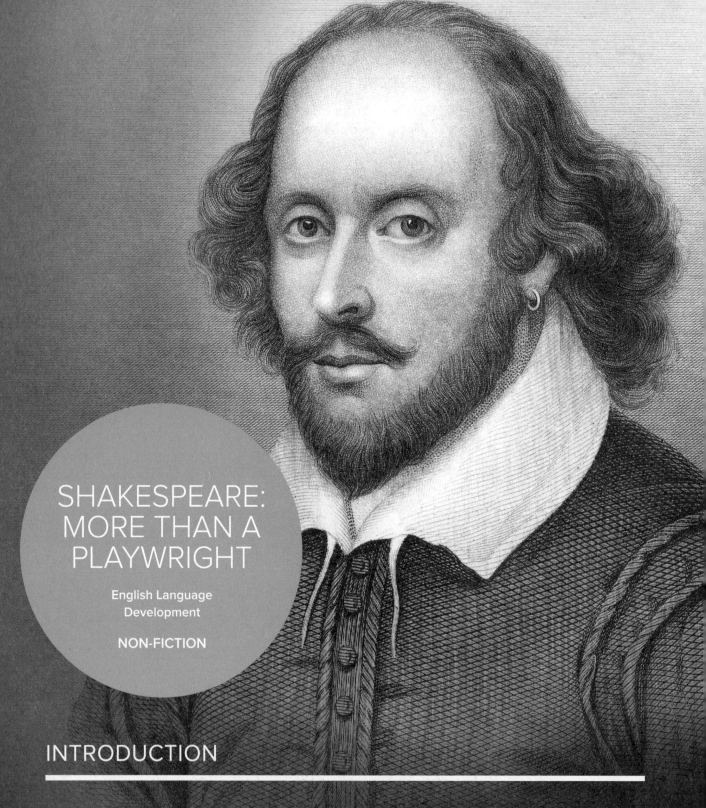

SHAKESPEARE: MORE THAN A PLAYWRIGHT

English Language
Development

NON-FICTION

INTRODUCTION

Before William Shakespeare wrote his famous plays, he was an actor in London. This article examines what scholars know about how Shakespeare went from being a young man in Stratford-upon-Avon to an essential member of a London acting company.

"Before writing the plays that would make him an icon, Shakespeare was an actor."

 FIRST READ

1   In *As You Like It,* William Shakespeare wrote, "All the world's a stage, and all the men and women merely players." Shakespeare would know. He had firsthand experience of being such a "player." Before writing the plays that would make him an **icon,** Shakespeare was an actor.

2   William Shakespeare is a frustrating man to study. He left behind no diary and no personal letters explaining how he went from a young man in the small town of Stratford-upon-Avon to being the world's most famous playwright.

3   Historians know that in 1582, when he was 18 years old, Shakespeare married a woman named Anne Hathaway. Historians call the period after the wedding "the lost years" because we have no written records of what Shakespeare was doing. Suddenly, in 1592, he is mentioned as an **"upstart"** actor and playwright in a pamphlet written by a critic and dramatist named Robert Greene.

4   Somehow between 1582 and 1592, Shakespeare left his family in Stratford and established himself in the London theater scene. It is unlikely that Shakespeare left home on his own. At the time, actors needed to work for official acting companies, which were supported by rich **patrons.** Luckily for Shakespeare, these acting companies spent time traveling around England performing in towns like Stratford. Some scholars propose that Shakespeare joined a company called the Queen's Men when they passed through Stratford in 1587. It just so happened that the leading actor of the Queen's Men had died in a fight right before the performance in Stratford. They would have needed someone to fill in. Did a young Shakespeare volunteer? We don't know for sure. If he did, Shakespeare would have accompanied them back to London.

NOTES

5   In London in the late sixteenth century, plays were not a new form of entertainment. However, the theater itself was a new concept. Before the 1570s, plays were performed in public spaces like parks or in private homes. Actors earned money asking for pennies after performances. That all changed when James Burbage built the Theatre in London in 1576. Like modern theaters, the Theatre was a dedicated building for showing plays. These playhouses could charge admission. This guaranteed an income for actors and playwrights.

6   In the 1590s, Shakespeare performed with the Lord Chamberlain's Men, first at the Theatre and later at the Globe Theater. We don't have any contemporary reviews that mention Shakespeare as a good or a bad actor. Theatergoers in the 1590s were not quiet, polite audiences like today. If they disliked an actor on the stage, they spent the entire performance **heckling** him. They even threw the apples and oranges sold in the theater at him. If Shakespeare were a poor actor, he would not have kept his job.

7   How did Shakespeare move from actor to playwright? Unlike contemporary Broadway theaters that show the same play every night, theaters in Elizabethan England were **repertories.** That means they performed a different show every night. On Friday audiences could see *Romeo & Juliet.* Saturday might be *Richard III* instead. Theaters needed to get audiences to return to the theater regularly and keep handing over their pennies. Because of this system, acting companies performed around 40 plays a year—20 new plays and 20 popular plays from previous years. To fill the Globe, Shakespeare stepped up and started writing.

8   From the beginning, Shakespeare's plays were a draw. Did Shakespeare act in his own plays? He was listed as a principal player with his company even after he started writing, so probably, but we don't know for sure which roles he played. He was not a leading actor. He may never have played his most famous characters, such as Macbeth or King Lear. Some historians believe that his last role was Hamlet's father in *Hamlet,* written around the year 1600.

9   By that point, Shakespeare was working in both the business and creative side of the theater. In addition to writing and acting, he was one of the managing partners of the Lord Chamberlain's Men and a part-owner of the Globe Theater. These businesses, not publishing his plays, made Shakespeare wealthy. The plays weren't collected and printed in the First Folio until 1623, seven years after his death.

USING LANGUAGE CA-CCSS: ELD.PI.11-12.12.a.Ex

Read each sentence and note the boldfaced word. Choose the domain-specific theater word from the options below that best replaces the boldfaced word to make the sentences clearer.

New Word Options					
playwright	critic	principal player	theatergoers	reviews	playhouse

Sentence	New Word
The **writer** told stories about his own life and the history of his country.	
We went to the **building** to see the new play everyone was talking about.	
During intermission, the **people** mingled in the lobby and discussed their favorite scenes.	
The **articles** in the local newspaper raved about the cast of the play.	
The **man** performs in all the company's shows, and he is always one of the best performers.	
On her blog, the **person** describes shows she's seen and whether her readers should also attend.	

Please note that excerpts and passages in the StudySync® library and this workbook are intended as touchstones to generate interest in an author's work. The excerpts and passages do not substitute for the reading of entire texts, and StudySync® strongly recommends that students seek out and purchase the whole literary or informational work in order to experience it as the author intended. Links to online resellers are available in our digital library. In addition, complete works may be ordered through an authorized reseller by filling out and returning to StudySync® the order form enclosed in this workbook.

Reading & Writing Companion   **77**

👥 MEANINGFUL INTERACTIONS CA-CCSS: ELD.PI.11-12.7.Ex

Work with your partner or group to discuss the effects of the language choices listed below. Use the chart to take notes on the effects of each language choice, and then use those notes to participate in the discussion. Use the self-assessment rubric to evaluate your participation in the discussion.

Language Choice	Example	Effect
Using a quotation	In *As You Like It*, William Shakespeare wrote, "All the world's a stage, and all the men and women merely players."	
Questions	Did a young Shakespeare volunteer?	
Use of plural personal pronoun "we"	Historians call the period after the wedding "the lost years" because we have no written records of what Shakespeare was doing.	
Connections to today	Like modern theaters, the Theatre was a dedicated building for showing plays.	

⚙️ SELF-ASSESSMENT RUBRIC CA-CCSS: ELD.PI.11-12.1.Ex

	4 I did this well.	3 I did this pretty well.	2 I did this a little bit.	1 I did not do this.
I affirmed others' ideas during the discussion.				
I contributed effectively to the group's decisions.				
I understood the author's language choices in the selection.				
I helped others understand the effect of language choices in the selection.				
I completed the language choices chart carefully and accurately.				

REREAD

Reread paragraphs 1–5 of "Shakespeare: More Than a Playwright." After you reread, complete the Using Language and Meaningful Interactions activities.

 USING LANGUAGE CA-CCSS: ELD.PII.11-12.4.Ex

Read the sentence in the first column and note the boldfaced noun. Read the sentence in the second column that provides additional information about the noun. Then, in the third column, write a noun phrase that could replace the bolded word with the additional information provided in the second column.

Sentence	Additional Information	Noun Phrase
William Shakespeare wrote the **play** *Romeo and Juliet* in the 1590s.	*Romeo and Juliet* is dramatic.	
Shakespeare lived in **Stratford-upon-Avon**.	Stratford-upon-Avon was a small town.	
Robert Greene criticized Shakespeare in a **pamphlet**.	The pamphlet was vague but nasty.	
James Burbage built a **theater** in 1576.	Burbage's theater was the first in London.	

Please note that excerpts and passages in the StudySync® library and this workbook are intended as touchstones to generate interest in an author's work. The excerpts and passages do not substitute for the reading of entire texts, and StudySync® strongly recommends that students seek out and purchase the whole literary or informational work in order to experience it as the author intended. Links to online resellers are available in our digital library. In addition, complete works may be ordered through an authorized reseller by filling out and returning to StudySync® the order form enclosed in this workbook.

Reading & Writing Companion   **79**

MEANINGFUL INTERACTIONS CA-CCSS: ELD.PI.11-12.1.Ex

What are the key ideas in the first half of "Shakespeare: More Than a Playwright"? Work with a small group to identify and discuss the key ideas, using the speaking frames. Then use the self-assessment rubric to evaluate your participation in the discussion.

- A key idea in paragraph 2 of the text is . . .

- In paragraph 3, the author introduces the key idea of . . .

- A key idea in paragraph 4 is . . . This idea builds on the other key idea of . . . because . . .

- In paragraph 5, the author describes . . .

- That key idea is also included in . . .

- The author also says that . . .

SELF-ASSESSMENT RUBRIC CA-CCSS: ELD.PI.11-12.1.Ex

	4 I did this well.	3 I did this pretty well.	2 I did this a little bit.	1 I did not do this.
I expressed key ideas clearly.				
I provided coherent and well-articulated comments.				
I added additional relevant information to others' ideas.				
I was courteous when adding additional information.				

REREAD

Reread paragraphs 6–9 of "Shakespeare: More Than a Playwright." After you reread, complete the Using Language and Meaningful Interactions activities.

USING LANGUAGE   CA-CCSS: ELD.PI.11-12.6.c.Ex

Read each sentence. Look at the desired connotation in parentheses. Then choose the word that more closely matches the desired connotation to complete the sentence.

1. Theatergoers in the 1590s were not _____, polite audiences like today. (less sound)

   ○ silent   ○ quiet

2. If Shakespeare were a/an _____ actor, he would not have kept his job. (more negative)

   ○ poor   ○ awful

3. That means they _____ a different show every night. (more formal)

   ○ performed   ○ put on

4. From the beginning, Shakespeare's plays were _____. (more professional)

   ○ liked   ○ a draw

5. These businesses, not publishing his plays, made Shakespeare _____. (more permanent)

   ○ rich   ○ wealthy

MEANINGFUL INTERACTIONS   CA-CCSS: ELD.PI.11-12.6.b.Ex

What is the author's attitude towards the subject in "Shakespeare: More Than a Playwright"? What evidence from the text supports your inference? Explain your thoughts and opinions using the speaking frames below.

- The author's attitude is . . . because . . .

- Based on the text, I can infer that . . .

- This evidence suggests that . . . because . . .

Please note that excerpts and passages in the StudySync® library and this workbook are intended as touchstones to generate interest in an author's work. The excerpts and passages do not substitute for the reading of entire texts, and StudySync® strongly recommends that students seek out and purchase the whole literary or informational work in order to experience it as the author intended. Links to online resellers are available in our digital library. In addition, complete works may be ordered through an authorized reseller by filling out and returning to StudySync® the order form enclosed in this workbook.

Reading & Writing
Companion   **81**

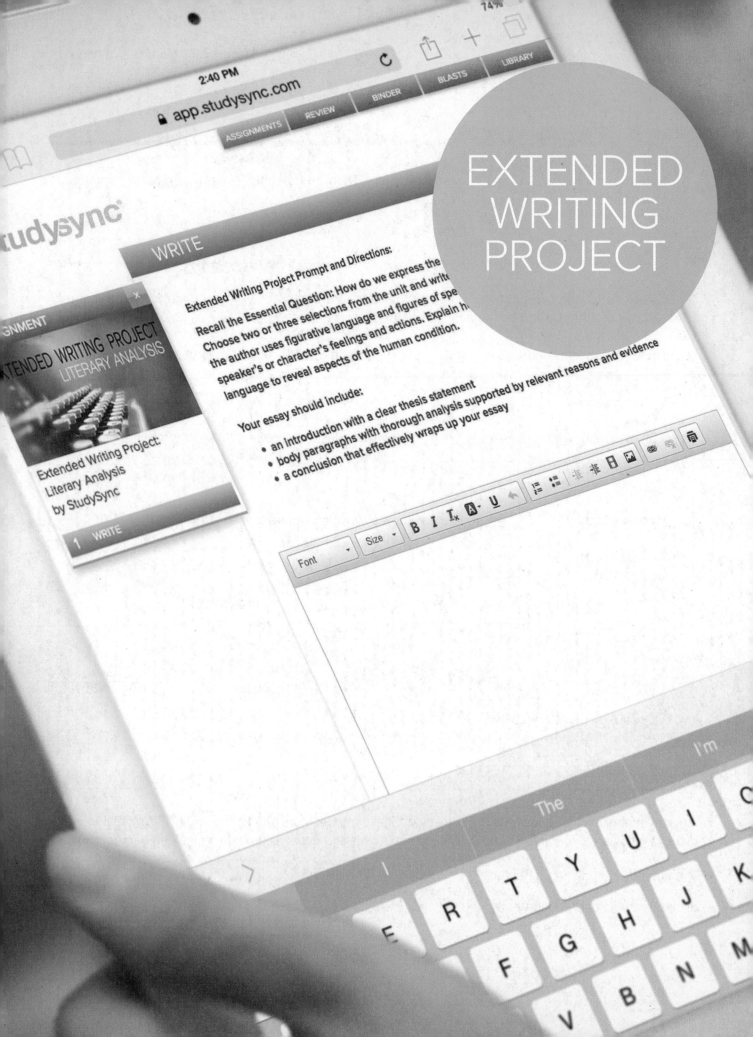

EXTENDED
WRITING
PROJECT

WRITE

Extended Writing Project Prompt and Directions:

Recall the Essential Question: How do we express the
Choose two or three selections from the unit and write
the author uses figurative language and figures of spe
speaker's or character's feelings and actions. Explain h
language to reveal aspects of the human condition.

Your essay should include:

- an introduction with a clear thesis statement
- body paragraphs with thorough analysis supported by relevant reasons and evidence
- a conclusion that effectively wraps up your essay

EXTENDED WRITING PROJECT
LITERARY ANALYSIS

Extended Writing Project:
Literary Analysis
by StudySync

1   WRITE

NOTES

LITERARY ANALYSIS

WRITING PROMPT

Recall the Essential Question: How do we express the complexities of being human? Choose two or three selections from the unit and write a literary analysis focused on how the author uses figurative language and figures of speech to help readers understand a speaker's or character's feelings and actions. Explain how each author uses figurative language to reveal aspects of the human condition.

Your essay should include:

- an introduction with a clear thesis statement
- body paragraphs with thorough analysis supported by relevant reasons and evidence
- a conclusion that effectively wraps up your essay

Literary analysis is a form of **argumentative writing.** There are different purposes for argumentative writing. For example, an argument might intend to change readers' perspectives, sway them into taking action, or convince readers to accept the writer's ideas and beliefs. In an essay focused on literary analysis, a writer makes claims about the meaning or the value of a literary work and analyzes sections of a text to support a conclusion about or interpretation of the work. The writer develops claims in the analysis using **reasons** and **relevant textual evidence.**

To build a strong literary analysis, writers introduce a thesis statement that makes a specific **claim** about a text, usually an interpretation of events, characters, symbols, or other aspects of one or more works of literature. They will then support their assertion with relevant evidence from the literature being discussed. All quotations should be introduced and explained, including any names of authors, titles, and context needed. The analysis should stay focused on the writer's claim or claims, and include transition words to help create flow and make connections between supporting details that help build the argument.

To be convincing, writers of literary analyses should establish and maintain a formal style and objective tone. In addition, writers should include rhetorical devices (such as use of logic, appeal to emotion, or use of analogies) that help support assertions.

The features of a literary analysis include the following:

- an introduction with a clear thesis statement that makes a claim about one or more works of literature
- supporting details and relevant evidence from the texts mentioned in the introduction
- a logical organizational structure
- cohesive and clear relationships between ideas
- specific rhetorical devices, such as appeals to logic or emotion
- citations for all sources consulted
- a conclusion that follows from and supports the argument presented

As you continue with this extended writing project, you'll receive more instructions and practice to help you craft each of the elements of literary analysis writing in your own essay.

 READ

Before you get started on your own literary analysis, begin by reading this essay that one student wrote in response to the writing prompt. As you read this student model, highlight and annotate the features of literary analysis that the student included in her essay.

Feelings Hidden under Trappings and Suits:
Figurative Language in *Hamlet* and "On Monsieur's Departure"

The "human condition" encompasses the unique mental features and behaviors that separate humans from animals. Falling in love, missing a friend, or feeling self-doubt all represent parts of the human condition. In addition, mixed emotions and feelings of inner conflict play a key role in the human condition. In William Shakespeare's play *The Tragedy of Hamlet, Prince of Denmark*, readers experience the inner thoughts of a young prince in turmoil as expressed through his soliloquies.

Early in the play, Hamlet's depression and grief overwhelm his private thoughts, but he must put a brave face forward if he is to avenge his father's murder. Queen Elizabeth I's poem "On Monsieur's Departure" describes the sadness felt by a speaker whose beloved abandoned her. Both Shakespeare and Elizabeth I use figures of speech to help readers understand and relate to the experience of holding intense feelings inside, hidden from public display. This act of hiding makes characters human and reveals an important aspect of the human condition.

Elizabeth I was queen of England from 1558 to 1603 ("Elizabeth I"). During her long rule she never married, despite calls from her court to find a king and produce an heir. In her poem "On Monsieur's Departure," the speaker struggles to keep her true feelings hidden. The speaker of the poem is not necessarily Elizabeth, but she would have undoubtedly understood the importance of cultivating a public image. In addition, literary scholars believe the poem was inspired by the breakup of marriage negotiations with Francis, Duke of Anjou, a one-time suitor to Elizabeth (Abrams 998). The speaker sets up her dilemma in the first line: "I grieve and dare not show my discontent" (1.1). The use of the verb "dare" implies that a strong force keeps her from showing her grief. She continues the use of strong language in the second line: "I love, and yet am forced to seem to hate" (1.2). Here the speaker clarifies her problem—she is in love with someone, but the outside world "forces" her to "seem to hate." The use of the word "seem" is important. No one can actually force her to hate a person, but she can pretend. The whole stanza comprises a list of paradoxes—figures of speech that seem to be contradictions but actually reveal truth. The truth in this case is that the feelings projected on the outside of a person may be entirely different from what he or she is actually feeling inside.

Like Elizabeth's speaker, Hamlet is torn between his true, inner feelings and the image he needs to project in public. In the first act, when Hamlet sees his uncle Claudius a month after his father's death, Claudius addresses Hamlet's grief: "How is it that the clouds still hang on you?" (1.2.6). Hamlet replies that what they see is only the tip of the iceberg. He hangs on his mother's use of the word "seem"—much like Elizabeth's speaker—when he says:

> Seems, madam? Nay, it is, I know not "seems."
>
> 'Tis not alone my inky cloak, good mother,
>
> Nor customary suits of solemn black,
>
> Nor windy suspiration of forc'd breath,
>
> No, nor the fruitful river in the eye, . . .

Together with all forms, moods, shapes of grief,
That can denote me truly. These indeed seem,
For they are actions that a man might play,
But I have that within which passes show,
These but the trappings and the suits of woe.   *Hamlet* (1.2.17-27)

Here, Shakespeare uses figurative and descriptive language to convey Hamlet's hidden emotions. Hamlet may be dressed in mourning ("customary suits of solemn black"), sighing ("windy suspiration of forc'd breath"), and crying ("fruitful river in the eye"), but his true grief is on a deeper level inside. The "windy suspiration" is an example of hyperbole. The exaggeration gives the feeling that Hamlet's sighs are bigger and more poignant than the sighs of other people. The metaphor of crying as a "fruitful river" shows Hamlet's grief as endless and rushing, like a river. Later in the speech, Hamlet uses a metaphor to compare himself to an actor, saying what his family sees is "actions that a man might play." Anyone can "play" at grief by doing what Hamlet describes, but he has "that within which passes show"—something hidden and abstract, yet real. Later in the scene, Hamlet realizes he needs to better conceal his emotions, and he ends his first soliloquy with the metaphor "But break my heart, for I must hold my tongue." It is the first indication that Hamlet will "hold his tongue" and avoid taking his revenge, or that he might not act at all.

In the second scene of Act 2, Hamlet again compares himself to an actor. In a soliloquy, Shakespeare uses hyperbole to describe how an actor would behave had he experienced a real tragedy: "He would drown the stage with tears, / And cleave the general ear with horrid speech." Hamlet wants to express himself in this way, but he cannot. Comparing oneself to another is an aspect of the human condition. Hamlet wonders if he is a "coward," and then he says he is "pigeon-liver'd" and lacks "gall" (2.2.130). This implies that the actor represents the opposite—a brave man with guts. The speaker of "On Monsieur's Departure" also insults herself when she says: "For I am soft, and made of melting snow" (3.14). Using this metaphor, the speaker admits her own weakness. Some readers may think that the speaker describes herself as "soft" to garner sympathy, because women, especially in Elizabeth's time, were expected to be weak. But, on closer examination, the line is really another connection to the paradoxes of the first stanza. Melting snow is neither water nor snow. It stands in between phases, which is what the speaker wants to be out of, as she says later: "Let me float or sink, be high or low" (3.16). It is the feeling of being stuck in between that is so painful to the speaker.

Many people, especially those in high places—say a queen or a prince—need to cultivate a public persona to avoid appearing weak. This limit on behavior develops from the complications of human social structures. Authors of literature such as "On Monsieur's Departure" and *The Tragedy of Hamlet, Prince of Denmark* use figurative language to explore the line all people have to walk between the expression and concealment of feelings. What society deems acceptable plays a central role in what people determine to share or conceal. Deciding what to share or keep hidden inside during social interactions forms an essential part—and challenge—of what make humans human. The use of figurative language in these works gives resonating, tangible expression to these unsaid, intangible feelings.

Works Cited

Abrams, M. H., ed. *The Norton Anthology of English Literature,* Sixth Edition.

New York: W. W. Norton & Company, 1993. Print.

"Elizabeth I." *Encyclopædia Britannica.* Encyclopædia Britannica Inc., 2014. Web.

27 Aug. 2014.

Elizabeth I. "On Monsieur's Departure." *StudySync.* BookheadEd Learning, LLC.

2015. Web. 4 May 2015.

Shakespeare, William. *The Tragedy of Hamlet, Prince of Denmark. StudySync.*

BookheadEd Learning, LLC. 2015. Web. 4 May 2015.

Please note that excerpts and passages in the StudySync® library and this workbook are intended as touchstones to generate interest in an author's work. The excerpts and passages do not substitute for the reading of entire texts, and StudySync® strongly recommends that students seek out and purchase the whole literary or informational work in order to experience it as the author intended. Links to online resellers are available in our digital library. In addition, complete works may be ordered through an authorized reseller by filling out and returning to StudySync® the order form enclosed in this workbook.

Reading & Writing Companion

87

THINK QUESTIONS

1. What works of literature is the author analyzing, and what main ideas is she developing? Which sentence from the first paragraph states the main idea of the essay?

2. What point does the writer make about Hamlet's outward signs of mourning? How does she support this idea?

3. What comparison between the two texts does the author make in the fourth paragraph? How does this comparison support the writer's thesis statement?

4. Thinking about the writing prompt, which selections, Blasts, or other resources would you like to use to create your own literary analysis? What are some ideas that you may want to develop into your own piece?

5. Based on what you have read, listened to, or researched, how would you answer the question: *How do we express the complexities of being human?* What are some ways authors in this unit have expressed what it's like to be human?

NOTES

PREWRITE

CA-CCSS: CA.W.11-12.1a, CA.W.11-12.4, CA.W.11-12.5, CA.W.11-12.6, CA.W.11-12.9a, CA.W.11-12.10, CA.SL.11-12.1

WRITING PROMPT

Recall the Essential Question: How do we express the complexities of being human? Choose two or three selections from the unit and write a literary analysis focused on how the author uses figurative language and figures of speech to help readers understand a speaker's or character's feelings and actions. Explain how each author uses figurative language to reveal aspects of the human condition.

Your essay should include:

- an introduction with a clear thesis statement
- body paragraphs with thorough analysis supported by relevant reasons and evidence
- a conclusion that effectively wraps up your essay

As you prewrite your literary analysis, think back to the texts you've read so far in this unit. Which texts have vivid figurative language or figures of speech? Do any examples of figurative language stick out in your mind as particularly fresh, beautiful, or insightful? What new ideas about the human condition do these texts include? Do any of the texts make you think about the human condition in a new way?

Make a list of the answers as you brainstorm these questions for two or three texts. As you write down your ideas, look for patterns that begin to emerge. Which two or three texts have similar ideas? What claim about the human condition can you make based on the texts? What relevant evidence can you gather to support that claim? Answering these questions may help you solidify the ideas you want to discuss in your essay. Use this model to help you get started with your own prewriting, remembering that you can use as many details from a text as needed:

Text: "On Monsieur's Departure"
Figurative Language: "For I am soft, and made of melting snow" (metaphor)
Comment on the human condition: It is painful to be in an in-between state.

Please note that excerpts and passages in the StudySync® library and this workbook are intended as touchstones to generate interest in an author's work. The excerpts and passages do not substitute for the reading of entire texts, and StudySync® strongly recommends that students seek out and purchase the whole literary or informational work in order to experience it as the author intended. Links to online resellers are available in our digital library. In addition, complete works may be ordered through an authorized reseller by filling out and returning to StudySync® the order form enclosed in this workbook.

Reading & Writing Companion **89**

SKILL: THESIS STATEMENT

 DEFINE

In a literary analysis, the thesis statement introduces the writer's claim, in this case his or her interpretation of the literary text to be analyzed. The thesis statement expresses the writer's central or main idea about that text, a position the writer will develop in the body of the essay. A vague, obvious truth does not make a good thesis statement; a thesis statement should be specific and clearly answer the prompt. The thesis statement usually appears in the essay's introductory paragraph and is often the introduction's last sentence. The rest of the paragraphs in the essay all support the thesis statement with facts, evidence, and examples.

 IDENTIFICATION AND APPLICATION

In a literary analysis, a thesis statement:

- provides the key idea, or claim, about the writer's interpretation of a text or texts
- is a precise interpretation or claim based on relevant textual evidence
- lets the reader know what to expect in the body of the essay
- sets up the essay so that the reader has a clear idea where the analysis is heading
- appears in the first paragraph

 MODEL

The writer of the student model literary analysis essay "Feelings Hidden under Trappings and Suits" puts the thesis statement near the end of the first paragraph. The writer sets the stage for this thesis by tying the unit's essential question to two works to be discussed in the analysis, thus answering the prompt:

> The "human condition" encompasses the unique mental features and behaviors that separate humans from animals. Falling in love, missing a friend, or feeling self-doubt all represent parts of the human condition. In addition, mixed emotions and feelings of inner conflict play a key role in the human condition. In William Shakespeare's play *The Tragedy of Hamlet, Prince of Denmark,* readers experience the inner thoughts of a young prince in turmoil as expressed through his soliloquies. Early in the play, Hamlet's depression and grief overwhelm his private thoughts, but he must put a brave face forward if he is to avenge his father's murder. Queen Elizabeth I's poem "On Monsieur's Departure" describes the sadness felt by a speaker whose beloved abandoned her. **Both Shakespeare and Elizabeth I use figures of speech to help readers understand and relate to the experience of holding intense feelings inside, hidden from public display.** This act of hiding makes characters human and reveals an important aspect of the human condition.

Notice the bold-faced thesis statement. The student's thesis statement contains a claim that focuses on the figurative language used in the play and the poem that she will analyze in the essay. The writer's interpretation or claim is that the figurative language in both works serves to help readers understand the characters' experiences with hidden feelings. Put another way, the interpretation stated in the thesis involves connecting figures of speech and the theme.

The thesis statement is strong in that it shows the reader what direction the essay will take. The reader can expect to learn how each text treats hidden feelings and how figures of speech emphasize this theme.

 PRACTICE

Write a thesis statement for your literary analysis that articulates your main idea or claim in relation to the essay prompt. When you are finished, trade with a partner and offer each other feedback. How clear was the writer's main point or claim? Is it obvious what this essay will focus on? Does it specifically address the prompt? Offer each other suggestions, and remember that they are most helpful when they are constructive.

Please note that excerpts and passages in the StudySync® library and this workbook are intended as touchstones to generate interest in an author's work. The excerpts and passages do not substitute for the reading of entire texts, and StudySync® strongly recommends that students seek out and purchase the whole literary or informational work in order to experience it as the author intended. Links to online resellers are available in our digital library. In addition, complete works may be ordered through an authorized reseller by filling out and returning to StudySync® the order form enclosed in this workbook.

Reading & Writing Companion   91

SKILL:
ORGANIZE ARGUMENTATIVE WRITING

DEFINE

A literary analysis is a type of argumentative essay. It is intended to convince readers of an author's position or point of view on a subject that is related to one or more pieces of literature. Authors introduce a precise claim in a thesis statement, which is the basis for an author's argument. Then they support that claim with valid reasoning and logical, relevant evidence from reliable sources. To do this, the author must organize and present the reasons and relevant evidence—the details and quotations from the text or texts—in a logical and convincing way. The writer must select an organizational structure that best suits the argument.

The writer of a literary analysis can choose from a number of organizational structures, including compare and contrast, sequential order, problem and solution, cause and effect, and chronological order. If the purpose is to analyze a series of events, a **chronological or time-order structure** might work best. If the purpose is to describe steps in a process, a **sequential structure** might be more appropriate to the task. If the purpose is to show how events build upon one another, **a cause-and-effect structure,** which can be quite similar to the chronological structure, might be more effective. If two or more texts or ideas are being analyzed together, **a compare-and-contrast structure** may help the reader understand how one group of ideas and details is related to, or differs from, another.

Once claims have been established, writers of a literary analysis should acknowledge counterclaims, or alternative points of view about the literature being analyzed. These counterclaims should be included in a logical way. The compare-and-contrast structure is a useful approach in arguing against opposing claims or points of view.

IDENTIFICATION AND APPLICATION

To answer a writing prompt involving literary analysis, the writer should choose an organizational structure that addresses the requirements of the prompt. In general, an argumentative essay follows this pattern:

- The writer develops an opinion or point of view on the topic and states a claim.
- The claim is stated in a thesis statement and is supported by logical reasoning.
- Text evidence in the form of specific details from the text supports the author's claim. In a literary analysis this would include examples and quotations from the texts that support the claim and do not include bias or personal opinions.
- A restatement of the claim is found in the concluding paragraph.

To address the prompt in this unit: (1) the writer chooses two to three selections; (2) the writer analyzes figurative language to show a speaker's or character's feelings and actions; and (3) the writer chooses figurative language that reveals aspects of the human condition. An organizational plan for addressing the prompt might have the following compare and contrast structure:

- The introduction includes a clear thesis statement. The thesis must significantly address an aspect of the human condition. The introduction also indicates which literary texts the writer will be analyzing.
- For each literary text that is analyzed, there is at least one paragraph providing examples of figurative language from that text that help a reader understand the character or speaker's thoughts and feelings, and that help reveal an aspect of the human condition.
- Body paragraphs also identify similarities and differences between the ways the various texts' characters or speakers comment on the human condition.
- Transitional words and phrases help show how ideas are connected.
- A conclusion revisits the thesis and summarizes its importance.

MODEL

The author of the student model literary analysis "Feelings Hidden under Trappings and Suits" chose to discuss the Unit 2 texts *The Tragedy of Hamlet* and "On Monsieur's Departure."

The writer reread the selections and found examples of figurative language that seemed to answer the prompt. Then she used the following table to organize ideas generated during prewriting. The table helps the writer organize the body of the essay and ensure that all ideas support the thesis statement and answer the prompt.

Thesis Statement: "Both Shakespeare and Elizabeth I use figures of speech to help readers understand and relate to the experience of holding intense feelings inside, hidden from public display."

LITERARY TEXT	FIGURATIVE LANGUAGE	INTERPRETATION AND CONNECTION TO HUMAN CONDITION
"On Monsieur's Departure"	"I love, and yet am forced to seem to hate"	The feelings projected on the outside of a person may be entirely different from what he or she is actually feeling inside.
Hamlet	"But I have that within which passes show, These but the trappings and the suits of woe."	His true grief is on a deeper level inside.

First, the writer stated her thesis. Next, the writer used the three headings in the first row of the chart to organize details and information in the table. These details serve as key ideas for the body paragraphs. For example, the details from second row are in the first body paragraph of the essay. The third row serves as a point of organization for the second and third body paragraphs.

 PRACTICE

Fill out a version of the three-column chart from the Model using your chosen selections from the unit. Use the chart to state your thesis and identify the selections you will analyze, as well as to record key details and interpretations you may want to include in your literary analysis. Keep in mind that the inclusion and sequence of items may well change or evolve during the writing process.

SKILL:
SUPPORTING
DETAILS

 DEFINE

In informative and argumentative writing, a writer develops the thesis statement with relevant information, called **supporting details.** Relevant information consists of any fact, definition, detail, example, or quotation that is important to the reader's understanding of the topic and is closely related to the thesis or claim. Supporting details can be found in a variety of places, but to be relevant they must provide support for the thesis. Relevant supporting details include the following:

- Facts important to understanding ideas
- Research related to the thesis
- Quotations from experts or other authoritative sources
- Conclusions of scientific findings and studies
- Excerpts from a literary text

Writers can choose supporting details from many sources. Reference books, articles in scholarly journals, news accounts, graphs, biographies, critical reviews, and authoritative websites can all provide relevant information for source material. The writer must be careful to evaluate the quality of information to determine which sources are most important and most closely related to the thesis. If the information doesn't relate to the topic or if the information doesn't strengthen the thesis, it is not relevant.

 IDENTIFICATION AND APPLICATION

Step 1:

Review your thesis statement. To identify relevant supporting details, ask this question: What is my key interpretation for this literary analysis? Here is the thesis statement from the student model:

Both Shakespeare and Elizabeth I use figures of speech to help readers understand and relate to the experience of holding intense feelings inside, hidden from public display.

The key interpretation is that the two authors are revealing an aspect of the human condition by using figures of speech to show how people sometimes keep their true emotions hidden inside.

In those cases when you have difficulty finding strong supporting details for your thesis statement, you should consider revising your thesis so that it fits better with the sources you have reviewed.

Step 2:
When answering the extended writing prompt, you need to ask yourself which passages in your chosen texts would best support your key interpretation, or claim. The writer of the student model chose a poem and a play. The writer needed to find strong support in both texts to craft an effective literary analysis.

Here is a quotation that the writer chose from "On Monsieur's Departure" to support her thesis.

> **I love, and yet am forced to seem to hate.**

This is a figure of speech called a paradox: it seems like a contradiction but it actually reveals truth. The speaker feels forced to hide her feelings by showing the opposite. Notice how well this connects with the thesis above.

The other text that the student chose to analyze in the literary analysis essay is *Hamlet*. Here is one of the quotations the writer chose to use as supporting evidence.

> **But break my heart, for I must hold my tongue.**

"Hold my tongue" is a figure of speech that means not talking when you want to say something. This is another way of holding in feelings, so it connects with the interpretation in the thesis.

 MODEL

Writers of a literary analysis should recognize both the strengths and limitations of any evidence presented, anticipating the audience's level of knowledge, interests, or biases. As a result, a writer of a literary analysis must explain why details are included, especially when a longer quotation serves as a supporting detail. In addition, the relevant evidence may be spread across several sentences or lines and require the reader to use inference skills. The writer of the student model found some strong supporting evidence in a group of lines spoken by Hamlet. The writer uses some introductory sentences to show how the quotation is relevant to the thesis and to draw a connection to the other text in the analysis. Note that because the writer can assume her readers know the texts, she only needs to provide limited context:

> In Act I, scene ii, when Hamlet sees his uncle Claudius a month after his father's death, Claudius addresses Hamlet's grief: "How is it that the clouds still hang on you?" (1.2.6). Hamlet replies that what they see is only the tip of the iceberg. He hangs on his mother's use of the word "seem"—much like Elizabeth's speaker—when he says:

> Seems, madam? Nay, it is, I know not "seems."
> 'Tis not alone my inky cloak, good mother,
> Nor customary suits of solemn black,
> Nor windy suspiration of forc'd breath,
> No, nor the fruitful river in the eye, . . .
> Together with all forms, moods, shapes of grief,
> That can denote me truly. These indeed seem,
> For they are actions that a man might play,
> But I have that within which passes show,
> These but the trappings and the suits of woe.   *Hamlet* (1.2.17-27)

The student model writer notes that the key line is the next-to-last one: "But I have that within which passes show." The writer points out in the paragraph that follows, "Anyone can 'play' at grief by doing what Hamlet describes, but he has 'that within which passes show'—something hidden and abstract, yet real." This means Hamlet is holding something inside. The phrase, "Anyone can 'play' at grief," seems to anticipate that some readers might disagree with her analysis. By emphasizing that Hamlet is not doing something that just "anyone" would do, she may convince her readers of her view. The previous lines of the quotation provide the context for the reader to infer what is being held "within": negative emotions such as grief. Hamlet indicates that the emotions hidden inside him are much worse than the gloom he is showing on the outside, "the trappings and the suits of woe." Indeed, words from this line of the quotation are used in the title of the literary analysis.

NOTES

PRACTICE

Write a paragraph for your literary analysis that states a claim or main idea and then supports it by drawing relevant evidence from one or more of the unit texts. The paragraph should also support your overall thesis. First, write your thesis statement. Next, review the evidence listed in your Organize Argumentative Writing Chart to use as you craft your paragraph. As you note your evidence, be sure to include an explanation of how the evidence supports the claim you are making. Exchange your paragraphs with a partner and provide each other feedback. Remember that you can use this paragraph or a revised version in later stages of the writing process.

PLAN

CA-CCSS: CA.W.11-12.1a, CA.W.11-12.5, CA.W.11-12.9a, CA.SL.11-12.1

WRITING PROMPT

Recall the Essential Question: How do we express the complexities of being human? Choose two or three selections from the unit and write a literary analysis focused on how the author uses figurative language and figures of speech to help readers understand a speaker's or character's feelings and actions. Explain how each author uses figurative language to reveal aspects of the human condition.

Your essay should include:

- an introduction with a clear thesis statement
- body paragraphs with thorough analysis supported by relevant reasons and evidence
- a conclusion that effectively wraps up your essay

Review the information you listed in your three-column chart listing two to three selections, figurative language examples, and an interpretation about the human condition. Review your preliminary thesis from the Thesis lesson. This organized information and your thesis statement will help you create a road map to use for writing your essay.

Consider the following questions as you create the roadmap you'll use to develop your main paragraph topics and their supporting details:

- What vivid examples of figurative language do your chosen selections have?
- How do you interpret these instances of figurative language?
- What does the figurative language show about the character or speaker?
- How does your interpretation of the figurative language connect to the human condition?

- What aspects about the human condition does the author reveal through the figurative language used in the text?

Use this model to get started with your road map:

Thesis statement: Both Shakespeare and Elizabeth I use figures of speech to help readers understand and relate to the experience of holding intense feelings inside, hidden from public display.

Paragraph 1 Topic: How figurative language in "On Monsieur's Departure" reveals an aspect of the human condition
    Supporting Detail #1: Quote containing figurative language
    Supporting Detail #2: Interpretation

Paragraph 2 Topic: How figurative language in *Hamlet* reveals an aspect of the human condition
    Supporting Detail #1: Quote containing figurative language
    Supporting Detail #2: Interpretation

Paragraph 3 Topic: *Hamlet* and "On Monsieur's Departure"
    Supporting Detail #1: Quotations
    Supporting Detail #2: Interpretations

SKILL: INTRODUCTIONS

⭐ DEFINE

The **introduction** to an argumentative text usually states in the first paragraph the **main idea** or **claim** that will be examined or argued in the subsequent paragraphs. In addition, the writer may try to engage or "hook" the reader with an interesting piece of relevant information that sets up the significance of the analysis or the process to be described. For example, a scientific article might pique the reader's interest by promising to argue that a recent archeological discovery may shed light on our current understanding of backaches, or a food essay will entice the reader with pictures of a luscious chocolate cake and then argue that desserts should be made with less sugar. The introduction may also set forth the basic structure of the text that will follow, providing readers with a roadmap of sorts before the trip officially begins.

⚫⚫⚫ IDENTIFICATION AND APPLICATION

- In argumentative writing, the introduction should indicate the subject as well as the **claim** the writer will be making. Whether the writing is in the form of a report, a news article or an interpretation of literature, the writer with a point to argue needs to make the claim and topic clear.

- The introduction should include the **thesis statement** that contains the claim that the author will be supporting. In a literary analysis, the thesis statement should include the authors or titles of any works of literature to be discussed.

- The thesis should be specific and not be an obvious truth that everyone agrees with. A strongly stated thesis engages readers' attention and makes them more likely to read the whole analysis. A dull thesis with generic language may cause readers to stop at the end of the introduction.

- It is customary to build interest in the topic by beginning the introduction with a **"hook,"** or a way to grab the reader's attention. This awakens the

Please note that excerpts and passages in the StudySync® library and this workbook are intended as touchstones to generate interest in an author's work. The excerpts and passages do not substitute for the reading of entire texts, and StudySync® strongly recommends that students seek out and purchase the whole literary or informational work in order to experience it as the author intended. Links to online resellers are available in our digital library. In addition, complete works may be ordered through an authorized reseller by filling out and returning to StudySync® the order form enclosed in this workbook.

Reading & Writing Companion **101**

reader's natural curiosity and encourages him or her to read on. Hooks can, for example, ask open-ended questions, make connections to the reader or to life, or introduce a surprising fact.

- In a literary analysis, the introduction should give information about the literary text or texts being analyzed. It should also provide some background information about the text to provide context for the reader.

- Some introductions may require more than one paragraph. For example, an author of a literary analysis may need to use the first paragraph to establish the text or texts and to provide background information, using a second paragraph to build to a thesis statement.

 MODEL

The writer of the student model literary analysis "Feelings Hidden under Trappings and Suits" uses the first paragraph of the essay as the introduction. The writer begins by explaining the topic and then introduces the two texts being analyzed. Then the writer presents the thesis statement.

> **The "human condition" encompasses the unique mental features and behaviors that separate humans from animals.** Falling in love, missing a friend, or feeling self-doubt all represent parts of the human condition. In addition, mixed emotions and feelings of inner conflict play a key role in the human condition. In **William Shakespeare's play *The Tragedy of Hamlet, Prince of Denmark,*** readers experience the inner thoughts of a young prince in turmoil as expressed through his soliloquies. Early in the play, Hamlet's depression and grief overwhelm his private thoughts, but he must put a brave face forward if he is to avenge his father's murder. **Queen Elizabeth I's poem "On Monsieur's Departure"** describes the sadness felt by a speaker whose beloved abandoned her. **Both Shakespeare and Elizabeth I use figures of speech to help readers understand and relate to the experience of holding intense feelings inside, hidden from public display.** This act of hiding makes characters human and reveals an important aspect of the human condition.

The topic of the literary analysis, as required by the extended writing prompt, is how authors use figurative language to express the human condition. The writer begins the essay by explaining what the phrase "human condition" means. The hook is contained in the idea of the second sentence, which expresses examples of being human that readers can relate to: "Falling in love, missing a friend, or feeling self-doubt all represent parts of the human condition." After defining the topic, the writer gives a couple of examples to

NOTES

reinforce the reader's understanding and serve as a hook. Next, the writer indicates that the literary analysis will cover a play by William Shakespeare and a poem by Elizabeth I. The thesis statement is an interpretation that connects a theme that appears in both texts.

 PRACTICE

Write an introduction for your literary analysis that includes the following: 1) the names of literary works or authors; 2) a hook to engage the reader; 3) a thesis statement that states the main idea or claim; and 4) a preview of how the analysis will be structured. When you are finished, trade with a partner and offer each other feedback. How convincing is the language of your partner's thesis statement, and how strong is the claim? How clear is the topic? Were you hooked? Offer each other suggestions, and remember that they are most helpful when they are constructive.

Please note that excerpts and passages in the StudySync® library and this workbook are intended as touchstones to generate interest in an author's work. The excerpts and passages do not substitute for the reading of entire texts, and StudySync® strongly recommends that students seek out and purchase the whole literary or informational work in order to experience it as the author intended. Links to online resellers are available in our digital library. In addition, complete works may be ordered through an authorized reseller by filling out and returning to StudySync® the order form enclosed in this workbook.

Reading & Writing Companion **103**

SKILL: BODY PARAGRAPHS AND TRANSITIONS

 ## DEFINE

Body paragraphs are the section of the essay between the introductory and concluding paragraphs. It is in the body paragraphs that you support your thesis statement by developing your main points with reasons and relevant evidence from the text in the form of supporting details. You will use the reasons and evidence to shape your own analysis of the information you present. Typically, each body paragraph will focus on one main point or idea to create clarity. The main point of each body paragraph must support the thesis statement or claim.

In each body paragraph, a writer needs to show the relationship between his or her ideas and textual evidence. To make sure the reader follows all the claims and reasons put forth in the essay, a writer needs to provide **clarification** by using **transitions.** Transitions are connecting words and phrases that clarify the relationships among ideas, reasons, and evidence in a text. Transitions work at three different levels: within a sentence or between sentences, between paragraphs, and for indicating organizational structure. By using words, phrases, clauses, and varied syntax to show relationships between major sections of text, writers create **cohesion,** or a sense that the literary analysis is a unified whole.

 ## IDENTIFICATION AND APPLICATION

The body paragraphs provide the reasons and evidence needed to support the claim a writer makes in his or her thesis statement. Typically, writers develop one main idea per body paragraph.

- A body paragraph for a literary analysis could be structured as follows. Note the use of transitions within a paragraph:
  - › **Topic sentence:** The topic sentence is the first sentence of your body paragraph and clearly states a claim, or the main point of the paragraph. It's important that your topic sentence develops your thesis statement.

> **Reason:** State the reason you believe your claim to be true and in support of your thesis statement.
>> **Transition:** Use a transition word, phrase, or clause to link your reason to the evidence you will use to support it.
> **Evidence #1:** Present evidence to support your reason. Evidence includes relevant facts, definitions, concrete details, quotations, or other information and examples.
>> **Transition:** Use a transition word, phrase, or clause to link your evidence to the analysis you will use to explain it.
> **Analysis/Explanation #1:** After presenting evidence, you will need to analyze that evidence and explain how it supports your claim or main idea and, in effect, your thesis statement.
>> **Transition:** Use a transition word, phrase, or clause to link this analysis to a second piece of evidence you will use to support the claim.
> **Evidence #2:** Provide a second piece of evidence to further support your claim or main idea.
>> **Transition:** Use a transition word, phrase, or clause to link your evidence to the analysis you will use to explain it.
> **Analysis/Explanation #2:** Analyze this second piece of evidence and explain how it supports your claim and, in effect, your thesis statement.
>> **Transition:** Use a transition word, phrase, or clause to link your analysis to the claim, restated in the conclusion.
> **Concluding sentence:** After presenting your evidence, you need to wrap up your main idea and transition to the next paragraph in your conclusion sentence.

- Transition words help readers understand the flow of ideas and concepts between paragraphs as well as within a paragraph.
  > Some of the most useful transitions are words that indicate that the ideas in one paragraph are building on or adding to those in another. Examples include: *furthermore, therefore, in addition, moreover, by extension, in order to,* etc.

- Clarify ideas by varying your syntax, or sentence structure.
  > Use a combination of simple, complex, and compound sentences.

 MODEL

In the student model essay "Feelings Hidden under Trappings and Suits: Figurative Language in *Hamlet* and 'On Monsieur's Departure,'" the first body paragraph aims to analyze the figurative language in "On Monsieur's Departure." Recall the essay's thesis statement, and pay attention to the sentence that concludes the introductory paragraph:

*Both Shakespeare and Elizabeth I use figures of speech to help readers understand and relate to the experience of holding intense feelings inside, hidden from public display. **This act of hiding makes characters human and reveals an important aspect of the human condition.***

Note that the sentence that follows the thesis statement, which refers to "an important aspect of the human condition," should serve as a transition to the body paragraph that will follow. However, the writer begins the first body paragraph with some background information on the poem without the benefit of a transition.

Elizabeth I was queen of England from 1558 to 1603 ("Elizabeth I").

The writer has missed an opportunity to tie the introductory paragraph more cohesively to the first body paragraph. For example, the writer might have picked up on her introduction's concluding sentence to transition to the opening of the next paragraph: **"One person who knew well the many problems of the human condition** was Elizabeth I, who was queen of England from 1558 to 1603." The words "human condition" could help create a clear transition between paragraphs. Still, the writer is supporting her thesis statement in this body paragraph. The third sentence is the topic sentence, which introduces the paragraph's main idea or claim: "In her poem 'On Monsieur's Departure,' the speaker struggles to keep her true feelings hidden." A few sentences later, the writer introduces her first piece of evidence from the text:

*The speaker sets up her dilemma in the first line: "I . . . **dare not show** my discontent" (1.1).*

Then the writer begins to analyze and explain why she included this evidence, using the word "dare" to create her transition:

***The use of the verb "dare"** implies that a strong force keeps her from showing her grief. She continues the use of strong language in the second line: "I love, and **yet am forced to seem** to hate." Here the speaker clarifies her problem— she is in love with someone, but the outside world "forces" her to "seem to hate." The use of the word "seem" is important. **No one can actually force her** to hate a person, but she can pretend.*

The writer presents a detailed explanation of the vivid language in the first two lines of the poem. She uses the words "forced" and "force" to connect her evidence and her analysis. However, while the explanation is not incorrect, it does not support the writer's claim that Elizabeth uses figures of speech to express her intense feelings. To build a stronger relationship by examining figurative meanings, the writer might have explored the choice of the verb *force*, for example, and what such a word might mean for a queen such as Elizabeth. A queen, of course, is one who is used to using force and being a force, and not being forced. The body paragraph then introduces the idea of figures of speech without any evidence:

> *The whole stanza comprises a list of paradoxes—figures of speech that seem to be contradictions but actually reveal truth. The truth in this case is that the feelings projected on the outside of a person may be entirely different from what he or she is actually feeling inside.*

While this analysis is not incorrect, it is not supported by the evidence presented by the writer. Stronger transitions and more specific evidence (including examples of paradoxes) are needed. Overall, the writer needs to clarify the relationship between the thesis statement and the ideas presented in this body paragraph.

 PRACTICE

Write one body paragraph for your literary analysis that follows the suggested format, being careful to link the body paragraph to your introduction and thesis statement. When you are finished, trade with a partner and offer each other feedback. How effective is the topic sentence at stating the main point of the paragraph? Is there a claim stated that is tied to the thesis? How strong are the reasons and evidence used to support the claim? Are all quotes and paraphrased evidence cited properly? Did the analysis thoroughly explain the reasons and evidence ? Did the writer use transitions to make the paragraph cohesive? Offer each other suggestions, and remember that they are most helpful when they are constructive.

CONCLUSIONS

sync•skills

SKILL: CONCLUSIONS

 DEFINE

The **conclusion** is the final paragraph or section of a nonfiction text. A strong and effective conclusion should follow from and support the argument presented in a text, or restate the central or main idea. It should also articulate the significance of the topic, noting any interesting or important implications the analysis or explanation may have for the reader. Perhaps most important, it should provide the reader with a sense of closure, the satisfying feeling that the central idea or argument has been thoroughly addressed.

 IDENTIFICATION AND APPLICATION

When your composition is a response to a writing prompt, it is a good idea to use the conclusion to review how your essay has met the requirements of the writing prompt. Based on the dictates of this unit's prompt, here is a list of items that should be included in the conclusion of your literary analysis:

- The titles of the two or three selections discussed
- A summary of the analysis of each author's use of figurative language and figures of speech to help readers understand a speaker's or character's feelings and actions
- A restatement of the thesis, or claim
- A reminder of the aspects of the human condition explored in the essay
- A tie to the Essential Question: How do we express the complexities of being human?

The order of these elements is not important, except that they should be organized logically and with transitions. Consider examining the conclusion side by side with the introduction, which includes the same information. Remember, the conclusion is the writer's way of referring back to this information in a way that will help the reader evaluate whether or not the writer's position has been argued effectively. Ultimately, a writer will use the conclusion to, in some way, connect the claims and supporting ideas to guide readers' understanding.

 MODEL

The author of the student model literary analysis "Feelings Hidden under Trappings and Suits" created a flowchart to outline the conclusion to the analysis.

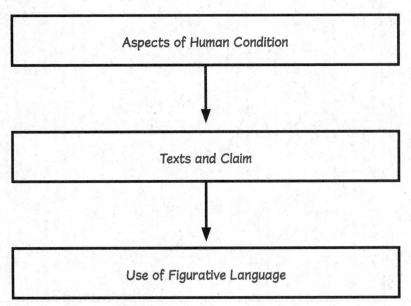

Aspects of Human Condition

Texts and Claim

Use of Figurative Language

This graphic organizer shows that the conclusion will begin with a review of the ideas about the human condition included in the literary analysis. Then the conclusion will review the texts analyzed and the claim made. It will finish by explaining how the figurative language reveals human complexities. A writer could then place under each heading some drafts of sentences that develop these ideas. To complete the conclusion, a writer should leave readers with some kind of final thought. For example, the writer of the Student Model closed in this way: "The use of figurative language in these works gives resonating, tangible expression to these unsaid, intangible feelings."

 PRACTICE

Write a conclusion for your literary analysis. To develop a conclusion, first reread your introduction, supporting details, sample body paragraph, and other notes. Then you might try outlining your conclusion ideas using a

Please note that excerpts and passages in the StudySync® library and this workbook are intended as touchstones to generate interest in an author's work. The excerpts and passages do not substitute for the reading of entire texts, and StudySync® strongly recommends that students seek out and purchase the whole literary or informational work in order to experience it as the author intended. Links to online resellers are available in our digital library. In addition, complete works may be ordered through an authorized reseller by filling out and returning to StudySync® the order form enclosed in this workbook.

Reading & Writing Companion   **109**

graphic organizer like the one above, in a formal outline, or through a simple list. When you are finished, trade with a partner and offer each other feedback. How effectively did the writer restate the thesis or claim of the introduction in the essay in the conclusion? What final thought did the writer leave you with? Offer each other suggestions, and remember that they are most helpful when they are constructive.

DRAFT

CA-CCSS: CA.W.11-12.1a, CA.W.11-12.1b, CA.W.11-12.4, CA.W.11-12.5, CA.W.11-12.6, CA.W.11-12.9a, CA.W.11-12.10, CA.SL.11-12.1a, CA.SL.11-12.1d

WRITING PROMPT

Recall the Essential Question: How do we express the complexities of being human? Choose two or three selections from the unit and write a literary analysis focused on how the author uses figurative language and figures of speech to help readers understand a speaker's or character's feelings and actions. Explain how each author uses figurative language to reveal aspects of the human condition.

Your essay should include:

- an introduction with a clear thesis statement
- body paragraphs with thorough analysis supported by relevant reasons and evidence
- a conclusion that effectively wraps up your essay

You've already made progress toward writing your own literary analysis essay. You've thought about the topic and chosen your selections. You've identified what you want to claim about how the authors use figurative language to express the human condition in characters. You've decided how to organize information, and gathered supporting details and relevant evidence. Now it's time to write a draft.

When drafting, ask yourself these questions:

- How can I improve my hook to make it more appealing?
- What can I do to clarify my thesis statement?
- Which relevant facts, strong details, and interesting quotations should I include in each body paragraph to support the thesis statement and make it a strong claim?

- Would more precise language or different details about these texts create a stronger interpretation?
- How well have I communicated what the figurative language means and what it communicates about the human condition?
- What final thought do I want to leave with my readers?

Using your roadmap and your other prewriting materials, write a draft of your essay. Remember that writing a literary analysis begins with an introduction and presents a thesis statement. Body paragraphs provide supporting details and relevant information. A concluding paragraph restates or reinforces your thesis statement. An effective conclusion can also do more—it can leave a lasting impression on your readers. Before you submit your draft, read it over carefully. You want to be sure that you've responded to all aspects of the prompt.

REVISE

CA-CCSS: CA.W.11-12.1d, CA.W.11-12.4, CA.W.11-12.5, CA.W.11-12.6, CA.W.11-12.9a, CA.W.11-12.10, CA.SL.11-12.1

WRITING PROMPT

Recall the Essential Question: How do we express the complexities of being human? Choose two or three selections from the unit and write a literary analysis focused on how the author uses figurative language and figures of speech to help readers understand a speaker's or character's feelings and actions. Explain how each author uses figurative language to reveal aspects of the human condition.

Your essay should include:

- an introduction with a clear thesis statement
- body paragraphs with thorough analysis supported by relevant reasons and evidence
- a conclusion that effectively wraps up your essay

You have written a draft of your literary analysis. You have also received input from your peers about how to improve it. Now you are going to revise your draft.

Here are some recommendations to help you revise.

- Review the suggestions made by your peers and include those that will help strengthen your essay.
- Focus on maintaining a formal style. A formal style suits your purpose—analyzing literature to prove a thesis. It also fits your audience—students, teachers, and other readers interested in understanding your point of view and your ideas about works of literature that they have read.
  › As you revise, eliminate any slang.
  › Remove any first-person pronouns such as "I," "me," or "mine" and instances of addressing readers as "you." These are more suitable to a writing style that is informal, personal, and conversational.

> › If you include your personal opinions, remove them. Your essay should be clear, direct, and unbiased, with all ideas supported using textual evidence.
- After you have revised elements of style, think about whether there is anything else you can do to improve your essay's information or organization.
  - › Do you need to add any new details to your essay? Is there a particularly moving example of figurative language you could identify and analyze that would help to better support your thesis?
  - › Do you make any assertions that are not supported by quotations from the selections? Take the time to explain assertions with specific textual examples and be sure to cite your sources.
  - › Can you substitute a more precise word for a word that is general or dull?
  - › Consider your organization. Would your essay flow better if you strengthened the transitions between paragraphs or between ideas and examples?
- As you add new details or change information, check that you do not introduce errors.
  - › Check that you are using standard English capitalization and punctuation.
  - › Check that you spelled names and other words correctly.

SKILL:
SOURCES AND CITATIONS

 DEFINE

When writing a literary analysis, an informative/explanatory text, or an argumentative essay, writers cannot simply make up information or rely on their own subjective experiences or opinions. To thoroughly support the treatment and analysis of their topics, writers need to include information from relevant, accurate, and reliable sources and cite, or acknowledge, them properly. **Sources** are the documents and information that an author uses to research his or her writing, and writers should keep track of these sources as they research and plan their work. When it comes time to write, authors may need to acknowledge the sources they used to form their ideas. If they don't, authors can be accused of **plagiarism,** or stealing someone else's words and ideas.

Writers may need to provide a full list of sources in a **Works Cited** section or standard **bibliography.** This is a list of sources from which you locate any facts, quotations, statistics, or statements you include in your writing that are not common knowledge. In some academic texts, writers may be asked to provide sources and citations in **footnotes** or **endnotes,** which link specific references within the essay to the correlating pages or chapters in an outside source. Such notes may also provide explanations or additional information from the sources.

Some sources are **primary sources.** A primary source is a first-hand account of thoughts or events by the individual who experienced them. Examples of primary sources include letters, photographs, official documents, diaries or journals, autobiographies or memoirs, eyewitness accounts and interviews, audio recordings and radio broadcasts, and works of art.

Other sources are **secondary sources.** A secondary source analyzes and interprets primary sources. Some examples of secondary sources include encyclopedia articles, textbooks, commentary or criticisms, histories, documentary films, and news analyses.

NOTES

Writers should include information from a variety of sources in a way that maintains the flow of ideas. Writers should avoid relying too heavily on any one source. Whatever the source, information included in a text that is the result of research should be cited in some way. **Citations** are required whenever authors quote others' words or refer to others' ideas in their writing. Writers need to remember that using good sources to develop original ideas is key to strong analytical writing. Citing those sources is a vital part of the process.

IDENTIFICATION AND APPLICATION

- All sources must be **credible** and **accurate.** When writing a literary analysis, look for sources from experts in the topic you are writing about.
  › When researching online, look for URLs that contain ".gov" (government agencies), ".edu" (colleges and universities) and ".org" (museums and other non-profit organizations).
  › Don't neglect respected print sources. Many scholars do not publish online.

- Include a citation to give credit to any source, whether primary or secondary, that is quoted exactly. Make sure the quotation is presented in quotation marks. There are several different ways to cite a source.
  › If the author's name is mentioned in the essay, include the page number where the quotation can be located:
  › Collins points out, "These authors offer unique insights into the lives of people living in the Middle Ages" (83).
  › If the author's name does not appear in the text, include the author's name and the page number in parentheses at the end of the sentence in which the quote appears:
  › All of the authors discussed "offer unique insights into the lives of people living in the Middle Ages" (Collins 83).
  › If there is no author, use the title of the work:
  › The ideas of writers of this period are now being studied with great interest. ("The Middle Ages").
  › For online sources, as with the online encyclopedia above, no page number is needed.
  › When quoting Shakespeare, citations require special consideration. First, italicize the titles of plays. Next, because there are so many editions of his plays, do not use page numbers when referencing quotations. Instead, place a parenthetical reference after each quotation containing its act, scene, and line numbers separated by periods. Use arabic numerals for all reference numbers, as in this example:

"To be or not to be. That is the question—" *Hamlet* (3.1.55).
This means the line comes from the play *Hamlet,* Act III, scene i, line 55. In a literary analysis, the author's name is not always required in the citation as long as his name is stated in the essay and the authorship is clear.

- Citations are also necessary when a writer borrows ideas or takes facts from another source, even if the writer paraphrases, or puts those ideas in his or her own words. Follow the same citation rules as for exact quotations.

- At the end of the essay, include a Works Cited list with full bibliographical information on each source cited, formatted correctly in MLA style. Works are listed alphabetically by author's last name, and if there is no name, by title.

 ## MODEL

The writer of the student model essay "Feelings Hidden under Trappings and Suits: Figurative Language in *Hamlet* and 'On Monsieur's Departure'" used four sources in writing the literary analysis essay. In addition to the two texts she chose to analyze, the writer found background information in two reference sources: a literature anthology and an online encyclopedia. Note that while encyclopedias are fine for gaining an overview of a topic, they are not the strongest resources. Writers should always look first for scholarly articles or reputable essays over an encyclopedia entry. In any case, any resource should be cited.

The writer included the two reference sources in the second paragraph:

> *Elizabeth I was queen of England from 1558 to 1603* (**"Elizabeth I"**). *During her long rule she never married, despite calls from her court to find a king and produce an heir. In her poem "On Monsieur's Departure," the speaker struggles to keep her true feelings hidden. The speaker of the poem is not necessarily Elizabeth, but she would have undoubtedly understand the importance of cultivating a public image. In addition, literary scholars believe the poem was inspired by the breakup of marriage negotiations with Francis, Duke of Anjou, a one-time suitor to Elizabeth* (**Abrams 998**).

In the first sentence, the writer used a fact from the encyclopedia entry. That information is not common knowledge and needs to be cited. The entry did not have an author, so it is cited by the title of the article. Because the

Please note that excerpts and passages in the StudySync® library and this workbook are intended as touchstones to generate interest in an author's work. The excerpts and passages do not substitute for the reading of entire texts, and StudySync® strongly recommends that students seek out and purchase the whole literary or informational work in order to experience it as the author intended. Links to online resellers are available in our digital library. In addition, complete works may be ordered through an authorized reseller by filling out and returning to StudySync® the order form enclosed in this workbook.

Reading & Writing Companion   **117**

encyclopedia entry is online, she did not include a page number. The second citation in this paragraph is a paraphrase of someone else's ideas. The writer found this information in a literature anthology edited by M. H. Abrams. Because it is a book, it gets a page number. That way any reader can easily find the ideas the writer shared.

Later in the model essay, the writer quotes exactly from *Hamlet*.

> *Like Elizabeth's speaker, Hamlet is torn between his true, inner feelings and the image he needs to project in public. In Act I, scene ii, when Hamlet sees his uncle Claudius a month after his father's death, Claudius addresses Hamlet's grief: "How is it that the clouds still hang on you?"* **(1.2.6).**

The writer included in her citation the act number (1), the scene number (2), and the line number according to the digital source she used to write her piece (6), each separated by a period. She did not have to include the author's name, since the play's author is established in the beginning of the analysis. She also did not have to include the play's title since that is implicit in the paragraph.

Sometimes writers would like to include additional information from their source material, though it may not be directly related to their purpose for writing. This information often comes in the form of explanatory notes. For example, the writer of the student model might do this:

> *In addition, literary scholars believe the poem was inspired by the breakup of marriage negotiations with Francis, Duke of Anjou, a one-time suitor to Elizabeth (Abrams 998).[1]*

The superscript 1 indicates a footnote or endnote. A footnote would appear at the bottom of the page, while an endnote would appear at the end of the text. Here is a possible footnote or endnote example for this passage:

> 1. *While many scholars suggest other opportunities Elizabeth may have had for marrying, this example occurs at the time the poem was written (Abrams 998).*

While this informational note is not part of the writer's argumentative purpose, the fact that Elizabeth I had a complicated love life may be of interest to readers who want to know more about this fascinating monarch and poet.

PRACTICE

Use the information you have learned about MLA format to apply to citations in your own literary analysis. Find two examples of places where you need to cite a source, and then follow the correct format to write the citations within the text of your revision. Next, write a complete entry for each resource in a Works Cited section to place at the end of your essay. Exchange citations and Works Cited entries with a partner to see if you have formatted them correctly.

EDIT, PROOFREAD, AND PUBLISH

CA-CCSS: CA.W.11-12.1, CA.W.11-12.4, CA.W.11-12.5, CA.W.11-12.6, CA.SL.11-12.1, CA.L.11-12.1b, CA.L.11-12.2a, CA.L.11-12.2b, CA.L.11-12.3a

WRITING PROMPT

Recall the Essential Question: How do we express the complexities of being human? Choose two or three selections from the unit and write a literary analysis focused on how the author uses figurative language and figures of speech to help readers understand a speaker's or character's feelings and actions. Explain how each author uses figurative language to reveal aspects of the human condition.

Your essay should include:

- an introduction with a clear thesis statement
- body paragraphs with thorough analysis supported by relevant reasons and evidence
- a conclusion that effectively wraps up your essay

You have revised your literary analysis and received input from your peers on that revision. Now it's time to edit and proofread your essay to produce a final version. Have you included all of the valuable suggestions from your peers? Ask yourself: Have I fully developed my thesis statement with strong textual evidence? What more can I do to improve my essay's information and organization? Have I accurately and consistently cited my sources? Did I include a Works Cited page and use the correct format?

When you are satisfied with your work, move on to proofread it for errors. For example, check that you have used correct punctuation for quotations and citations. Have you followed hyphenation conventions and checked syntax and usage? Have you corrected any misspelled words?

Once you have made all your corrections, you are ready to publish your work. You can distribute your writing to family and friends, hang it on a bulletin board or post it on your blog. If you publish online, create links to your sources and citations. That way, readers can follow up on what they've learned from your essay and read more on their own.

Fulfillment
through StudySync

If you are interested in specific titles, please fill out the form below and we will check availability through our partners.

ORDER DETAILS

Date:

TITLE	AUTHOR	Paperback/ Hardcover	Specific Edition *If Applicable*	Quantity

SHIPPING INFORMATION

Contact:

Title:

School/District:

Address Line 1:

Address Line 2:

Zip or Postal Code:

Phone:

Mobile:

Email:

BILLING INFORMATION ☐ *SAME AS SHIPPING*

Contact:

Title:

School/District:

Address Line 1:

Address Line 2:

Zip or Postal Code:

Phone:

Mobile:

Email:

PAYMENT INFORMATION

☐ CREDIT CARD

Name on Card:

Card Number: Expiration Date: Security Code:

☐ PO

Purchase Order Number:

StudySync Text Fulfillment, BookheadEd Learning, LLC
610 Daniel Young Drive | Sonoma, CA 95476